To Morgan
With les
from
Chris

POLES APART

From Darkness, Fire and Chains

By

Chris Piechowski

Pen Press

© Chris Piechowski 2011

All rights reserved

No part of this publication may be reproduced, stored in a retrieval
system, or transmitted in any form or by any means, without the prior
permission in writing of the publisher, nor be otherwise circulated in
any form of binding or cover other than that in which it is published and
without a similar condition including this condition being imposed on
the subsequent purchaser.

While some of the events and characters are based on historical events
and figures, the novel is a work of fiction and the central characters and
incidents portrayed in it are the work of the author's imagination.

First published in Great Britain by Pen Press

All paper used in the printing of this book has been made from wood
grown in managed, sustainable forests.

ISBN13: 978-1-78003-027-2

Printed and bound in the UK
Pen Press is an imprint of Indepenpress Publishing Limited
25 Eastern Place
Brighton
BN2 1GJ

A catalogue record of this book is available from
the British Library

Cover design by Jacqueline Abromeit

To my father:

For his wisdom, patience and understanding,

Always the truest of friends and the most sagacious of

teachers,

I owe him everything.

ABOUT THE AUTHOR

Chris Piechowski was born and raised in England. The son of a Polish father and English mother, he served for over thirty years in the Police Force. He now lives in retirement with his wife, in a small village on the edge of Salisbury Plain.

CONTENTS

FOREWORD

The primary driving force for this book was a remarkable, heart-warming family reunion brought about in 2005 when the author traced the Polish born owner of a quantity of wartime letters and photographs that had been abandoned at Salisbury in mysterious circumstances some forty years ago. The investigation also uncovered the whereabouts of the owner's long-lost brother and this led to the rediscovery of his whole extended family, some of whom had been separated since the war. The family and the author were captivated by the amazing accounts of those missing years. The coincidences, time scales and twists of fate involved and the almost unbelievable adventures of the brave individuals concerned (and the many others who have been interviewed since), proved beyond any reasonable doubt that fact really is stranger than fiction.

Almost without exception these Polish veterans have spoken most passionately and vehemently of their personal and sudden loss of family and home life with its once treasured and seemingly secure bonds of brotherhood, duty and shared responsibility. It seemed that everything but their humanity had been savagely stolen from them by the sadistic, racist hatred of the Nazi and Soviet doctrines and pogroms. They told of terror and tragedies beyond understanding: of parents, grandparents, brothers and sisters dead on the battlefield or murdered by the occupiers, with the surviving relatives catapulted into slavery across Europe and beyond, or sent to the death camps or the Gulag. They all bitterly resented the rape of their country and the loss of nationhood but it was, above all else, a return to the familiarity, security and continuity of family life for which they truly yearned.

The author's involvement in the reunion of one family combined with those numerous personal tales of horror, flight, capture, forced labour and an overwhelming desire to fight for freedom, motivated him to put pen to paper. He wanted to tell the human story behind the wartime experiences of his father's generation and define their frequently undervalued contribution to the allied war effort, where they fought against a level of malevolence never seen before or since. In view of what he had seen and heard it seemed natural that he should tell his story through the eyes of a Polish family.

The current threat from terrorism and the political and social controversy surrounding the latest wave of Polish immigration into Britain added a contemporary relevance and menace that could not be ignored. For this reason the author also wanted to show that the veterans had, more than most, earned the right to live, work and prosper here and that their civic and national qualities had made integration a relatively smooth process.

In a fiercely competitive and financially driven literary world, good intention, hard facts and a true story are seldom enough to secure publication and reach out into a wide public arena, as many people understandably want to read and be entertained by their favourite established or celebrity authors. Nevertheless, the author remained convinced that this story must be told and its present-day significance understood and so, after a great deal of thought and in an effort to reach as large a general readership as possible, his vehicle of choice became the historical novel. The result is a gripping, fast moving, action packed tale of assassination, fortitude, heroism, death and survival as the family are split asunder; firstly by their own history and then by the unrelenting violence and horrors of the Nazi and Soviet invasions. Divided, they must flee the blitzkrieg and death camps at home; suffer the privations and cruelty of the Gulag in Siberia; fight in the streets and sewers of Warsaw and across the battlefields of Normandy, Holland and Italy. Whilst struggling to endure in such an alien and terrifying world of darkness, fire and chains, they were each driven on by the dream of reunion.

It is accepted that such a format will, by definition, blur and sometimes cross the boundaries between fact and fiction but it should be made clear at the outset that the vast majority of events described are true and accurately reflect the extraordinary experiences of real people, some known, admired and cherished by the author. Two of the surviving characters in this fictitious family are based on a veteran's individual account - including his own travels, encounters, experiences, major battles (both military and psychological), anecdotes and, indeed, even personal characteristics. One is the author's father and the other his Godfather. The others, introduced to widen and deepen the readers vicarious experience, are founded on the accounts given by other veterans, their relatives, colleagues and friends, many of whom did not escape from occupied Poland, and they replicate the lives and tribulations of tens of thousands of service personnel and civilians alike.

For the reader's convenience, the author's ease of telling, and in order to illustrate the devastating impact of the war on Poland's population, these characters, real and imagined have been brought together as a representative family and, taken together, they bring history back to life. Through their eyes, actions, thoughts and voices these ordinary people, living in extraordinary times, expose the reader to the most awe-inspiring events, right across the huge range and depth of the Polish war. This most vivid, turbulent and uncompromisingly poignant emotional experience could never be matched by any amount of historical text, explanation or analysis.

Their exploits are by no means unique. The devastation visited upon them was repeated by the brutal occupation forces throughout the land and it spread ever onwards, multiplying like a virulent virus to infect a million such families. The tortuous route home for the survivors has been travelled by tens (perhaps even hundreds) of thousands of Polish Servicemen and their families. Many more died in the effort and others were lost along the way but their pride, indomitable spirit and bravery has inspired whole generations since. It is difficult in present times of relative comfort and wealth (despite the credit crunch and recession) to imagine the horrors and privations experienced by the Poles, many little more than children.

It is not commonly known that the Polish Armed Services were the fourth largest contingent of the 1939 to 1945 allied coalition, after the USSR, the US, and Great Britain. Uniquely amongst the allies her personnel fought in every European theatre of war and were in the field for all six years of the bloody and unforgiving conflict. Most of those who risked so much to fight in all three Services under Allied Command did so in the hope and belief that it would lead to the liberation of a partitioned and brutalised Poland. Yet it was not to be, as post-war history was being driven by a mixture of Western political self-interest, Soviet expansion and general war weariness. In consequence the allies consigned this decimated, fiercely patriotic and intensely Christian nation to another forty-five years of hardship and deprivation under rigid Russian atheist occupation. Those Poles who returned during this period did so at considerable personal risk: many were arrested, imprisoned and even executed.

The events of the Second World War are characterised by unprecedented levels of ethnic and religious hatred, destruction and mass-murder that form a macabre benchmark against which the real nature of today's terror threat can be measured. That is not to underestimate the seriousness of current events, but to put them in an historical perspective and balance. The frighteningly cold statistics of the death toll alone, without even considering the cruelty, barbarism, slavery, ethnic cleansing and state managed mass-murder that was unleashed against civilian populations (none more so than the beleaguered and isolated Poles) prove that this was a real war on terror. We must also remember that it was so very nearly lost because of bickering between the allies, based on selfish national interests. Is history now repeating itself - have we, or have we not, learnt its bitter lessons? Are we any better prepared and have we the mental and physical will of our parents and grandparents to persevere through overwhelming adversity? We must certainly hope so, but recent worldwide events cast serious doubt on our ability to prevail and, as before, only time will tell.

It is not surprising that the vast majority of the demobilised Free Polish Forces accepted the invitation of the United Kingdom to make their futures here and have since made a fine contribution to our social, political and economic development. Initially, many faced discrimination and hostility from their new neighbours, particularly in education, employment and housing, but over time they were able to assuage such suspicion and xenophobia. Their assimilation has been mutually beneficial and a positive example of what can be achieved by hard work, tolerance and an honourable sense of indebtedness to the host nation.

I REMEMBER   I REMEMBER

I remember, I remember

The Fir trees dark and high

I used to think their slender tops

Were close against the sky

It was a childish ignorance

But now 'tis little joy

To know I'm farther off from heav'n

Than when I was a boy.

Thomas Hood, 1799 to 1845

Prologue

Death in Lisbon
7th June 1930

At first glance Franz did not readily stand out from the crowd as it merged from the side-streets and formed into an animated but orderly procession heading expectantly towards the docks. He looked every inch the merchant sailor he was: just under six feet tall with broad, well-muscled shoulders, weathered and tanned features, sun-bleached fair hair, a rolling gait, large callused hands and, being thirty nine just four days ago, he was still at the peak of his physical and professional development. However, a closer examination would reveal several distinguishing features. Set in an angular face, with slightly protruding cheekbones, he had a very long nose, which resembled that of a boxer, being slightly crooked at the bridge and bulbous at the end. He had a prominent lower jaw and unsymmetrical ear lobes, with the left heavily scarred, thickened and slightly longer than the right. He also had a two-inch scar running almost vertically down the forehead above his right eye. These peculiarities reinforced his overall appearance as that of a hard man, well used to defending himself and a figure best avoided: certainly not one to be trifled with.

He was also a man of few words, with an iron will and a physical strength to match. He was self-reliant, resilient to hardship, resourceful and not normally given to panic or trepidation, but today he was already nervous and sweating profusely from the heat and an uncharacteristic inner tension, so fully sprung that it quivered near breaking point. He visibly winced when he noticed

1

the exceptionally heavy police and security presence as he joined the long queue at the harbour-front guardroom. Whilst he waited and slowly composed himself, he took the opportunity to look all around as nonchalantly as possible and check the faces of those walking behind him. He was convinced that he was being followed, but despite his best efforts during the long walk from the hostel to the quayside, he had been unable to identify those responsible.

Over the years he had become very surveillance conscious and routinely employed a host of counter measures to mislead, confuse and ultimately throw his pursuers right off the scent, but as he had so obviously failed to spot even one of them on this occasion, he concluded that these must be the best in the business. He pictured a determined team of perhaps half a dozen highly trained agents: seasoned professionals who regularly switched positions and used simple disguises and other tricks of the trade to change their appearance and melt into the background. He became very wary of walking right into another trap and his apprehension soared again as he took his false identity papers and forged mariner's pass from his jacket pocket.

He knew his documents were not of the best quality, certainly not up to his usual standard, and would probably only withstand a cursory inspection. Unfortunately, his meticulous preparations had been disrupted by the fallout from his aborted action at the Consul General's Office. During the surveillance stage he had become increasingly alarmed as, day by day, the levels of security there had been progressively raised until Portuguese uniformed and plain-clothes police officers were guarding the entire perimeter and manning mobile checkpoints on the approaches. Heavily armed German soldiers were now patrolling inside the compound and everyone entering the public areas was being searched. The place had become a fortress, in stark contrast to his first reconnoitre two weeks earlier at the start of this, his most vital mission, when he had seen very few security personnel and had entered the building unchallenged.

To justify his presence then, he told staff that he was penniless and stranded without a ship or local accommodation and begged for a loan of funds, sufficient to cut his losses and return home to Germany. As he expected he was given short shrift and sent on his way. He now felt sure that somehow he had aroused their suspicions and had only succeeded in drawing even more unwanted attention to himself. He wondered if they had learnt of his plan. Had he been betrayed? Perhaps the American Military Intelligence Service had tipped them off; after all he had narrowly escaped their elaborate ambush at the American embassy the previous month. He was almost within touching distance of their Ambassador, found pruning his roses in the garden: an apparently unprotected sitting target, inviting him to strike, but as he reached the gate he had sensed danger all around. It was too easy. Everything about it felt wrong and so he calmly walked on by. Bitter experience had taught him never to ignore his feral instincts and, when he later replayed the incident over and over in his mind, he concluded that the figure in the garden was a secret service doppelganger: the irresistible bait in the trap.

In any event, an attack at either embassy was now impossible and having been forced to change the venue he was convinced that this was his last chance to rescue the entire Portugal operation. However, the new truncated timescale had meant that a number of operational compromises, including the use of imprecise documentation, had to be made. This additional and to him, unaccustomed risk, now left him feeling rather ill-prepared and particularly vulnerable, but he had to follow his new orders even if they undermined his own operational rules and eroded his confidence of success. He was to seize the unexpected and sudden opportunity that the diplomat's offshore visit and fate had offered him before his enemies once more closed in and this time perhaps, silenced him for good.

Traffic was far heavier than normal, as unusually large numbers of the public were also being admitted to the naval dockyard and Franz had to stand on tiptoe and crane his neck to look beyond the first line of uniformed security personnel at the red and white hatched barrier that blocked the road ahead. He saw that several people right towards the front of the queue were being singled out, searched and questioned by the naval guards. A senior police officer, who appeared to be in charge of the whole security detail, supervised the operation as two guards closely examined their identity papers before allowing them to pass through. Franz knew that if he were searched he would either have to surrender or once again fight for his life and his hard-won freedom. The former would lead to the discovery of incriminating evidence that would seal his fate and the latter would most probably lead to the loss of more innocent life, something he was determined to avoid. He had decided years before, when the persecution first started, that he would fight back with all the power and resources at his disposal but he would never stoop to the levels of cruelty so readily and enthusiastically employed by those who had tormented him. Nevertheless, if it came to a fight here, then escape looked impossible. He could see at least another twenty police and security officers deployed within the concourse beyond the gate, all were armed and there would surely be many others, both uniformed and plain clothes, scattered throughout the massive quayside complex. At the first sign of serious trouble all would be lost as they rushed to seal the place up tight, trapping him inside their contracting cordons where he would be captured, or worse, while his target was spirited away to a place of safety, well beyond his reach.

Fear of capture and torture flooded back and with it came the painful memories of his youth and he was briefly tempted to simply turn and run rather than risk more misery. As he deliberated with uncharacteristic indecision he suddenly realised that he was even more afraid of failure, especially at such an early point in his plan of attack. He had personally come too far, suffered too much and seen his countrymen pay too high a cost in humiliation and subjugation to give up now. This clarity of purpose momentarily held him rooted to the spot and after a second or two, as he contemplated the countless numbers depending on him for their salvation, he forced himself to breathe deeply and the misgivings passed, allowing him to shuffle forward in the line.

As he approached the barrier he held his pass up at shoulder level and to his immense relief the police officer, without a second glance, simply waved him through the small entrance gate through which the queue was being funnelled. The guards, accustomed to the appearance, bearing and mannerisms of members of the Merchant Marine, currently more focused on the visiting civilians, paid him scant regard and immediately turned their attention to those behind. He was safely inside and quickly made his way, again unchallenged, past the additional security patrols and on towards the back of the large throng of spectators that was rapidly gathering and being marshalled along the dockside.

When he heard the Captain's barge approaching the jetty, Franz pushed his way through the ranks of onlookers and stood one row back from the front, positioning himself a few yards from the rear of the powerful and gleaming open-topped car and its waiting chauffeur. Two uniformed police officers stood facing the crowd twenty yards to his right and another three about fifty yards to his left. They all appeared relaxed and unaware of any threat and as he watched they confirmed this view by turning around to look at the anchored warship, the SS Konigsberg, as it noisily saluted the boatload of departing dignitaries.

He did yet another sweep of the crowd around him, looking for any indication of a possible threat to his plan. He prided himself on his ability to spot plain clothes police or military personnel and although he saw nothing obvious close by, he knew they were there somewhere, waiting and watching for him. As the point of action finally approached, Franz continued to fret and he struggled to hold himself together and, although he rallied at the sight of the barge coming alongside, he realised that he was now only being driven on by an all-consuming hatred and bitterness.

He was relieved to hear the familiar and imposing voice of his controller once more, but then disturbed by his scornful words as they echoed around his head, "Don't take on so! You were chosen for this task because you had the strength to succeed where others would fail, but what have you become in recent days: a man of honour or a spineless mouse?"

During his fateful, tortured journey Franz had been guided, harangued and even goaded by his controller, and so it continued, "It's entirely up to you and you alone must decide: decide here and decide now. Come on then, what's it to be; hero or coward? Will you stay and fight or run and cower?"

He shook his head to silence the mocking voice and as his attention refocused on his surroundings he found himself staring intently at the mighty warship. He knew then that he would do battle, because the Cruiser seemed to embody all the power, authority and arrogance of the nation that had hounded him, tormented him and violated his rights for as long as he could remember. He thought it fitting that such a symbol of German dominance, control and international muscle would now be utterly powerless to stop just one man from humiliating them in the eyes of the whole world. He shuddered when he, yet again, mentally rehearsed his intentions and broke into a cold sweat as he tried to ignore the enormous spiritual, political and practical consequences of his actions. He finally accepted that he no longer knew exactly who he was, where he truly belonged or who he could trust, but he was absolutely clear about the identity and guilt of those who had driven him to this point.

The German Minister to Portugal marched purposefully down the quay towards his car, dressed resplendently in full ceremonial regalia, cheerfully conversing with his escort, the local Counsellor of Legation. They were in good humour as their 'Inspection' of the warship had gone well and the Captain and his officers had spared no expense on their enthusiastic and alcohol enriched entertainment. Until recently Franz had never once heard mention of the Minister's name, but latterly there had been much talk regarding his wife and her close relationship with the widow of the late, great, German Foreign Minister, Gustav Stresemann. The papers were full of stories of these two women who had become the centre of Berlin High Society and the talk of the whole nation. It was rumoured that the Minister's sudden and surprising promotion to the Portugal position had more to do with his wife's friendship than his diplomatic abilities. In the eyes of Franz such privilege, patronage, wealth and most of all, the direct link back to Poland's arch-antagonist Stresemann, made him the ideal target.

As the two men approached the car Franz sensed that his whole life, the painful catalogue of suffering, had been toughening him up for this one extraordinary, defining moment. He had at last reached the point of no return: he was ready and he would succeed. He breathed deeply, said a silent prayer of thanks, wiped his sweaty hands on his jacket, and then carefully and slowly pulled the Mauser from his pocket. He held it down in front of his body, shielding it from those around him. It was his favourite weapon with which he was very familiar, well practiced and proficient. He had obtained it the previous year in Antwerp, where he once again gave the police the slip, and he had even given it a name, synonymous with its intended purpose: 'Liberty'. It would free him and write his name in history. It was a modified 1916 'Prussian Contract' military Red 9: a semi-automatic or, more correctly, a self-loading pistol. He felt the familiar and reassuring feel of the ridged Walnut panels of the grip (with the large eponymous number 9's embossed and painted thereon) in his right hand as, without looking down and

6

by touch alone, he smoothly slid in and engaged the detachable six-shot magazine which he had pre-loaded with 9mm parabellum rounds. It was a reliable and very accurate weapon and ideal for his purpose.

He sprang into action as soon as they took their seats and the chauffeur was back behind the wheel preparing to drive off. As the adrenaline pumped through his veins any remaining doubts and ambiguities fell away and his mind was completely clear for the first time in days. He was utterly focussed as the target ceased to be a human being and transformed into the personification of state power, oppression and neglect. He barged between the two men in the front row and covered the remaining distance in a split second, the weapon coming up smoothly into the well-balanced double-handed aim position. He instinctively leaned forward slightly, distributing his weight evenly as he bent and braced his knees in the classic hand-gun stance. There was no hesitation as the barrel came to rest almost touching the Minister's head. Before anyone had a chance to react he squeezed the trigger three times in rapid succession and then, as his own face and torso were splattered with blood, tissue and brains, he realised that he had succeeded. In that instant the energy and bitterness that had sustained his lonely struggle and fed his need for power and violent release completely drained from him.

Although he was mentally and physically spent, the relief that he had succeeded was overwhelming. Now he knew questions would be asked and he would finally be given his day in court, his chance to accuse and condemn from the safety of a foreign stage. The world would now listen because the act was so sudden, violent and shocking. He had successfully challenged the raucous, garish high cockalorum of German nationalism and military aggression so personified by the Ambassador. The pompous giant master and his strutting servant had now been toppled, reduced to the grey slumber of death and desolation, and soon they would also be shamed in the court of public opinion.

Both the Minister and the Counsellor had slumped forward and remained motionless as did the chauffeur who, although uninjured, had instinctively dived across the front passenger seat in an effort to protect himself. In his peripheral vision Franz saw the five police officers closing on him and, as he instinctively half turned towards the closest, he saw two men in civilian clothes with pistols raised burst through the front of the crowd twenty yards away. At the same time someone screamed in German, "Shoot the bastard: he's murdered the Ambassador, for Christ's sake kill him before he fires again!"

Having achieved his primary aim Franz could take no further risks if he was to live to see the plan through to completion, and as the drive for self-preservation took over, he threw his weapon into the car, raised his hands and shouted, "I'm from Gdansk…I've killed the diplomat because I have been persecuted for years…all my life…it must stop!" As he screamed his justification, the first police officer, by now unwittingly blocking the line of fire of those men with weapons drawn, and without even breaking his stride, shoulder charged Franz and they both crashed into the side of the car. Franz lost his balance and fell face down onto the concrete with the policeman on top of him. He was held down for several minutes as other police officers piled in and the area was fully secured. The two dignitaries were rushed to hospital and then, to the jeers of the section of crowd that had just witnessed the brutal execution, Franz was pulled to his feet, searched and arrested.

As he was manhandled away Franz noticed that the two men with guns were nowhere to be seen and their sudden and mysterious disappearance confirmed his suspicion that they were two of the German agents who had been following him all day, but yet again, when it came to the crunch they were too late and too slow. Many Germans and locals in the crowd swore, taunted and spat at him as he was dragged along the quayside towards a police car but Franz, satisfied with his decisive victory and Germany's utter humiliation, had now withdrawn into himself and he heard nothing. Nothing that is, save for the voice in his head that would continue to ridicule and control him.

Two of the shots had entered the Minister's head, one through the brain and the other shattering his jaw. He had no chance of surviving such horrific injuries. The third bullet passed clean through the Counsellor's hat and miraculously left him physically unscathed. Mentally, he never fully recovered from the violence and shock of the attack and the sudden and bloody loss of such a close colleague, friend and innocent victim.

ONE

The Reckoning
10th June 1930

Franz felt like a caged animal as he continually paced back and forth across his isolation cell. Despite the short time of his present confinement he was now so familiar with his claustrophobic surroundings that he could safely and silently move around with his eyes closed. This was a skill he had learnt back at his home and it had served him well. He remembered coming down the stairs in the middle of a particularly dark night and literally bumping into a 'watcher' who was caught unawares as he waited on the landing. Franz had reacted first and punched out blindly with both fists, catching the intruder in the face with a lucky right arm jab. The unmistakable squelching sound of the impact was followed by a stream of curses and then, as Franz followed up his initial attack with a further flurry of punches, the intruder stumbled and fell backwards down the stairs into the hallway. Franz drew his pistol, as his adversary struggled to his feet and reached for the door and the safety of the street, and fired once, calmly aiming for the wall above the front door. Plaster and dust fell onto the head and shoulders of the retreating watcher, who was sent on his way with a few choice words. He did not look back as he ran down the road towards safety and Franz was lifted by the memory of how good it had felt not being a victim but being in total control.

His thoughts stayed with his home: Danzig, or Gdansk as the Poles knew it. The city had belonged to many nations during its long and distinguished history, most recently to Prussia until 1919 when it ostensibly became a free city under Polish Governance, within the overall control of The League of Nations. In truth most of the current population were ethnic Germans. The native Poles had been forced to leave or change allegiance during the last century when the population had been systematically 'Germanised' under Prussian rule. The Legislative Assembly, encouraged by the huge German majority that then existed within the city, seemed to take particular delight in antagonising the Polish authorities. It was also actively discriminating against and victimising those Poles who had remained or had returned following the Great War. They found it far more difficult than the Germans to obtain suitable employment, housing, education or common justice. Although a prosperous, major industrial city and thriving port, few of the financial and social benefits filtered through to the dwindling Polish population. The German Government was deaf to their appeals and complaints, being determined to maintain the status quo and The League of Nations (which was a paper tiger without USA membership) lacked even the will to intervene.

Although officially a German citizen, Franz, like his forefathers, considered himself to be Polish and directly blamed the German Government for the decades of hardship and suffering inflicted on his nation. Poland was partitioned and ceased to exist as a country in 1795 when it disappeared from the world map, but for the next 123 years Polish nationalism simmered just beneath the surface and frequently erupted into insurrection, with four major uprisings and numerous political and military conspiracies aimed at restoring independence. Each struggle was put down with ruthless and increasing violence and over time the downtrodden Poles came to revere and romanticise their country as 'Martyred Poland', driving ever-larger sections of the fractured population towards revolt. Ironically, when hostilities broke out in 1914 two million Poles were conscripted into the separate German, Russian and Austrian armies, according to which partitioned area of Poland they resided in. Instead of fighting their enemies they were forced to fight each other!

The eldest of three brothers, Franz went to sea at seventeen hoping to escape from the poverty and oppression at home and to help contribute to the family income. His parents had been struggling to support all three sons during such economically hard times, especially after his father lost his job. His mother was then forced to take in washing and every day became a constant but impossible quest to find sufficient food for them all. His father, previously a very proud man, grew increasingly frantic with their desperate situation and a growing antipathy towards all things German fed his self-pity, which contributed to his mental and physical decline. Franz, seeing his father's deterioration, found it hard to cope with the added responsibility and became even more discontented and determined to find a better life.

He was initially glad to decamp and leave the hunger and deprivation behind him but as the months passed he began to feel guilty for abandoning his mother and brothers in an increasingly hostile and potentially dangerous situation in Gdansk. He became even more embittered when he was unable to offer any help to his younger brothers at a time when they needed him most - during the Great War. In 1913 he was living in America and working as a seaman on their merchant fleet but shortly after he embarked from New York on one such trip, in July 1914, the war broke out and he found himself in very difficult circumstances. His ship was in mid Atlantic approaching Cuba at the time and being 'of German citizenship' he found he was now no longer eligible for employment on most vessels registered in neutral countries. As this also included the United States, he was paid off as soon as the ship docked and he found himself stranded in Cuba without any means of support. As he was determined to have nothing to do with Germany's war effort, he knew that he could not return home. To do so would risk immediate arrest and conscription into the armed services.

As things stood his future prospects looked dismal, so he decided to take on another identity, as a neutral Swiss citizen. With a little subterfuge and a convincing persona, he successfully obtained the relevant passport and was then able to gain further employment at sea and in the short term it also provided some protection against the German Authorities. He soon became aware of the naval blockades that were rapidly being established in the Baltic and decided to avoid the area altogether and travel elsewhere. Over the next four years he sailed to Africa, South America and back to the United States several times, frequently changing his identity and nationality.

Franz's burden of remorse and concern for his brothers' welfare

11

and safety increased even further when in Philadelphia, after he had been arrested for entering the country on false papers, he received a letter from his mother informing him of his father's death. To make matters worse, when Franz was eventually able to talk himself out of detention and return home in 1918 he discovered that both his brothers had also left and his mother, who had since heard nothing from them, had no idea where they had settled.

As the years passed his discontent, anger and sense of isolation increased and as a result he had searched for a way to strike out at those whom he believed had treated him and his community with such contempt and disdain. His resentment and belligerent attitude towards the authorities inevitably brought him into conflict with the police and he was repeatedly arrested and imprisoned for violent and disorderly behaviour and assaulting bureaucrats and police officers. He felt he was unfairly targeted and hounded by the law to the point of persecution and he took every opportunity to antagonise his accusers, ridicule the police and criticise the Government. They, in turn, reacted increasingly robustly to his hostility and growing subversion and frequently reminded him that he would get his comeuppance. He could stand such taunting no longer when he realised that the man that he had discovered on his stairs had obviously not taken his warning seriously. He could not believe his eyes when he saw him, the police watcher, openly following him from his home in broad daylight, making no attempt to hide the fact. When Franz stopped, turned and looked at him, he too stood still and then smirked at his target and waved. Franz was infuriated at the audacity of the man and was left in no doubt that he was waiting for the opportunity to get his revenge. Franz quickly considered his options, made his decision and walked slowly and purposefully towards him. Feeling safe in the busy street, the watcher did not run: he stood his ground but only until Franz pulled out his gun. This time he did not aim off target and he felt a great sense of relief as the man went down. At the sound of the shot bystanders ran for cover, but Franz posed no further threat as he calmly pocketed his weapon and walked away.

The Authorities denied any involvement and said the critically injured man was an innocent neighbour, the local blacksmith, but they prevented Franz from standing trial and testing the evidence by simply locking him up and forbidding any access to him.

He remembered, as clearly as if it were yesterday, the sense of euphoria and success he felt when he had escaped from the Asylum at Lebork (Lauenburg) in Pomerania. It had taken him three months to rehearse and perfect his plan and it had worked like clockwork. He was over ten miles away and safely on a train to Berlin before the hospital staff and the authorities had organised a proper search. He had won their trust and was rewarded for his good behaviour by being allowed to join an organised and supervised walk in the nearby woods. He had concealed the knife in his clothing that morning and then, as intended, he slowly fell behind the main party until only one guard was left escorting him. As the path narrowed he grabbed the surprised orderly from behind, pulled the knife and held it firmly to his throat. In total control, he threatened to cut the terrified man's throat and gradually increased the pressure on the blade until it drew blood but then, as the orderly lost control of his bladder, started trembling uncontrollably and begged for mercy, he lost the impulse to kill and merely threw him to the ground before running off. A week later he made his way from Berlin to the Hamburg bank where he had placed all his seafaring savings, only to discover that they had been seized by the state.

Although left virtually penniless, from that day on he drew strength from the fact that they were unable to incarcerate him then, despite categorising him as a high security risk and injecting him with chemicals. They said, that like so many sailors, he had contracted the pox and the injections were the correct and only effective treatment, but he knew that throughout his detention they had continued to use him as a human guinea pig to trial their new diagnostic tests and experimental treatments. He remembered how he had protested, punched out and screamed defiance at the staff but they drugged him into acquiescence.

The accepted treatment for syphilis was salts of mercury, yet in addition to that toxic remedy they were slowly poisoning him with additional and repeated doses of arsenic, not only injected into his body but also secreted in his food and drink. He had no doubt that if he had not escaped he would have become just another dead inmate, an expendable statistic used to develop their medical knowledge and power. He was certain that if he were sent back there they would certainly finish him off one way or another: they could not allow him to expose the lies, the abuse, the false imprisonment and the complicity of the highest Government officials. He was proud of the fact that, despite their efforts, for eight years he had kept one step ahead of his pursuers, led by the detective Kellermann, and outwitted them by a combination of his considerable linguistic skills, numerous false papers and passports and an acquired ability to go native and blend into the background. Nevertheless, he had been labelled a 'murderer' and even a 'vicious lunatic' by his pursuers, who were proving very persistent.

He dwelt on the detail of how he had been hounded from normal life and, whenever the dragnet closed right in, how he had been driven to full flight, living rough as a vagrant and hiding out in the countryside, sleeping under bridges or in barns and avoiding all human contact. He could no longer use his Swedish or English identities or his genuine Swiss, German or Polish passports and, as he was driven deeper and deeper underground, it was becoming harder to obtain good quality stolen or forged documents. He would go for days without food and creep across international borders under the cover of darkness and there assume yet another false but fragile identity, to buy himself a week or two of respite. Even then his enemies ruthlessly plotted his demise and suborned witnesses as they unremittingly built their case against him. He thought it so ironic that he, alone, homeless and made so unwelcome in every one of the growing list of countries where he had sought sanctuary, had been labelled a spy, a traitor and a dangerous enemy of the state. What state? He had none.

He still drew solace from his defiance. Having reached his lowest point, literally in the gutter, exhausted, filthy, starving and friendless, he, unlike many driven to such wretchedness, had not given up and abandoned his struggle, but instead, for hours on end, had calmly and repeatedly recited his personal covenant of revenge. He recalled how he had drawn so much strength and resolve from the familiar words as he underwent a final and critical metamorphosis. In order to survive and to succeed, the exhausted, beleaguered quarry was abandoned and the steadfast, ruthless hunter was born.

That powerful memory reminded Franz that his actions at the docks had not only been justified but also crucial if he was going to survive and nullify the German plans to have him liquidated. The most blatant attempt had been in Naples where he and several of his crewmates were openly attacked on the street whilst on shore-leave. Franz, quick to identify the reality of the situation, had managed to escape down a side-alley as a desperate, full-scale fight broke out behind him, but one less fortunate colleague - mistaken for him in the melee - was beaten to death by the local gang of thugs in the pay of Kellermann. Two other sailors, trying to defend themselves and their colleagues, were hospitalised with serious injuries but the gang, which outnumbered the sailors two-to-one, carried away their own wounded. This incident showed that the German Police and Security forces were also quite prepared to kill and maim anyone who stood in their way. Even inside this prison he could not feel safe, but he believed he had finally found a way of bringing their institutionalised, systematic and unforgivable crimes out into the open: into the full glare of public and international judgment. He was confident that his future trial in a foreign and less denouncing country would ensure that his voice and the pleas of the thousands he represented would be heard across the whole world. He hoped that the public outcry and the international condemnation of his enemies could, not only save his life in the short term, but just might be the only way to ensure his future protection.

Nevertheless, just for a moment or two, as he again contemplated the destructive power of the forces arraigned against him, he found himself wondering whether the constant accusatory and erosive mantra of his enemies did actually contain a shred of truth. After all, he had committed serious criminal acts and he had struck at the very heart of the beast that taunted him, but despite his doubts, it all came back to the fact that they, not he, were the aggressors, the persecutors and the deceivers. Every time he had reached out for help or kindness he had been betrayed, belittled and condemned.

Above all else, he resented the fact that both Germans and Poles had come to consider him as an outsider and he now felt that this discrimination had, to a significant degree, followed him all his life, holding him back and often causing open hostility on board ship as he travelled across Europe and to the Americas. He was incensed that Germany and Poland were once again engaged in an increasingly resentful and rancorous war of words: this time over their respective rights in Gdansk and along the Polish Corridor. Hitler, who was becoming more popular and dominant as he travelled the length and breadth of Germany, making powerful speeches during his election campaign, was striving for overall control of the whole country. He was now making barely veiled threats of hostile military action in support of German citizens in Danzig. There was also a supportive groundswell of anti-Polish feeling within the press and the more militant sections of the Government. The Poles in return were also becoming more uncooperative and belligerent. Franz fervently wished that both leaderships would spend just a fraction of their energies and taxes on helping the poor and downtrodden through the depression rather than antagonistically confronting each other.

As he reminisced he again realised that every convoluted twist and turn in his life had led directly to this very time and place and an overwhelming sense of personal destiny filled him with confidence and courage. He gave voice to the simple but heartfelt basis of his proposed defence, "I had no choice. I acted to protect myself."

At that moment the trap at the bottom of the cell door rattled open and a meal of bread, sausage and milk was placed on the concrete floor. When Franz picked up the tin plate the guard spoke slowly and deliberately, so Franz would not misunderstand his muffled words, "I'm sorry to be the one to tell you this but I've just found out that you're going to be tried within the next few days by a closed military court. They say you'll be executed immediately afterwards. Our masters have decided that there won't be a public trial, so no publicity for you. It seems they want your passing to go unnoticed. I suggest you use the time left to prepare yourself my friend."

Franz threw his plate and contents against the wall screaming, "Bastards! They're all evil bastards. For the love of God - they must pay for this." He slowly sank to his knees and repeatedly punched the floor, so hard that his knuckles split and the searing pain burst through his anger. Then he wept: not because of his shattered fists or any fear of death, but because of the cold realisation that if the hand of his enemy could reach out so far and so easily, to silence him, just one lonely man, then he must fear for the very future of his homeland.

TWO

Darkness Descends
1st September 1939

Ewa and her devoted husband embraced on the overcrowded platform, their sons already excitedly climbing into the carriage. As Henryk raised his voice to be heard above the noise and bustle of several hundred other anxious passengers, his tone was unfamiliarly serious and pleading, "Please write home whenever you can. Take care of the boys and keep them on a tight rein. I love you so much - but you must go now - and please stay safe!"

She saw the pain of separation and worry in his eyes as he hugged and kissed her, and sensed with striking certainty that their comfortable life together, surrounded by friends and family and wanting for very little, was about to change forever. She was to board an evacuation train for the families of the railway workers from all across the Lower Vistula. Its departure was arranged to coincide with the repositioning of rolling stock to the east, facilitating the movement of troops westwards to the front. It was hoped that taking the women and children to safety would ensure that the husbands and fathers remained at their posts to re-supply and transport reinforcements to the hard-pressed defenders to the west. In truth these front-line forces would shortly be overwhelmed and cut off by a tidal wave of military armour and aerial bombardment as the unremitting Nazi war machine rolled right over them.

Such an evacuation of civilians had first been planned in March following the German occupation of Czechoslovakia, which had exposed the whole of western Poland as an extremely vulnerable salient within the voracious jaws of Hitler's Germany. Final preparations were made in August when German intentions became obvious, as she massed armoured divisions along her eastern border and raised tensions over the Polish Corridor to an unprecedented level, with aggressive sabre rattling and actual territorial incursions.

The Railway Authority had arranged for the Nowaski family to be moved from their home to a host railway family, living outside Luck, a city in the Polish Ukraine on the relatively safe eastern side of this vast country. Their flight however, unbeknown to all at the time, was taking them from the onset of a cruel, ferocious blitzkrieg into the path of another equally dire but more insidious danger.

Ewa returned her husband's kisses and squeezed his hands with loving tenderness, anxious to spend every possible second with her soul-mate but also desperate to do all in her power to protect her children. She turned to her daughter Maria, "I know father must stay my dear but I wish you would leave, it's not too late to change your mind, even now. Please come with us."

They too embraced, then fighting back the tears Maria kissed her mother and said, "We've discussed this for hours already and we agreed I should stay and look after Papa and, in any case, I'll be needed at the hospital. We can only do our jobs properly back here if we know you are all safe, so no more discussions please, take the boys away from this chaos and madness."

"I know it's for the best but I feel so guilty leaving you behind, so promise me you'll both take care of each other and look after the house properly until we can come back."

Maria linked her arm through her father's and patted his hand, as a signal of her new responsibility of care and reassured her mother, "We'll do our best and don't worry, I know deep inside that whatever happens we'll all be back together before too long."

Ewa wept openly as the train pulled away with the boys lining the windows waving goodbye to their father and sister. She dreaded the thought of such a long and difficult journey and, although a robust and intelligent woman, she was totally disconcerted by the speed at which current events were unfolding. Poland was at war: her enemies many and powerful, her friends few and weak. In just one momentous day, as the Nazi government launched operation 'case white'- the invasion of Poland - everything had irrevocably changed for millions of citizens across the face of Europe. The Nowaski family, like so many others, would be sorely tested.

Ten days before, Hitler had addressed his senior commanders and sadistically empowered them and, in the minds of many subordinates, also absolved them with the following words, 'We must kill, without pity or mercy, all men, women and children of Polish descent or language. Only in this way will we obtain the living space (Lebensraum) that we need for our greater Germany.'

Henryk, a very private man who never spoke of his origins, his antecedents or his childhood, had been born in Danzig of Polish parents. After leaving school, along with his elder brother, he left the hostile atmosphere of the 'free' city in search of safety, work and better prospects, taking advantage of the general confusion and upheaval caused by the outbreak of the Great War. They found lodgings and full time employment as labourer/gardeners at the Cistercian monastery in the small historic town of Pelplin. Four years later, following the rebirth of Poland and whilst undergoing training on the National Railway he met Ewa in the nearby town of Gniew. They courted, fell in love, worked hard and saved for their future together. Just over a year later they could wait no longer and, much to the delight of their friends and Ewa's family, they were married. Henryk's brother Roman was the best man and the only member of his family to attend. Their close and happy union was subsequently blessed with five children: four boys and a girl.

Thirteen-year-old Jan, an adventurous outdoors lad, dreamt of becoming a train driver and spent all his spare time playfully annoying the staff around the railway yards at Pelplin where his father was now the station telegraphist. He was very close to his mother and although she showed no favouritism she had the strongest of maternal bonds with her youngest son. She could accurately predict how he would behave in any given situation and could often tell how he felt, what was worrying him and even what he was thinking. Although he was sometimes embarrassed by this closeness he treasured their relationship and would do anything to avoid hurting his mother. He was described in school reports as an average student but he worked hard and enthusiastically took part in all classroom and extracurricular activities. His sociable, helpful and considerate attitude to his classmates made him very popular both with students and teachers alike.

Tomek and Jacek were fifteen and although twins were as different as chalk and cheese. Tomek was physically tall, well built, very strong and a sportsman: always hunting and shooting across the numerous marshes and lakes that surrounded their home. He was also mischievous and headstrong: his schemes and adventures frequently getting himself or more often his brothers into trouble with their father or neighbours. Jan looked up to him and often sought his company as they had similar interests, but being older, Tomek tolerated the hero worship but did not relish his younger brother as a constant shadow. Although he never voiced the opinion he worried that Jan would deliberately, or more likely, inadvertently reveal his secret escapades to their mother. He was also very good with his hands, constantly whittling and carving toys and household items from discarded pieces of wood he found on his hunting trips. He had just started an apprenticeship as a carpenter with a furniture maker in the centre of town.

Jacek was a loner, a book worm, top in his class at school and a music lover, naturally gifted at the piano and graced with a fine singing voice. He was three inches shorter than Tomek and his pallid indoor complexion, slight physique and serious expression set him apart, both within the family and amongst his peers. He was seldom seen with his twin and, in fact, did all he could to avoid sports, games, country pursuits and anything too strenuous. His greatest attribute was an inner strength of unshakeable resolve, being highly self disciplined, single-minded and not easily diverted when tackling any subject that truly held his interest or challenged his thirst for knowledge. Like his twin he had just left school and had been looking forward to starting at college where he had enrolled to study music.

The eldest son at sixteen was Jozef, the only one who was truly dedicated to his religious studies, a master of the catechism who served at the altar every day and was determined to train for the priesthood. He was intelligent, sensitive, and considerate of others and a very deep thinker with high moral values and a keen sense of family duty. He was hoping to go to university one day but suspected that his parents on their own would be unable to afford to support him through his studies. He had therefore, on the advice of the local priest, who had taken on the role of mentor and hinted at the possibility of the church providing some financial assistance in the future, enrolled at college where he was studying theology.

Maria had inherited her mother's fine looks and benevolent temperament and was a natural organiser and problem solver. This skill was frequently required to mitigate the exuberant excesses of her brothers who had come to rely on her at such times as a placatory buffer between them and their parents. Now nineteen and a qualified nurse at the local hospital, she still continued to enthusiastically help her mother run the home and look after her brothers. It was really her own choice to remain behind and, as the hospital was already receiving casualties from air strikes, her mother understood and respected her viewpoint. Nevertheless Ewa was devastated by the separation. The boys, despite their varied commitments at home, had been given no option by their parents other than to travel with their mother, in line with the Railway Authority's recommendation that all those under seventeen years of age should be evacuated.

Twenty-four hours later, Ewa reflected on the farewell and their slow progress towards the capital. They had spent hours in sidings as troop trains and wagons loaded with horses and military hardware, speeding towards the west, were given priority along this arterial route. She shivered, recalling the huge hospital train that had passed, heading towards Warsaw earlier in the day. Its vast, garish red crosses and the casualties crammed within its seemingly unending number of carriages telling her more about what was really happening than the constant reassuring messages on the wireless and in the newsletters, saying all was well as 'the brave defenders gallantly held the line.'

The train had stopped at Torun and, in order to take on more distressed families, those already aboard had been forced by the Railway Police to abandon their meagre possessions, leaving their cases, packages, bicycles and even livestock scattered across the platform. As the train pulled out the desperate and unnatural image of those former travel necessities and personal comforts, now reduced to an irrelevant mishmash of pitiful flotsam, was forever imprinted into Ewa's mind. It left her with a deep sense of finality, loneliness and foreboding.

Suddenly they were all thrown to the floor as the train's brakes were applied so fiercely and without warning, some half a mile from the main station in Warsaw. As Jan tried to pick himself up and help his mother he heard the deafening and terrifying noise of the diving Stukas and the answering fire of the anti-aircraft guns. The spats above the wheels of the dive-bombers had been fitted with wind fuelled sirens, aptly named by the Germans as 'the trumpets of Jericho': these had a demoralising effect on those on the ground, numbing the senses and causing disorientation. To cause further dread, the bombs had been specially designed with tubes inside their fins so that each one whistled loudly and shrilly as it plummeted earthwards. The planes were able to dive almost vertically onto their targets with deadly accuracy because they were fitted with an autopilot system, which controlled the dive and safely brought the plane back to level flight once the bomb had been dropped. This allowed the pilot to devote all his attention to successfully aiming the bomb and, even if he temporarily passed out (which happened quite regularly) from the G-forces involved, the plane would recover automatically.

The continuous but belated warbling wail of the air-raid sirens sounding across the city added to the thunderous cacophony that painfully assaulted their ears. All around the overcrowded train passengers were screaming and children crying and, what had started the previous day in Pelplin as an adventure for the boys, had rapidly descended into a nightmare for all the family. Ewa, although terrified by the attack, scrambled to her feet and gathered her children around her. Not for the last time, she feared for the lives of her boys and screamed at them, "Stay close to me. We must get off this train…now!"

Somehow they managed to keep together and stay on their feet as, caught in the stampede of dozens of passengers, they jumped from the now stationary train. Hundreds of people were literally running for their lives along the tracks away from the inferno within the station. As the panic spread some of the less able were knocked over by the sheer weight of those pushing through from behind, or simply stumbled, tripped and fell onto the ballast: in either case they were immediately trampled underfoot as the swarm of frightened travellers desperately ran for shelter.

Enemy planes seemed to fill the sky and the return fire had almost been silenced, leaving the station at the mercy of the Luftwaffe. The acrid smell of smoke, the ramped screeching of the dive-bombers, and the sheer force of heat and blast from the nearby explosions turned panic into pandemonium. As they ran they could see another train stopped about five hundred yards ahead and already its passengers were jumping onto the tracks. Ewa physically pulled her charges away from the vicinity of the trains towards the embankment, "Let's get off the tracks, hurry up! Make for the road. Come on…run...this way…we must stay together."

As they climbed up the steep bank on their hands and knees, surrounded by dozens of others desperately attempting to scale the same escape route, one of the planes screamed overhead at about a hundred feet swooping straight towards the second locomotive. The noise of the Junkers Juma 1200 horse-power engine was deafening and they instinctively fell flat on the ground and huddled together, but Jan's gaze was fixed on the plane as its twin machine guns strafed the engine, its carriages and the running passengers. He watched, mesmerised by the altogether alien sights and terrifying sounds, as men, women and children, some babes in arms, died by the dozen in and alongside the shredded carriages. The sprinting survivors were suddenly scythed down like ripe corn by the shock wave from a bomb, which had scored a direct hit on the front of the train. One carriage was thrown high up into the air and another was tossed along the tracks, end over end like a giant caber, spewing out bodies, smoke and flame through gaping holes, which only moments before had been the doors and windows of a seemingly secure and comfortable refuge. The other crashed horizontally back to earth onto its roof and was instantly reduced to matchwood by the massive impact which shook the ground with an explosive force, killing anyone who might have survived the original blast. Jan felt furious and ashamed that their soldiers had not prevented this from happening. In fact there wasn't a single soldier anywhere to be seen, only terrified and shocked civilians. But, as a plane climbed away into the grey autumn sky, vapour pouring from its wings, he noticed for the first time the black crosses and swastikas, symbols that he would grow to hate with a bitter intensity.

Jozef was lying across his mother in an attempt to protect her. He was terrified and praying for the strength not to show his fear or let his family down when he noticed three boys of about his own age a hundred yards away, using a wrecked power stanchion to scale the perimeter wall and gain access to the relative safety of the road above. They had just reached the top of the tower when there was a loud crack and another blinding flash, as all three were electrocuted and left dangling and twitching like puppets, entangled in the twisted metal and sparking overhead power lines. Just a few seconds later as smoke drifted away from their corpses they were shrivelled, blackened and unrecognisable, totally ignored by the crowd fleeing from the carnage in a frantic effort to save themselves. Jozef would never forget these appalling images even though they presaged ever-greater horror and hardship that would severely question his physical and mental resolve and test his faith to breaking point.

Jacek was sobbing as they finally joined the throng on the main road, seeking shelter from the attacking aircraft, and moving away from the railway. He was supported by Tomek who was also struggling to retain control of his own emotions, being full of hatred for the Germans and, although trembling with fear, he ached to join up, fight back and defend his country. Despite his strict Catholic upbringing he already prayed for revenge against his enemies. As he walked along, in his naïve enthusiasm, he imagined himself as a pilot, shooting down the bombers and helping to drive the invaders back from his home and country.

"Come on boys, keep up, we'll make for uncle Roman's in Old Town. I'm sure he'll help us find some transport east," Ewa almost shouted to make herself heard above the noise of the receding explosions, fires and general mayhem in the streets. She hoped her brother-in-law was safe and in a position to help. She had the necessary evacuation tickets and passes to take the children to safety, but right now they needed food, shelter, and the opportunity to recover from the shock before planning the next stage of their journey.

As they walked Jacek tried to rationalise what he had seen. The dreadful slaughter, the fear on everyone's face, the fires and the screaming of the injured made him feel physically sick. He couldn't understand why the Germans were attacking his family and all the other civilians who were seeking safety and posed no threat to them. Surely the planes should be at the front-line or attacking the Polish air force, not here in the centre of Warsaw. He felt so dejected and miserable, longed to be home again and wondered how far it was to the Ukraine.

I opened the metal zip on the small leather case (measuring only eighteen inches by nine inches by three inches deep) which, on returning from the shops, I had found parcelled up in my porch. It had been hand delivered. My curiosity aroused, I very carefully emptied the contents onto my desk. There were six letters, five written in Polish, but oddly, one in German and most without envelopes; several dozen old photographs; a small concise English-Polish dictionary; a set of rosary beads and ten yellowing postcards. I put them all aside for later examination and opened the accompanying letter dated two days earlier.

Dear Mick,

This case was found last week by a friend whilst sorting out her parents' cupboards in preparation for the house sale. Her mother had first mentioned it to her about ten years ago after her father had died, and I gather that a man who stayed at The Red Lion Inn at Salisbury, when her dad was the owner in about 1970, deliberately left the case behind. He was smart, well dressed, looked to be in his forties, and spoke with a strong Polish accent and he asked the licensee to hold on to it for safekeeping. He only stayed for about a week, then said he had to rush off to deal with an emergency and that things were difficult for him. He did not elaborate and gave no indication of his destination, but intimated that he would return for the case when his circumstances were resolved. The owner had taken a liking to the chap who was well mannered and personable and, although initially reluctant to retain the case, after further pleas he relented.

Needless to say, the mysterious visitor never came back and my friend's parents never saw him again. The letters and some photographs are dated in the late Thirties and Forties, and obviously were of sentimental value to have been kept in the case for thirty odd years. I can offer no explanation as to the owner's disappearance or his failure to collect his property. Unfortunately my friend was unable to furnish any further detail, as she never discussed it again with her mother before she died. She had forgotten all about it in the interim period and, to be honest, she was tempted to throw it out but I thought, with your Polish background, you might attempt to trace the owner if he's still alive or failing that, his next of kin. I know it's a long shot and I don't hold out much chance of success but it doesn't seem right to dispose of it when the mum and dad had kept it safe all these years. I feel that some attempt should be made to return these very private and personal documents to the owner: anyway, perhaps you could give it some thought.

Thanks for your time: let me know what you think in due course.

Yours Dave.

I had known Dave for forty years, having joined the police together as sixteen-year-old school-leavers in 1966. By the time we retired in 1998 we had been involved in the investigation of many high profile cases together. Contrary to popular belief, Wiltshire can be as violent as anywhere else in England.

We had also been heavily involved in policing the riots at Stonehenge; the so-called 'Battle of the Bean field' in 1985 and again in 1988 where, on that one night, over a thousand police officers were deployed in the Neolithic Circle site and the surrounding fields on Salisbury Plain. In an unprecedented operation for the Wiltshire Police, officers had travelled from numerous County and Metropolitan Forces across England and Wales in order to control a hostile crowd of some ten thousand, a small but significant contingent of which was intent on causing mayhem and damage at the World Heritage Site.

Over the years we had been in several particularly tight spots together and had somehow managed to save each other from both physical injury and considerable embarrassment. As a consequence we had developed a mutual respect for the other's professional abilities and had also become close friends, meeting socially on a regular basis for 'a trip down memory lane', where the stories became more exaggerated and the jokes more corny with each telling. I readily decided to see what I could do.

26

I was also intrigued by the fact that the 'Polish Gent' had disappeared and so little was known about him. Why would he leave these articles with a passing acquaintance if they really meant anything to him? What stopped him from returning? Could he still be alive? Surely he would now be well into his eighties! Perhaps the documents themselves could answer some of these questions.

Having thumbed through the papers I picked up the earliest letter, written in Polish on a single sheet of plain off-white paper that had been ripped from a book or pad and dated 2nd September 1939. Although the paper had faded slightly, the writing was small, neat and clearly legible. The language was old fashioned and I had difficulty translating several phrases but finally settled on:

My dearest Henio,

We are safe at Roman's. The authorities in Warsaw will not allow us to continue until the bombing stops and so we have been forced to break our journey. You should be proud of the boys who are so well behaved and they were delighted to see their uncle again. I don't know when you will receive this, as things seem to be getting more difficult. I miss you both already and how I long for our lives to be the way they were: perhaps it won't be for too long. I hope you are taking care of each other and not working day and night. I pray for us all the time and ask God to keep the boys safe. We hope to get back on the train tomorrow, but as I write this I feel that Luck is a world away from my home and all that I hold dear. Yet we must make the best of our situation and remain strong and determined to see this through. Young Jan is so brave and tonight I gave him my rosary to keep him safe, and now he is wearing it proudly around his neck. He says he is never going to take it off! How he reminds me of you. I must go now and prepare a meal, I am truly grateful for your brother's larder! Take care my darling and give my love to Maria.

Your loving wife, Ewka.

I picked up the rosary and let it run through my fingers, its wooden beads worn smooth and polished by years of use. The crucifix was silver but tarnished and as I stared at it I wondered what secrets it held, and whether they would be given up easily.

They were woken by Roman at 6am. "I've been to Central Station, which is still closed down, but the noon train to Lublin has definitely been scheduled to leave sometime today. It's now setting out from Wschodnia station instead: so we must cross the river. The Germans have virtually destroyed the railway bridge but one or two of the road bridges are still just about passable. We'll have to get a move on!"

The next two hours were spent giving the boys a decent breakfast and raiding Roman's wardrobe and cupboards for clothes and supplies that could replace some of those lost at Torun. "Take what you need," invited Roman as he cut bread and cheese for the journey, "There aren't many shortages yet, and anyway I can get by on very little: unlike my brother, I'm a man of simple tastes and requirements!"

Both Roman and his wife Mella were teachers and he had moved to the capital after she died from tuberculosis in the winter of 1933. As they had no children he decided on a fresh start in Warsaw, where the prospects and wages were far better than in the provinces. His wife's death had shaken him badly, and although a lively and sociable man, he had never wanted to marry again. As they left the flat Roman said quietly to Ewa, "I'll see you all safely to the train but I've decided I'm going to join up later today if they'll have me. There's a recruiting centre just round the corner but when I went three weeks ago, following the local call-ups for the reserves, they said I was too old at 45! Surely they must take me now after all that's happened since."

By 8 am the streets were packed and by stark contrast to the previous day, soldiers, particularly armed military police, were everywhere. They had only walked a hundred yards when they joined a queue at the first of the four checkpoints they would encounter. The Authorities were desperately hunting Polish speaking German spies who had been planted inside the capital long before hostilities broke out and who were now providing critical, up-to-date and extremely valuable military intelligence to the enemy.

All documents and identities were thoroughly checked before the family was allowed through and it took them over two hours to reach the station. Several times during the journey they heard distant explosions and everyone ran for cover when three German fighter planes screamed low overhead. Fortunately the pilots must have had pressing business elsewhere that morning as they carried on westwards. The four or five soldiers, who fruitlessly fired their weapons at the retreating aircraft, only served to further frighten those already cowering on the pavement nearby. How wonderful it was when seconds later two Polish fighters flew by, hugging the rooftops in hot pursuit of the Messerschmitts: They all cheered and shouted support; it was so comforting to see that, here at least, the Germans were not in total control of the skies.

There were clear signs that this station had also been attacked, with large holes in the platform roofs, craters in the platform itself and scorching from several fires within the structures of the trackside buildings. Sections of the line and overhead power cables had also been repaired overnight but it was evident that the raid had not been as determined, prolonged, or as effective as that on the central station. It was also clear from the army of workers milling about across the whole station that the civic authorities were at last beginning to bring some organisation to the chaos. Several shunting engines were already operating, removing wreckage, repositioning rolling stock and replacing ballast. On the concourse they bade a tearful farewell to Roman, thanking him for his kindness and his practical and emotional support, before they boarded their train and settled down in the front carriage, breathing a collective sigh of relief to be leaving the capital and its all too obvious dangers behind.

Over a hundred miles away at a dispersal airbase (little more than a couple of fields and a few hastily converted farm buildings) in the countryside, five miles from Lublin, Kapitan Piotr Maczewic was ranting at his senior officer. "Why won't they listen to the commanders in the field? You know our aircraft are just not up to the task, we're facing the best-equipped and trained air force in the world and, as we fight, our self-satisfied senior command personnel are living in cloud-cuckoo-land, dreaming of an impossible victory. For God's sake! Our defence is disorganised, our aircraft too few, too scattered and too far away from support, fuel and ammunition. We're already losing this war, yet the fool Generals spend their time arguing with each other and placing bets on when our troops will march into Berlin."

Major Garczek smiled benignly at his protégé, shook his head as he would at an intransigent child and said, "Piotr, you really mustn't speak like that, it's so insubordinate, defeatist and bad for morale."

"But their dithering and incompetence is criminal and it's coming from the same geriatrics that are stupid enough to think that Hitler is just hot air and idle bluff. Is there nothing you can do to make them see sense and get some organisation back into this shambles?

"I don't think so, but you do, at least in the privacy of this pigsty they call an office, deserve an honest answer. Of this I'm absolutely sure, things have slipped too far too quickly and we won't recover now, no matter what we do. There's no co-ordination between the army and us and our supply lines have been obliterated. I'm afraid we're on our own and we won't last much longer. As for you, if the Luftwaffe doesn't get you first, you'll probably be shot for your disrespect and rebellious talk. In fact I should shoot you myself, but the truth is I can't afford to lose my best pilot while we still have a few planes left."

Piotr had trained under the Major at the Air Officers' Academy at Deblin before being posted to operational command in September 1938. He now commanded a flight of six planes: P11c fighters, which had only half the speed and one eighth of the Messerschmitt 109's firepower. Although state of the art machines when first manufactured in 1934, rapid development in warplane technology had rendered them obsolete. They even looked old fashioned with their fixed undercarriages, high wings and open cockpits. Piotr's section had, however, been among the very few aircraft hastily fitted with radios just a few days before the war started. Previously only Squadron Leaders had radio contact with base and even now most of the pilots across the country had to rely on hand signals to communicate with each other. The P11c's one slight advantage however, was its superior manoeuvrability in very close-quarter combat and Piotr had used this edge and his own innate flying skills to achieve four 'kills' so far.

30

In the first minutes of the war he shot down an enemy bomber that crash-landed in a field and, acting on his strong sense of chivalry, and in total contrast to the German disregard of the Geneva Conventions, he landed alongside the stricken and smoking plane. He then helped to rescue the crew, shook them all by the hand and only when he was satisfied that they were in no further danger did he take off to resume the battle. The cost since that first engagement had been heavy, as he had lost three of his own aircraft and two pilots. He could hardly believe his eyes when he had seen enemy pilots deliberately machinegun his own colleagues as they were suspended helplessly in their parachutes. He was even more offended when he heard that some Polish pilots had since adopted the same practice in retaliation.

Piotr's remaining planes had only sufficient fuel and ammunition for one more sortie. The Major had promised to scour the countryside for replenishments but, from what Piotr had seen from the air, their lines of communication had been so well targeted by enemy bombers that any support was out of the question. There had even been rumours that morning that the whole air force was to be ordered to escape across the border into neutral Romania. Piotr had decided that he would refuse any such order, as he would not desert his comrades fighting on the ground. Until his plane gave out he would stay, and only then would he consider running for the border. The Major was taking his leave when the unit was scrambled, and just a few minutes later the three remaining fighters were in the air heading west in search of the enemy.

The first couple of hours on the train had passed without incident and Ewa had begun to relax somewhat when Jacek shouted out at no one in particular, "Look over here! Soldiers. I've never seen so many all in one place: where do you think they're off to?"

The train started to slow down and the troops could be seen marching along the road running parallel to the track. There were column upon column of cavalry and scores of horse-drawn artillery pieces, intermingled with trucks, motorcycles and units of infantry. Their progress was painfully slow and deliberate as the roadway had been churned into a sea of mud by a recent spate of localised thunderstorms, triggered by the exceptionally long hot summer.

"They must be reinforcements for the front," replied Jozef as he squeezed his way through the line of passengers at the window, "They'll be marching for days yet but there must be thousands of them: God willing, this many fresh troops will make a massive difference when they go into action. What a sight for sore eyes this is."

No sooner had he spoken than the soldiers started running from the road into the drainage ditches alongside the railway line and the cavalry charged off into the adjacent fields. All around troops were diving for cover and running in all directions away from the exposed level-crossing immediately ahead of the train. Orders were shouted by the officers, the horses pulled to the ground and weapons of every type pointed skywards.

Once again all the passengers cowered on the floor as they heard the now familiar sound of screaming aircraft engines overhead. They felt even more exposed and vulnerable as the train was now almost stationary, providing a sitting target to their attackers. Fortunately the enemy planes were initially more intent on destroying the soldiers and their equipment, and this gave the engine driver crucial moments to increase speed over the now deserted crossing and put critical distance between them and the fire-fight.

From seven thousand feet Piotr looked down at the battle scene below and was relieved that he had the advantage of height and, to some degree, this mitigated against the vast superiority of the ME 109s and Stukas which were dropping bombs and pouring cannon-fire into the ground units. He was not surprised that the return fire from the inexperienced troops was mostly wildly inaccurate and of little practical effect. He counted eight enemy aircraft and he hoped that if his section attacked and scored a couple of hits, the others would withdraw in search of undefended targets. This had been the case since the start of the conflict and he concluded that they would not stay and fight as they had probably been ordered to inflict as much damage as possible, without unduly risking their aircraft. This thought increased his confidence as he ordered, "Attack, attack, let's drive them off, take the 109s first. Remember your training and our lost colleagues. Follow me now and break right…break right."

As Piotr dived through the enemy formation he managed to

fire a full burst into the cockpit of a yellow-nosed 109 before the pilot had even seen him. Clouds of oil poured from the damaged plane which continued to fly straight and level, the pilot already dead at the controls, until it burst into flames, then exploded with huge chunks of wreckage spiralling to earth, each section trailing whirling patterns of smoke, flame and sparks like a display of giant fireworks.

When he levelled out he pulled a very tight turn which brought him up on the tail of another Messerschmitt, but his first burst of canon-fire screamed harmlessly underneath the German plane as the pilot spotted his enemy and climbed steeply to shake the Pole off. Piotr used every ounce of engine power and all his physical strength to stay inside the Messerschmitt's turn but he knew that within seconds it would inevitably pull out of range. He took his last chance and fired a long burst towards the escaping fighter, more in hope than anticipation and he was surprised to see his enemy's tail disintegrate, and the once sleek and powerful aircraft was immediately transformed into a useless heap of scrap metal that hurtled back to earth like a massive ungainly bomb. At that very moment, before he could savour his success, his own aircraft shuddered and he felt machine gun bullets rip across the tail end of his fuselage. He broke left and dived to escape his own unseen pursuer and the controls immediately became heavy and sluggish. As he slowly regained some control the enemy fighter that had attacked him streaked past above: the pilot making the classic error of overshooting the target in his exuberance to finish Piotr off.

The Pole realised that he had had a lucky break and his good fortune held as the enemy did not turn and seek to push home his initial advantage, but continued on, presumably in pursuit of his own comrades. Before it disappeared into the distance the Pole noticed a series of distinctive red and yellow bandings on the rear fuselage and tail of the fighter and made a mental note to mark it out for special attention should he manage to fly again.

Piotr was brave but knew he was now in grave danger and, if he was to survive, it was time to head for home. "It's cut and run for us if we want to fight again," he shouted into the radio as he started his turn. He was relieved to see only four enemy planes heading south-west, probably for their base and one of them was trailing a great deal of smoke. He was delighted that his flight had

33

apparently managed to destroy four enemy aircraft and force them to call off their attack but there was no reply to his radio message and, with increasing concern, he unsuccessfully searched the sky for his comrades. He hoped that they had survived but he had been so absorbed in his own personal dogfight that he hadn't seen either of them since their initial dive. The radio remained ominously silent except for the constant static and so he lost height and started to search the ground for wreckage.

The troops below were already returning to the road and reforming, tending to their dead and wounded. It appeared from above that casualties had been remarkably low and he mused that this was probably due to the very soft waterlogged ground absorbing much of the explosive power of the bombs and even preventing some from detonating. As he searched he saw the train again, some five miles ahead. Suddenly his heart sank when he also spotted the same 109 that had so nearly destroyed him appear from a cloudbank and rapidly close in on the rear of the train.

High velocity, large calibre bullets ripped through the carriages with the effect of an eighteenth century naval broadside: the red hot metal, shrapnel and impact splinters the size of axe blades raking through metal, wood and flesh without discrimination or hindrance. The full devastating impact of the attack was felt only at the rear of the train because the pilot, in order to line up his weapons, had fired too early. He had not reached the front carriages of the train before he was forced to release the fire button to prevent the guns overheating.

As Ewa found the courage to look out the window she saw the German plane scream low overhead and then start to turn in preparation for another pass, this time towards the front of the train and she knew that her family would be lucky to survive another attack. She gathered her children around her on the floor and, taking cover as best they could, they started crawling under the seats. Jozef had begun praying as he heard the aircraft and Jan clutched his rosary tightly to his chest.

"Don't be frightened," whispered Ewa, "I promised father that we would stay safe and we will," but secretly she had no faith or confidence in her own words.

"I wish we were back home not stuck on this train, what have

34

any of us done to deserve all this?" Tomek complained as he crawled closer to Jozef.

"Once we get to Luck things will get better: father said we were in far more danger back home and he knows what he's talking about. We owe it to him to look after each other and get to safety. We'll be all right, you'll see," replied Ewa, in a half-hearted effort to placate her family.

Piotr, even with a damaged plane, rushed towards the 109 with a combined closing speed of well over four hundred miles per hour and, as he approached the rear carriage, he was determined that the train would survive. He flashed over the engine and had the other plane in his sights. They fired simultaneously at extreme range but after a few seconds Piotr's ammunition was expended. He flew on as bullets stitched the fuselage and his right wing, and he was completely enveloped in smoke and hot oil. He felt a sudden intense pain in his lower legs and he couldn't feel the pedals through his feet. A numbing coldness crept across his arms and chest and he started to choke as the acrid fumes reached his lungs. He shook his head in an attempt to clear his vision, gritted his teeth and drew on every second of his limited combat experience to keep his crippled plane in level flight.

As he struggled with the controls he saw blood spurting from his right hand where his thumb and index finger had been shot clean off but he forced himself to ignore the frightening injury and look ahead towards his enemy. His options had all but expired: he was about to die. With this recognition came an overwhelming sense of purpose and he relaxed back into his seat accepting his fate as he realised, with complete certainty, that the determination already shown by this particularly stubborn and lingering enemy pilot meant that he would relentlessly press home his attack no matter what. Piotr felt he had his measure and gambled that this German's pride, his need to make up for his initial mistakes, and his belief in his own superiority would convince him that the Pole was bound to blink first and break off to avoid a collision. Such hubris would cost the young German his aircraft and his life.

A huge explosion rocked the train as the two planes collided a short distance ahead, with such force that they virtually disintegrated.

Seconds later the train broke through the dense cloud of smoke and as debris rained down they steamed on: many lives saved by the skill, resourcefulness and bravery of a man unknown to them all.

For the next two hours Ewa and her family, who had suffered nothing worse than a few minor cuts and bruises, were busy helping the one doctor and two nurses aboard to comfort the bereaved and tend the wounded. They also helped to remove the dead to the rearmost carriage, which although severely damaged and open to the elements, was still serviceable as a temporary mortuary. The train came to a final halt a mile short of Lublin where two bridges had been completely destroyed by enemy bombers. They waited all night for help, dreading the return of enemy aircraft, and when transport and medical staff arrived at first light the able-bodied passengers helped to remove the dead and injured. The survivors were loaded onto carts and trucks and taken to Lublin where they were documented, fed and accommodated overnight in a school. Being so far from home, the level of organised medical and warm-hearted assistance surprised Ewa and her appreciation was increased further when many local people, who were already enduring their own hardships, brought blankets, clothes and the little food they could spare.

The next three days were spent trying to arrange transport on to Luck, but it became clear that there would be no further trains as most major bridges, depots, and stations had been destroyed from the air. In fact there was no longer any organised public transport out of Lublin.

Ewa summarised the position to the boys and concluded, "Now we have no choice, we have to go on and keep to the arrangements that have already been made, there's no way back now, we've come too far."

"How on earth can we get to Luck now? Can't we stay here?" asked Jozef.

"It's over a hundred and twenty miles and it's getting colder all the time. Please let's just stay here," added Jacek.

"We are expected at Luck, money has been provided to them to look after us. That's where father will make contact, and from what we hear, things are going badly at home. The Germans are likely to be in Warsaw within a few weeks and so the further east we go the safer we'll be. We've got warm clothing and the people here will give us sufficient supplies. We're all fit and healthy and I'm sure we'll obtain plenty of rides along the way. Things aren't too bad and anyway it will only take a few days," and so Ewa motivated them to continue. They left early the following morning as light drizzle fell from a leaden sky, increasingly dampening their mood as the day progressed.

Both the weather and their fortune improved the following day when they were given several lengthy lifts and late in the afternoon they gratefully climbed onto a cart heading for a farm on the river Bug, north-east of Chelm. The jovial farmer was delighted to tell them that he had also been born in their part of the world, a small village not far from their home called Nova Wies. They talked about life in Pomerania and he later explained that he was, so far, unaffected to any great degree by the war. He was also kind enough to put them up for the night. The following morning they set off with the farmer who had promised to see them safely across the river, which fortunately was not in full flood as it usually was at that time of year. Their passage however turned into yet another painful reminder of how things had changed for them and it also announced the pitiless arrival of the war for the farmer.

Almost as soon as the small rowing boat cast off into the swift current they saw the first body floating by, followed by a procession of bloated corpses, mostly Polish soldiers but also a number of women and children: some were tangled together and, as they were rolled, tossed and turned in the flow, it seemed as if a ghastly underwater dance was in progress. In the centre of the river where the current appeared strongest the boat was buffeted and rocked as it was struck by the log-jam of spinning bodies and they held on to each other for safety and comfort. Several horse carcasses floated past and they were then rendered speechless as they watched the farmer pushing, poking and prodding with an oar to ease and propel the boat through what had thickened into a choking green, brown and grey carpet, not of river weed, but of the dead: a sightless and lost army stretching from bank to bank.

Ewa comforted her children as best she could but nothing she could say would lift the mood of despondency and sadness that remained with them long after they had left the river behind. The rest of the journey of about seventy miles was much slower as the lifts were few and far between and the traffic more localised. As they travelled further east they left the well-drained rich farmland north of the Lublin upland in their wake and entered a wetter, flatter, flood meadow landscape, interspersed with hundreds of small lakes, rivers and thick pine forest.

Progress was hampered even further as they traversed the extreme south-western corner of the vast Pripet (Pripyat) Marshes: the largest swamp area on the European continent that, throughout history, had been an impenetrable obstacle to the many invading armies. The road narrowed until it was little more than a footpath and they frequently found themselves up to their knees in black stinking mud that sapped their strength and occasionally the deepest and most dangerous sections brought them to a complete standstill. They were then forced to retrace their steps and search for another way around. As they stumbled, fell and struggled to help each other through the clinging ooze, it covered their clothes and their entire bodies until they looked like modern day mud wrestlers.

It took them two days to cover the ten miles through the swamp, but as their natural surroundings slowly changed so too did the infrastructure. The hamlets and villages now became more scattered, and noticeably poorer with many of the buildings neglected or completely derelict. The farms were much smaller, more dilapidated and far less productive. The locals appeared suspicious of them and quickly vanished inside their homes as the strangers approached. Many simply refused to answer the door but a precious few took pity on them and shared what they could. An old man, who must have been in his eighties and described himself as a lifetime slave to the land, listened to their account of war to the west and unconcerned he confidently predicted that it would pass him by as had many other conflicts. He put them up in his barn for the night and, as they bedded down on sacks of straw, Jan's physical weariness and mental anguish got the better of him, "Is the place we're going to just like this? The people here are all dirty, uneducated peasants, the whole place is filthy and I can hardly understand their accents. To be honest I've had enough of it already. It's a dump and if Luck is the same then I say we should go on to somewhere more civilized."

Before his mother could answer Jozef snapped at his brother, "I know you're the youngest and you're fed up but you really should show more sense and grow up a bit. None of us are in any condition to go much further and we certainly wouldn't have got this far without the help and support of these 'dirty peasants' as you so derisively call them. You should know better."

Ewa had heard enough and sat up, "Please, no arguments! We're nearly there, so there's not long to wait before we see exactly what our new home is like. None of us should rush to judgement, so let's make the most of our circumstances whatever we find. I'm sure we're through the worst of it already. Even if life is hard for us, it's a whole lot better than getting bombed or shot at. So ALL of you, get used to the idea that we're going to Luck, exactly as father intended, and no further."

The following morning the old farmer gave them directions and wished them well, gladly sparing a little food and water for the final leg of their journey. In his uncharacteristic outburst the night before Jan had inadvertently touched on one truism. Life in the east was indeed maintained at a subsistence level and, while most of the family found this depressing, Tomek was diverted by the abundant presence of wildfowl, beaver, deer and the many species of hawks and falcons, which he found fascinating, and he longed for the chance to go hunting. Nevertheless, even his enthusiasm waned as the constant walking took its toll and they gradually succumbed to exhaustion. When they finally arrived at their destination (about fifteen miles south east of Luck) three days later, they were disgustingly filthy: looking like bedraggled, beleaguered aliens and were exceedingly footsore, tired and ravenously hungry.

THREE

LUCK!
11th September 1939

Despite their experience of the last few days, the smallholding was still a huge culture shock for the Nowaski family. Their own home in Pelplin, provided by the National Railway, was a modern, mellow stone and tile, two-storey house surrounded by a sizeable, productive garden with a variety of fruit trees and shrubs. The well-maintained building contained two warm and cosy rooms on the ground floor in addition to a kitchen, a scullery with a copper boiler for the laundry and bathing, a small lean-to which housed the toilet and an outhouse where the logs and coal were stored. The four bedrooms upstairs accommodated the whole family quite comfortably with the twins and their brothers doubling up in two of the larger rooms. Although they already enjoyed a relatively good standard of living, the basement was rented out and this provided extra income for family luxuries and an annual holiday or two. They sometimes spent a week or fortnight visiting Ewa's relations, some nearby in Pomerania, but also those in Poznan and Kaszuby. It was made more affordable because Henryk's employment entitled the whole family to special railway passes that allowed them to travel anywhere inside Poland at half fare.

Jan thought it strange that they never saw or heard anything from his father's side of the family and had once asked him why. Henryk rather abruptly said that he had no previous family other than Roman, and became uncharacteristically angry and forcibly closed the subject when Jan tried to question him about his grandparents.

Ewa later told the boys that their father had always refused to talk about his childhood or his parents and that Roman was the same. She said they had experienced a very difficult time when they were growing up and did not want to be reminded of it. Seeing the disappointment on their faces she told them that whatever happened in the future they should always remember that their surname was ancient, noble and honourable. She informed them that a village near Gdansk had been named after their forefathers who had been the Lords of the Manor and owned the whole area, and that with such a proud, chivalrous history they must never bring dishonour on their family name. This heritage had never been mentioned before and the boys were delighted with their apparent elevation in status and wanted to tell everyone but she beseeched them never to mention it outside the family. She insisted that they should all respect their father's wishes about his past and so the subject was never broached again.

The contrast between their home and the new lodgings could not have been greater. Their host, his wife, their two small children, a working dog, a few chickens, ducks and geese all lived together in a large but rather ancient wood-framed, wattle and daub building with a dirt floor set out under a massive overhanging, and well patched thatch roof. There was only the one room, used for cooking, eating and sleeping. By their standards it was basic in the extreme, but durable, secure and warm, being dominated by a massive bread oven, measuring about fifteen feet by twelve feet, which was covered in thick straw to serve as the family bed.

A well was situated to the side of the front yard, alongside a small pond used by the animals. The one toilet was on the opposite side of the yard about twenty yards from the front door and consisted of a small, cold and draughty, wooden shed-like structure. Behind the ill-fitting and rickety door was a single bucket with a removable wooden seat. All the boys took it in turns to empty and bury the contents every day. Huge piles of logs were everywhere, both inside and, in even more impressive stacks of alpine proportions, propped up against all the farm outbuildings that surrounded the house. The most recent and well-maintained building on the whole farm was the small windmill situated on a grassy knoll, a hundred yards east of the house. It was in almost constant use for weeks on end following the annual harvest, when all the surrounding farmers brought their own grain to be ground down and then paid their bill in flour or other produce. A significant proportion of their host's 'income' and winter supplies depended on the efficiency and reliability of the mill which was sited to make optimum use of the prevailing winds.

After formal introductions, a good wash and change of clothing, they all sat on benches around the rough-hewn wooden table, sipping sweet dark tea from long glasses and eating a most welcome but basic traditional meal of bigos (a well seasoned hunter stew made from sauerkraut, tomatoes and in this case chunks of chicken, rabbit and sausage). Traditionally the pot was kept heated on the stove for days on end and ingredients added to top up the perpetual dish as and when they became available. As they satisfied their hunger the friendly but earnest farmer, Dominik Dabrowski told them about himself. Despite his feudal surroundings and circumstances it soon became obvious that he was an intelligent and well-educated man.

"I had to leave university early as my parents couldn't afford to keep me there once their business collapsed during the recession. My future looked bleak with no income, no country and no prospects and so, with a few of my single mates, I emigrated to America to seek my fortune in what they called the land of the free."

Jan clearly understanding every word, and now feeling guilty over his earlier peasant references, was instantly intrigued by this revelation. He could not contain his enthusiasm, "What was it like? Where did you live? Did you see any cowboys or Indians? Do you speak English? When did you........"

He was cut short by his mother, "Please Jan, don't interrupt, I'm sure there will be plenty of time later on for such questions, but for the time being we should let Mr. Dabrowski speak. He doesn't want us constantly butting in."

Their host thanked Ewa but, before continuing, told Jan in a sympathetic tone that he would try to answer all their questions in time and added, "If you're really interested in life in America I'll let you look through the diary I used to keep. It will certainly help you understand what was going on at the time."

Jan eagerly accepted his offer and Dominik explained that he had lived in Chicago, "It's a huge city like Warsaw and there were tens of thousands of us, all living within the Polish quarter, a city within a city."

He explained to the boys that people had been emigrating there from all over Poland for over fifty years, most trying to escape the occupation, oppression and the terrible poverty at home. He described what everyday life was like and was addressing Jan's original questions when the lad asked, "When did you come back?"

"During the war, in the hope that we could help defeat our enemies and later return to a free and hopefully more prosperous Poland. Thousands of us tried to join up and fight with the French and British against the Central Powers. It seemed like the right thing to do, but for years the Americans wouldn't allow it, but finally in 1917, after they had declared war on Germany, we were authorised to cross the border into Canada and enlist in General Haller's Blue Army. We were then shipped across to France and we fought in the trenches as an independent Polish Division under our own national flag."

Jacek, who prided himself on his historical knowledge, knew that his countrymen had fought on both sides in the Great War: some with the Russians and others with the Germans and Austrians, but he was totally unaware of this particular episode on the western front and despite his mother's sudden look of disapproval asked, "Why was it called the Blue Army?"

"We were known officially as Haller's army but we wore distinctive French issue, grey/blue uniforms and the name stuck. Although I say it myself, we were well trained and equipped and fought with lots of pride and determination and the Germans who faced us called us the blue devils."

Jan, encouraged by his brother's intervention asked, "What happened after the war? Where did you go?"

"You might find this hard to believe, but by then there were about a hundred thousand of us in the Blue Army and after months of negotiation and diplomacy we were all transported back to Poland from France in nearly four hundred sealed trains, right across Germany. We even took all our equipment and vehicles, including about seventy tanks."

Dominik explained that he had readily taken to military life and that they had arrived back just in time to fight in their own war against the new Red Army that threatened to once again conquer Poland, just as the nation had been reborn from the ashes of the

Great War. Following early successes the Poles had suddenly been swept right back from Kiev and, with their backs to the Vistula, and apparently staring defeat in the face, it looked like Poland would fall within days. Against all the odds and with no small degree of desperation they rapidly regrouped and counter-attacked, comprehensively routing the Soviets at the very outskirts of Warsaw.

Jan, like all Polish children, knew this story well but even so he still felt his pride and patriotic anticipation rising as he asked, "I know about the miracle on the Vistula. Were you a hero?"

"No, I was just an ordinary young Lieutenant then and was slightly wounded early on and really didn't do anything terribly brave or noteworthy, but it was an outstanding victory for our army."

The Russians were humiliated in the eyes of the whole civilised world. Most of their best units surrendered or fled across the East Prussian border, rather than face the Poles again and were then detained by the Germans. The remnants of their army were chased right past Minsk and with them in full retreat the road to Moscow was wide open. Out of the one hundred thousand men of the Red Army, eighty-five thousand were killed or captured.

Tomek voiced his long held criticism, "If our victory was as overwhelming as we've been taught I can't understand why on earth we didn't push home our advantage and keep going and finish the job off once and for all?"

"The truth is we'll never know how complete our victory could have been because it was at that point that international pressure for a ceasefire became irresistible, and a couple of days later the armistice was signed and we were finally ordered to stop our advance."

Jozef who had been listening intently added, "It's probably just as well because the Soviets would have defended their new revolutionary capital at Moscow with the same passion and determination that we showed in our defence of Warsaw, and the killing would have gone on indefinitely, without any guarantee of final victory."

Dominik nodded his agreement, "That's very true, young man. Anyway, as you probably know, the peace agreement moved our border westwards from our stop lines to its present position but it still incorporated a huge chunk of the Ukraine that had historically been part of Poland's Eastern Borderlands."

Ewa politely declined the postprandial shot of Vodka being offered by their host and asked, "When did you settle here?"

"In 1922, after I left the army."

Ewa continued, "But why choose this remote area? I know it's steeped in history, legend, and intrigue but it has also been ravaged by war and hardship. Life must be very difficult."

"The government was anxious to make the area more secure for the future, so it offered financial incentives for people to move east. They started a massive programme of resettlement and they handed out land that had been confiscated from the Bolsheviks, or the Ukrainians who had fought alongside them, and were now either dead or stranded inside the new Russian border."

Having been there in the war he knew the land well. It was relatively flat, the soil very dark and quite fertile with the potential to be very productive if it was managed properly. There was ample forest for timber, fuel and charcoal and no shortage of water. Furthermore, once the fighting had ended, the Government, looking to cut the military budget, had no further use for a large proportion of the army and so, along with thousands of others, Dominik was discharged and found himself in fierce competition with his former comrades as they desperately, but unsuccessfully, looked for work. He told his guests that initially he had considered going back to America but the adventurer in him was attracted to the idea of returning to the very cradle of the Polish nation and so he took up the Government's offer to move.

He gathered his thoughts as he helped himself to another vodka and poured more tea for everyone else. He sat back down and then continued, "Like you say, life is far more basic here with few home comforts, but I've survived. At first I really struggled with the ferocious winters and the unrelenting labour and I don't mind admitting that I was on the point of giving up several times in those first few years."

When he had arrived he found that the land was scarred and pitted with the aftermath of countless battles and wars. There were shell holes everywhere, several deep and extensive bunkers and trenches and dozens of shallow graves scattered across the higher ground. The flotsam and jetsam of advancing and retreating armies were strewn across his land and it all had to be cleared and the ground made safe before it could be levelled and planted. Gradually he worked his way through it, and as the years went by he learnt how to get the most out of the land. As production and income increased he repaired and weatherproofed the dilapidated farmhouse and built the mill.

He then brought them right up to date, "I met my wife Bogdana in Luck and together we've built our lives and family around this farm, but as the children came along we had a few particularly bad winters and poor harvests and things started to get a lot harder again and so I've had to take a part time job at the railway yard in Luck, where I stay two or three days a week. With the extra wage we just about managed to keep our heads above water. Then, about a month ago, I was asked, or perhaps more accurately told, to put up a railway family to be evacuated from the west, and here you are."

The Nowaski family had become increasingly fascinated by the diversity, hardship and enterprise of their host's life story and had, for most of the time, listened in respectful silence. Ewa then gave their hosts a thumbnail sketch of her own family history before expressing her hopes for their immediate future, "We're very grateful to you and your wife and I'm especially sorry that we've added to your problems, but I'm sure we will all get along. We will of course do everything we can to help you, in the house and on the farm."

The farmer scratched his thick dark beard and frowned as he responded, "I wish we could offer you a proper welcome and show you the hospitality that you deserve rather than this sorry offering, but things have rapidly changed for the worse over the last couple of weeks. It's an understatement to say matters have become nigh on impossible around here since the war started."

He explained that there was no flour for bread as the authorities had requisitioned all their reserve supplies, together with most of the livestock and preserved meats and pickles to help supply the people in the city, many of whom had already completely run out of food, and to provision the local army garrison. In an apologetic tone he added, "There's been a great deal of panic buying and profiteering in Luck and now everyone is suffering because of the greed and thoughtlessness of a callous minority. We've been left

46

with some tea, coffee, eggs, potatoes, milk, dry biscuits, cheese and whatever we can hunt or trap, but we've already started to kill the remaining animals. To make matters worse the railway shut down this week and so there's no more work for me in the yards at Luck and I haven't even been paid for the last three weeks."

His wife said, "To be frank, we're broke. Prices have gone right through the roof and everything is in short supply or completely unobtainable. I'm ashamed to say we've already spent the money provided towards your keep, on feeding our own children. With you all here I'm certain that what we have won't last long and, to make matters worse, winter will be upon us soon, so things can only deteriorate further. I feel guilty saying it but as you've taken so long to arrive I found myself hoping that you'd decided to stay in Pomerania. I don't know how we can manage for more than a couple of weeks and, even so, we'll have to ration what we have. I accept that we're now all in this together, but none of us should underestimate the difficult challenges ahead."

Ewa, now becoming immune to bad news and simply glad of warmth and shelter, responded accordingly, "We can't thank you enough for agreeing to have us despite the obvious difficulties it will cause you all, and I deeply regret the extra burdens we've placed on you. For our part we undertake to do anything you ask to earn our keep and will help your family in any way we can. Perhaps it won't be for too long and, God willing, we can all return to some semblance of normality. Surely England and France will come to our aid. I heard in Warsaw last week that they've declared war in our defence."

Dominik shook his head and with cynical resignation replied, "I think they mean to help, but as a soldier, I feel their stance is of no practical significance as they are too far away and understandably concentrating on their own defences. This war will spread, of that I'm sure, and it will keep our allies busy, so we shouldn't rely on any outside intervention. If we're to overcome this invasion then it will be through our own efforts."

Over the next week life fell into a routine of domestic and farming chores and in addition the boys started to forage and hunt in the surrounding countryside for any food and supplies that would supplement their meagre rations and help to make life more comfortable for both families.

Jan lay on the oven amongst all the sleeping bodies sharing the warmth and straining his eyes to read a few more pages of Dominik's fascinating diary when, in the soft flickering firelight, he noticed the paper on the wall moving and undulating as if it was being rustled by an imaginary wind. He thought that perhaps it was an optical illusion caused by the strange shadows cast by the red and spluttering embers. Curious, he got up quietly, trying not to wake the others and examined the wall, peeling back a piece of loose paper. He jumped back with astonishment and fright as he saw that the wall was alive with lice, literally millions of them living under the paper, across the whole area of the wall.

As he stood there early that morning, wondering if the lice were eating the paper paste and debating whether he should say anything, just a few miles away the massive Red Army, some seven hundred thousand strong, was pouring across the border into Poland. Mile after continuous mile of troops, artillery, tanks and the deafening machinery of war, supported by hundreds of fighter and bomber aircraft crossed into Poland and engaged Polish troops and militia, in direct violation of its bilateral and multilateral non-aggression treaties with Poland. The defenders, already overstretched and massively outnumbered, were rapidly outflanked and separated to such a degree as to become totally ineffective, even as a defensive force. This surprise attack from the rear against a sparsely militarised area, combined with its deliberate ferocity, effectively sealed Poland's fate for the next sixty years.

The double invasion was no accident or coincidence. The Nazi and Soviet powers had conspired to deploy their full military might, agreeing, even before the war had started (in a secret appendix to the Molotov–Ribbentrop pact) to ignore international law and jointly attack and overwhelm their isolated neighbour. Their battle plan concluded with the rapid partition of Poland along predetermined borders and the subjugation of its citizens into forced labour. This virtual slavery was a pattern to be repeated across Europe, thus providing the human resources so necessary to maintain their respective military ambitions (which for one small moment in history happened to coincide in respect of a hapless Poland). This was a precursor to ever greater collaboration between this particularly malignant axis of evil. As the weeks wore on these two countries, sworn political and ideological enemies

48

would become allies in all but name. Russia would provide the Nazis with desperately needed raw materials such as wheat, oil, coal, rubber, timber and metals and, in return, Germany would give enthusiastic cooperation at every level, from senior political and military command right down to the troops and administrators on the ground, and even between the respective intelligence and secret police leaderships and functionaries.

In the cities, towns and villages across Poland German and Russian soldiers, bureaucrats and police were to meet, shake hands, toast each other and boast that between them they had dispatched Poland to the four winds. Although this claim was fancifully premature, even foolhardy at the time, it was chillingly prophetic because, at war's end, nearly seven million Poles had been killed by the cold brutality and ideological hatred of these two ruthless regimes. The enormity of this figure can best be illustrated by comparison to the United Kingdom's terrible loses in the Great War when almost a million of its citizens were lost in the trenches and on the battlefields of that terrible conflict. This was about 3% of her population and it was quite rightly described as a national and human catastrophe, 'the loss of a whole generation' and both Government and Press avowed that never again would such slaughter be countenanced.

Coincidentally the population of Poland in 1939 was very similar to that of Great Britain in 1914, approximately thirty five million, but its losses of almost 20% were over six times more staggering and almost unimaginable today. For example, the huge death toll was equivalent to a 9/11 every single day for the two thousand and seventy five days of the war, plus an additional two hundred and fifty five such disasters.

The British would also pay a very heavy price for Stalin's initial flirtations with Hitler. Despite her declared neutrality in the Western conflict Russia afforded Germany considerable covert military and naval assistance, including the provision of a naval supply base to the west of Murmansk at Western Litsa Cove on the southern coast of Motovsky Bay in the Barents Sea. Known as 'Base North' it was established as early as October 1939, so that German U boats and raiders deployed against the British could be secretly and safely rearmed and resupplied, without making the hazardous return trip to their home-ports. Ironically, some of the very same vessels would later repeatedly and successfully attack British Arctic convoys as they struggled against ice, storm, mountainous seas, and relentless torpedo attacks from the invisible marauding wolf-packs. These Merchant Navy crews and their escorts risked everything and suffered so dearly to reach Murmansk and Archangel to feed, equip, resupply and sustain the then beleaguered Red Army, so close to defeat and at the mercy of its erstwhile ally.

It was mid morning the following day when they all stood at the windows and watched a column of Russian cavalry riding towards Luck along the road at the end of the track to the farm. Bogdana warned them, "Please remember there's no love lost between the Russians and us Poles or Ukrainians, there's been too much blood spilt over this piece of land in the past."

In fact there had been no real peace there for generations and a mutual distrust and hatred had been handed down from father to son and then reinforced with a seesaw of repression and revenge."

Dominik added, "I think it's even worse than that. They're definitely Cossacks out there and they've despised us and everything Polish for centuries, so they'll be looking to make their mark before too long. You lads make sure you keep well out of their way. They're also bound to have some of those Ukrainians, who used to own this land, fighting on their side and if they get the chance they'll certainly take it out on the likes of us. Either way, we're in for a great deal of trouble."

They spent the whole day indoors, cut off from the rest of the world (the Polish radio bulletins had ceased before the Nowaskis arrived and had been replaced with boastful German, and latterly Russian, propaganda) and they saw no more soldiers that day, neither friends nor enemies. They were afraid to venture outside as the distant sound of heavy guns and nearby machine-gun fire was a constant reminder that the war was all around them and, with every passing hour, the tension and fear mounted inside the building. By late evening a sense of helplessness and despair descended on them all and, try as they might, the adults could find no small crumb of comfort on which to pin their hopes.

The following afternoon their wait was finally over as the Soviets arrived at the farm and gratuitous violence and brutality assaulted their lives. An infantry patrol crept up to the outbuildings, secured the perimeter and fired several bursts from a machine gun into the roof of the house. Timber, dust, straw and debris rained down on the occupants who cowered on the floor under the table and, after a minute or two of silence, a Russian ordered, in heavily accented and badly pronounced Polish, "You in the house, all of you in the building, come out the front with your hands up. Your cowardly senior officers have fled the country and your pathetic army wouldn't even stand and fight us. They're beaten and on the run, so come out immediately or we will blow the building up and send you to Kingdom Come. I don't intend to tell you twice."

They filed out with their hands in the air, Dominik and his Bogdana leading the pathetic, disheartened little group, which was then ordered to lay face down in the muddy yard whilst they were roughly searched for any weapons. As this was happening the Russian interpreter paced up and down and shouted at them, "This land, including this very farm and all its contents, truly belongs to us and so you will now have to do exactly as you are told or you will lose everything. We, the victorious Red Army, liberators of all oppressed people, are in charge now."

They were then told to kneel on the track and forced to place their hands behind their heads and kept under armed guard while the sergeant in charge and two of his men ransacked the house. The farmer's few trinkets, cash and food was then divided up amongst the patrol, his two shotguns and the radio destroyed and the poultry killed and carried off in sacks. Their hosts were left with nothing. Their final inexplicable act as they left reduced Dominik and his wife to tears. Because of their history and exposure to hardship and disappointment they could bear almost anything, but when the soldiers set fire to the mill, and laughed and danced around as the flames quickly reduced it to a skeleton of smouldering embers, they were devastated. Beyond comfort and bereft of hope they sat in the farmyard filth and sobbed. The self-deprecating veteran of another war, who had laboured incessantly to carve a living from a harsh and unforgiving landscape and made a stream of sacrifices to raise a family, was left humiliated and ashamed of his own impotence.

When this tiny contingent of the Red Army finally left, the interpreter proclaimed, "A curfew is now in force daily between 7pm and 6am and if you are found outdoors during curfew you will be shot. There are no exceptions. You will be executed on the spot. You may have been liberated from the capitalists, but like us Russians, you are not yet free to do as you want. In fact, if you don't comply with every single one of our orders we will come back and burn your house to the ground." The soldiers laughed and shouted more threats and insults as they walked away with their spoils.

Things very quickly became desperate for all as the full restrictions of the occupation took hold and the two families struggled to survive on little more than potato soup. They were prohibited from hunting or setting traps and hunger constantly gnawed at them and, despite the oven, they always felt damp, weak and cold. They were forced to register at a Soviet camp set up about two miles from the farm towards Luck and all the boys had to carry out menial work around the camp for four hours every day. The adults were confined to the farm and could not leave without documentation issued in the name of the camp commander who had been appointed as civil administrator for the district.

The boys scavenged, initially when travelling to and from the camp, but as their craft and confidence grew they began to steal from the camp kitchen and the soldiers' kit and property. They were amazed at the amount of food and supplies within the camp and, as time wore on, they discovered that most of it had been stolen from the local population or plundered from captured Polish Army supplies. After being short of the most basic provisions for what seemed a very long time Jan stood mesmerised as he watched a group of eight Russian soldiers sat around a massive iron cooking pot. They were all wolfing down piping hot stew from the cauldron using wooden spoons and, as he watched, he realised that they were slurping and grunting like pigs because the ones who could eat the fastest were the lucky ones who would eat the most. It was a race to gorge themselves and he stared in disbelief at their rapacious capacity until they finally chased him off with a stream of abuse and threats. The cruellest soldiers would also tease the local children by throwing them lumps of stale bread and then laughing, jeering and kicking at them as they scrabbled and fought in the mud or dust to claim the small scraps.

Against this background of hunger and competitiveness the boys became ever more inventive and furtive in their search for food. They thought nothing of crawling under fences and buildings or climbing over walls and gates, often only yards from the soldiers and guards. Jan naturally teamed up with Tomek and they took turns to act as 'look out' in order to steal enough food to keep both families from starving. Jozef and Jacek also tried to work together whenever possible, but at first limited their unlawful activities, as they lacked the bravado, confidence and guile of their brothers. Jacek initially also found the physical exertion particularly demanding but slowly grew in confidence as he pushed himself further each day to live up to the example set by his more active brothers. Unfortunately his budding self-assurance soon took a significant knock-back when he playfully saluted a Russian guard as he entered the camp. Instead of returning the gesture, as the Polish soldiers had frequently done, the guard grabbed him by the coat, violently shook him and repeatedly cuffed him around both ears whilst shouting a stream of obscenities. When the guard released his grip, Jacek, already reduced to tears, fell to the ground with his ears ringing and throbbing, unable to hear his own exasperated blubbing. He ran home in dismay and shame, and immediately told his mother what had happened. "Show me exactly how you saluted him?" she asked, suspecting she already knew the reason for the assault.

Jacek illustrated the traditional Polish two fingered military salute with the middle and index fingers extended but the ring and little fingers bent back, touching the thumb at the palm of the hand. Ewa explained her supposition, "The Russians don't really understand our salute. Do you remember why our soldiers do it that way?"

"Yes, it's about the legend of the brave soldier who had two fingers blown off by shrapnel. He was a hero because, despite his pain and injury, he still proudly saluted his senior officer with his other two fingers. All our soldiers have saluted like that ever since."

Ewa explained further, "You need to know that some Russians think it's a personal insult. They've been told by Stalin and his Generals that, while we pretend to salute them with two fingers, the other two are holding a stone ready to throw at them, so the guard probably thought you were deliberately making fun of him and nowadays they don't need much of an excuse to beat us or lock us up. I'm sorry, it's entirely my fault. I should have warned you about it, but what with everything else, it never even crossed my mind until you told me what had happened. Try to keep away from them as much as possible."

Jacek was left feeling very sorry for himself and frustrated at the unfairness of the whole situation. He just wanted to go home.

Jozef constantly struggled with his conscience over their need to steal to survive, and although he avoided it whenever he could, guiltily leaving it to his brothers, he prayed for forgiveness every night. He couldn't shake off the uneasy feeling that he was being tested and his failure to abstain from sin was slowly but inevitably destroying his soul.

All four heard grim tales from workers, trucked in from nearby villages, telling of how the Cossacks had stormed through the area in the first attack, raping, looting and shooting anyone who dared to speak out against their behaviour. They were also told that small remnants of the retreating Polish army had linked up with local Polish and Ukrainian underground units (whose forefathers had been fighting each other and the Russians for centuries) in an alliance of convenience and were now attacking the invaders and their supply lines on a hit-and-run basis. This news generated both pride and fear in equal proportion amongst the forced labour at the camp. Pride that the Poles were fighting on: some at least refusing to surrender and fear as to what the Russians' response would be.

Their enemies were definitely aware of not having it all their own way and, in a swift and vicious retaliation for partisan activity, the local Mayor and his family were executed by firing squad. It was carried out in front of their own villagers to ensure, as the local Russian Commander put it, 'full compliance with the emergency regulations issued by the occupying military authority.' These stories made the boys very careful to appear friendly and compliant to everyone and they soon became a familiar sight around the camp: eagerly willing to help the soldiers in any way possible with their daily routine and domestic chores. In a very short time both Jan and Tomek became more canny and sharp-witted as they were increasingly relied upon to supply most of the family food and constantly mixed with hard-bitten and often coarse and violent Russian soldiers. Nevertheless, continually stealing, smuggling food past the guards and surreptitiously creeping around the camp buildings, their luck was bound to run out and when it happened the consequences were sudden and brutal.

Early in the afternoon as Jan crawled out from underneath a hut with his contraband of two small loaves and a hunk of cheese under his jacket, he was suddenly seized by his collar. Before he could look up an immense pair of hands moved to his throat and he was dragged to his feet and violently thrown against the side of the building. The impact with the ice-covered boards sent a bolt of pain right through his body and as the breath was driven from his lungs his legs turned to jelly and he fell to his knees. He gasped for breath and his chest felt as if it was on fire but he slowly rose to his feet, supporting himself against the side of the hut and spitting blood from his bitten tongue and split lips. He stood there half-choked, dazed and bleeding from numerous other cuts to his face and head. Before he fully realised what had happened, his captor, a huge Russian soldier, now holding the loaves, shouted, "You ungrateful thieving bastard. This is how you repay us for our kindness. Well, you're about to learn how we deal with your treachery, you little shit."

Jan was then frog-marched around the corner of the hut and thrown to the ground under the huge coalbunker wall. His brother was already sat there under the watchful eye of another guard who was now pointing his rifle at them both. Jan stole a glance at Tomek and saw that he was also bleeding from the nose and mouth and realised that he too had been beaten up. The first soldier shouted an order and almost immediately two more troops came round the corner and set up a light machine gun on the ground, fifteen yards in front of the boys.

"Stand up you Polish trash," ordered the second soldier.

Although neither boy fully understood the Russian words, the intention was clear, but they were already shaking with fear and frozen to the spot. "Shoot them where they are then - the cowardly little bastards," he screamed.

As the machine gun was primed, with what sounded like a final deafening insult to Jan, who was desperately clinging to his older brother, a Captain marched around the corner. He stopped as the soldiers sprang to attention and taking in the scene he demanded, "What in Hell's name are you doing?"

The first soldier explained what had happened and his own response to the situation, without any trace of regret or guilt on his part.

"Alright, so they deserve to be executed, but after all they're only kids and we can't really afford to waste valuable ammunition on the likes of these thieving bastards. For Christ's sake, we'd end up shooting half the population. Give them a good hiding and lock them up, and then let's make sure we get some proper work out of the useless brats."

Both boys were viciously punched and kicked about the body and head by the four soldiers and, whilst bleeding profusely and still whimpering, were forcefully thrown into the total darkness of the coalbunker, where they were left imprisoned. During their incarceration they were given no water, no food and no medical attention. They were numb with cold and pain from their injuries and periodically fell into a semi-conscious state.

Tomek dreamt of life back home and their adventurous holidays in the Kaszuby Lakelands were a recurring theme. He loved the woods, lakes, meadows and rivers and if the rest of the family had allowed it he would have spent the whole time walking, hunting, fishing and exploring the unique countryside. He remembered the strange Kaszuby language that the locals spoke between themselves and the old man who had proudly told him that wherever Tomek was in Kaszuby, if he threw a stone it would land in the water because there were so many lakes and rivers, all with shoals of delicious fish.

When they were at the seaside and all the others were relaxed and enjoying themselves on the beach, he and Jan were always restless and wanting to move on. Their parents insisted that whilst on holiday the boys could not risk going out on their own in strange surroundings and so Tomek and Jan often went hiking or fishing together while the rest of the family went on a picnic or did puzzles, played games or visited the local churches and castles. He remembered the day Jan had caught a huge carp which, even between them, they could hardly carry back to the cabin where their mother used the monster to make a delicious meal of karp po zydowsku (served in aspic with raisins and herbs) for the whole family and the neighbours as well! His mouth watered as he remembered the feast of another family meal deep in the cool of the forest on a hot summer's day and their surprise at first seeing the massive ancient stones positioned so formally in the glade. In his dream he was laughing as his father sat on a huge rock and tried to be serious, explaining the mysteries of the Goths and the stone rings at Wesiory, as the boys chased their sister and mother around the circle, much more interested in trying to get at the chocolate they were hiding.

When they were both at their most lucid the frightening, uncertain present came flooding back and as they huddled together for warmth they discussed what they should do when they were eventually let out.

"How could father have let this happen to us? Pleaded Jan, "If we had stayed at home we wouldn't be in this mess."

"No, we wouldn't, but we don't know what it's like back there either and in any case it's not really father's fault, he did what was right at the time and it's our own carelessness that's got us locked up in here. We need to get away from the Russians. We can't go back to the farm or stay in this area because if they catch us again, after what that officer said, they're just as likely to kill us all and not think twice about it. We should go back to Pelplin on our own and not risk making it any worse for the rest."

"OK, if that's what you think, but we've got to stick together at all costs and try to let mother know what we're doing once we're free of the camp. Perhaps they'll also be able to get home easier without having us to worry about. Anyway, the sooner we leave this God-forsaken place the better. This trip has been nothing but a total disaster from start to finish."

They were eventually released three days later, emerging into the early morning fog, covered from head to toe in a mixture of thick clinging coal dust and dried blood and blinking against the sudden daylight. Almost immediately, without a word being said, buckets of ice-cold water were thrown over them by two orderlies, who then dragged the boys, still dripping black greasy sludge, into a nearby hut. The heat from the pot-bellied stove at the centre of the room hit them like a brick wall yet they still stood there shivering uncontrollably. The combined effects of their extended exposure to the cold, the pain from their cuts and bruises, the sudden dousing and a fearful anticipation of what was to come next left them terrified.

Sat at a desk smoking a cigarette and looking through a stack of papers, was the same officer that had saved them from being shot. He looked up and smiled at them, slowly stubbed out the cigarette end, and said in broken but deliberate Polish, "You've abused our trust, taken advantage of your privileged situation within the camp and stolen food that has been issued to my soldiers. It's a capital offence and you were so nearly shot on the spot. If it hadn't been for me you would both now be dead. For your punishment you're going to Russia where you will be gainfully employed in the fields. If you behave yourselves, work hard and cause no trouble, I believe you may survive."

He stood up, walked towards them and stared at them in turn, "Who knows, you may one day, after you've been re-educated in the ways of socialism, return to Poland as decent citizens, but if you cause any trouble or do not follow orders or become lazy, you will be shot. You must remember life is hard for all of us and the only way we can achieve progress is by constant toil and total allegiance to mother Russia. This lesson you will quickly learn."

As the officer finished speaking Tomek said, "Please Sir…" but before he could ask his question the captain swung a full-blooded, right-handed haymaker punch that caught him on the side of the head knocking him clean off his feet.

"Get up!" he screamed, and as the boy hauled himself painfully to his feet, "Never speak until you are told to." He then bent down with his crimson face, distorted with rage, only inches from Tomek's and through fetid breath reeking of tobacco and vodka he snarled, "You are prisoners and will at all times behave as such or take the consequences, which will be immediate and severe." He then addressed the guard, "Get them out of my sight and throw this impertinent little jackass back in the coal hole. He will learn or he will die in the process. Make sure the other one's on the morning's transport."

An hour later Jan was sat in the back of an army truck with three other lads of roughly his own age and two captured Polish infantry soldiers, guarded by two fully armed Russians. One of the prisoners had his left arm in a sling and was bruised about the head and face. He appeared exhausted and was stretched out on one of the side benches, supported by his colleague, whereas all the other detainees appeared unharmed. They had initially been forbidden to speak by the driver but the injured soldier's parents were originally from the Ukraine and he had been forced to learn Russian as a boy. He periodically exchanged words with the guards who did not appear unduly hostile and seemed prepared to answer his questions. The injured prisoner later translated the gist of the conversation for the benefit of his companions. Jan, however, was immersed in his own thoughts, worried about his brother's fate and ruing the fact that Tomek was dragged back to the coalbunker before they had an opportunity to speak. He was deeply troubled not only because he was now on his own, but because they had not embraced or said their goodbyes which he felt sure would have given him some degree of courage and hope for what lay ahead.

They had been travelling for about two hours on a fairly well-maintained but almost deserted road when the vehicle was thrown into the air by a massive explosion under the cab. One of the guards and a young Pole were blown out through the rear of the truck before it fell back to earth, skidding along on its side for twenty yards, then coming to rest in the roadside ditch, enveloped in a cloud of dust and smoke. Jan was buried under several bodies, he couldn't hear or see anything and at first he couldn't move his limbs, but he could feel the weight of the others pressing down on his face. For the survivors, time seemed to stand still and the heat inside the wrecked vehicle was intense as they were engulfed in a cloud of acrid smoke that carried the choking stench of burning rubber and cordite.

The first to react was the uninjured Polish soldier who, ears still ringing and coughing from the effects of the smoke, pulled himself to his knees, grabbed a pistol from the concussed guard's belt and coldly shot him in the chest before he could regain his senses. He then jumped from the vehicle and it only took him a glance at the front to see that both the driver and the soldier in the front passenger seat were dead, having been blown apart by the full force of the explosion. He then ran back down the road to where the other guard was lying unconscious in the ditch and, without a second's hesitation, he shot him twice in the head. On the other side of the road the young lad was sprawled on his back, obviously dead with a fractured neck, his head turned at an impossibly unnatural angle.

By the time he returned to the truck Jan and one of the other lads were struggling to pull themselves from the tangle of bodies. He helped them to their feet and was relieved to see that, although they were shocked, battered, still dazed and covered in gore and debris, they appeared to have escaped any serious injury. His fellow soldier, already injured, had not been so lucky. A large piece of shrapnel had been driven through his forehead deep into his brain causing a massive wound, which had killed him instantly. The two remaining Polish youths, who had been sitting next to the cab had also received fatal blast injuries and were badly mutilated.

The soldier salvaged what he could from the truck and made a pile in the road of a rifle, ammunition, several canteens of water, food and rations together with gloves, overcoats and other items of equipment all stripped from the Russians. He called the lads over and said, "Right, you two, I'll keep the pistol and have the rifle and ammunition, but you take whatever you need to keep you going for the next few days," inviting them to help themselves. He then put his arms around their shoulders and with a sense of real, almost paternal, urgency said, "We've got to get out of here before a patrol comes to investigate. There's no time to lose so we've got to leave the bodies where they are. The Russians will kill us for sure after this and whoever planted the mine is long gone. There's no one to help us but ourselves."

"Where can we go? It's not safe to travel around here and we'll soon be spotted, especially if they're going to come after us," asked Jan, while grabbing what he could from the heap, genuinely at a loss as to what to do next.

"We'll have to make for Romania, there won't be many Russians in the mountains, and some of the locals may help us. The guard told us we were heading for their Divisional Headquarters at Ternopol, where all the prisoners captured around here are processed. By my reckoning we've travelled about sixty miles, so it must be about twenty miles ahead. From there it's still over a hundred miles to the border. It's not going to be easy, but we don't really have any choice, we can't stay here."

The other lad spoke for the first time, "I'm not coming. I live just fifteen miles from here and I know my way around. I'm going home. I can hide out with the neighbours and maybe join the underground, but I'm not going to Romania. You can both come with me if you like, I'm sure we could hide you as well until things cool down."

"No, I've got a duty to try to get to my unit and they've definitely gone to Romania so that's where I'm headed. If you two want to go off together and stay that's fine, but make sure the Russians don't catch you again."

Jan thought for a moment, reluctant to leave Poland and his family behind, but after considering his bad fortune to date he decided his chances of survival would improve vastly if he accompanied the soldier. From what he had seen he already considered him to be a clear-headed, experienced and competent fighter. "I'll come to Romania with you, there's nothing here for me now," he said with a decisiveness and resolve that belied his years and cloaked his internal anxiety. With a final look around the two of them took their leave and set off due south for the Carpathians and the hope of freedom.

They walked until Jan felt he could walk no further and as they trudged they talked; about the war, their respective homes, family circumstances, anything that crossed their minds but they always returned to the same subject, the one that dominated their thoughts, their chances of reaching safety. The soldier was upbeat about both Poland's future and their own prospects, "This whole area has been a war zone for centuries, countries come and go, invaders move in and are then driven out but Poland always springs back and it'll be the same this time. We need to keep our wits about us, stay off the beaten track and avoid the towns and villages. We'll walk hard through the day, lie low at night, and if we have a good helping of luck we should make it across in one piece."

Jan had learnt that the soldier's name was Jerzy Padjavik, from Krakow and he had been captured, along with his wounded friend, while covering the retreat of units at Luck. They had been ordered south a few days after the Russian invasion on the 17th September. Jan was encouraged to hear that Jerzy was a true man of the countryside, having spent much of his youth skiing, hunting and hiking with his older brother in the mountains south of his home. The same mountains that Jan would have to cross soon enough, but some two hundred and fifty miles further east than those so well known by his new guardian.

They had not seen a soul since they left the destroyed truck but they had skirted around two farms and a small village in order to avoid any contact. When darkness fell they had covered about fifteen miles and were quite pleased with their progress when they settled down for the night, on the edge of a small copse some five miles north west of Ternopol.

At first, sleep was elusive and Jerzy said, "Tomorrow we'll work our way around the west of the city and head south-south-west, straight for the mountains. We're going to need some help to get across, but the trouble is we don't know who we can really trust. Only twenty years ago this whole area was ruled by Austria and there are as many, perhaps even more, foreigners living here as there are Poles and Ukrainians. So we must be careful who we approach and when we do, we need to control the situation."

Jan suddenly felt very vulnerable and alone. His body was stiff and sore from the beating and the explosion, and his feet and muscles ached from the march. He pulled his greatcoat away from his chin and held the rosary tightly as he said a quiet prayer for himself, Jerzy and his own family. He wondered if he would ever see them again and he shuddered as he thought of poor Tomek all alone, languishing in the coalbunker.

They spent a fitful night and were keen to set off at dawn, wanting to cover as many miles as possible whilst they were hidden, to some degree, by the drizzle and mist. For three hours they headed south and were indeed shielded by the inclement weather as they skirted Ternopol, always keeping to the higher ground. About mid-day, as the weather started to clear, they reached the foothills of the vast mountain chain and the ground rose far more steeply. With the weather clearing they exercised greater caution, always taking cover when any noise of human activity was heard and consequently their progress slowed considerably. Jan began to dread Jerzy's intermittent and muted cries of, "Down! Get down, stay here while I take a look," because the waits for him to return, sometimes as long as twenty minutes or more, were making Jan even more apprehensive and agitated. He also noticed that there seemed to be more farms and small settlements than had previously been the case since they left the destroyed truck, and he was becoming convinced that they would be discovered at any moment.

It was mid afternoon when they approached the top of yet another hill and saw smoke rising from a burning farmhouse on the valley floor, about five hundred yards away. A military vehicle was parked on the track nearby and, as they watched from their vantage point, hidden in the grass, three Russian soldiers escorted an elderly man at gunpoint out of a nearby barn and marched him off towards the rear of the truck. Suddenly a shot rang out and one of the soldiers fell to the ground and before the others reacted a second soldier was also shot down. As the remaining Russian and his prisoner dived to the ground, seven or eight Polish troops ran from behind another outbuilding about thirty yards from the burning house. Jan couldn't hear what was said but the Russian immediately got to his knees and put his hands up in surrender. The prisoner, showing a total disregard for his own safety and astonishing speed of reaction for his age, instinctively grabbed a rifle from the ground and covered the Russian before giving him a vicious kick in the ribs.

Jan immediately thought that safety was at hand and started to stand up but, as he did so, he was forcefully pulled back down by Jerzy, "Stay down, we don't know what we're getting into here. Let's see what happens first."

They then witnessed the Polish soldiers searching the remaining outbuildings and taking equipment from the military vehicle and the apparently dead Russians. They tied up the surviving Russian but he was not abused any further. One of the Polish soldiers appeared to be an officer: he was certainly giving orders and taking control of the situation. After a few minutes Jerzy had seen enough, "Come on, let's get down there."

He explained his initial reticence as they walked, "At first I was worried that they might be deserters, only looking out for themselves at everyone else's expense but that's not the case. From what I've seen I don't think they're conscripts either but proper professional soldiers. We've found some friends at last."

They discovered that the Lieutenant, Lance Sergeant and seven men had been garrisoned with their battalion between Lublin and Chelm when they were ordered, even as the Russians crossed the border, to fight their way south-east to reinforce the Romanian bridgehead. Things soon deteriorated further as they were squeezed between the two invading armies and sustained German and Russian attacks decimated their numbers as they attempted to bypass Lwow. The few survivors were now scattered far and wide, all looking for an escape route south.

Following the Germans' initial successes and having lost so much territory the original plan of the Polish High Command had been to withdraw their considerable land and air-force assets to the south east and there maintain a protracted defence until the allies could counterattack and relieve them. However, once it became clear that the British and French had no intention of honouring their treaty obligations to provide full-scale military assistance, and had therefore to all practical purposes abandoned them to their fate, the Polish priority changed to one of extricating as much manpower as possible through the Romanian bridgehead to reform in France.

With perimeter lookouts posted, the Lieutenant spoke to the two new arrivals inside the barn, "We walked in yesterday and the farmer was kind enough to let us bed down in the barn. He's a patriot, not worried about himself and content that his family is already safely over the border. We were going to rest up for a couple of days so this morning I decided to do a full reconnoitre and set up an observation post."

Jerzy asked, "What went wrong?"

"When we saw the Russians arrive I decided it was best to simply wait for them to leave but, unfortunately, about an hour ago they found some of our kit in the barn and arrested the farmer. Before we got back they burnt the place down to make him talk, but luckily we got here before they took him in for proper interrogation. I've also got one of the best snipers in the whole army, a gamekeeper from the Lakes and you saw the results of his work."

"Could they have told their base about us?" asked Jan as his feeling of security started to wear off.

"No, they haven't got a radio, but they'll be missed before long so we had better move out. The farmer has to come with us now or they'll kill him. I'll leave the Russian tied up here. I can't murder a prisoner and anyway, by the time he gets free, we'll be miles away and after what's happened to him and his mates, his own people are just as likely to shoot him."

"What's happening generally," asked Jerzy, "Is it a total collapse since the Russians came?"

"More or less, the few units we came across had received contradictory orders. Some told to hold their positions and fight on to the last, but some like us told to escape into neutral countries and others told not to engage the Russians at all because we have a non-aggression pact with them."

Jerzy shook his head, "I don't believe it! They've invaded us and yet soldiers who have taken an oath to defend their land, are told not to engage, but to run away?"

"Well, it's true, and another unit hadn't received any orders at all until we met them. They'd simply been abandoned to fend for themselves. Anyway, it's obvious that the enemy, Germans and Soviets alike, are closing in on all fronts and the war in Poland is virtually over so we've decided we'll fight our way out."

Thirty minutes later, refreshed with a meal of water, soup and biscuits, they were once again resolutely moving south and the rest of the day passed off without further incident. Although the farmer slowed them down slightly, his detailed local knowledge was invaluable and several times he was able to point out potential hazards and likely areas for Russian patrols. They also heard aircraft for the first time in a couple of days, but it was well to the west and caused them no real concern, other than to alert them to another potential danger.

The following afternoon they were well into the foothills and when they paused to rest the farmer surprised them all when, with much pride, he proclaimed that he would guide them across the mountains himself. He explained that he would avoid contact with the Russians by following the very animal tracks and paths that, as a young man, he had used regularly with his father to smuggle in goods, avoiding the scrutiny of the Austrian authorities and their crippling taxes.

As their journey became progressively more difficult they slowed dramatically and at times were forced to climb high into the mountains in order to avoid the more regularly used trails and passes. Jan, although used to the very cold Polish winters, had never experienced such bone-numbing chill. The icy winds penetrated through every item of his clothing and the air itself was so cold that it burnt his lungs every time he gasped for breath. At other times it alternately snowed and rained, until he was soaked to the skin and again so cold that he couldn't feel his hands or feet and ice was forming across his face. He was automatically putting one foot in front of the other, but his mind was so befuddled by fatigue and hypothermia that he was incapable of rational thought.

He craved respite, normality, warmth and above all, an end to the unrelenting pain. He was literally walking while he was asleep and, whenever conscious thought broke through his bewilderment, he just wanted to lay down, give up and die. He no longer had the will to go on. Every time he faltered, stumbled or simply

65

slumped down and refused to move, Jerzy was there with words of encouragement, a helping hand or literally a shoulder to lean on. On several particularly steep and rocky climbs Jerzy tied himself to the lad and carried him on his back or sometimes pulled or even dragged him across the snow and ice. The others fared little better and they became so disoriented as they climbed that they often wondered if they were even going in the right direction. Each of them at some time or another feared the worst and imagined themselves frozen to death on the trail and abandoned by his comrades. With every pace they weakened further and time seemed to pass ever slower as they stumbled, fell and crawled along the worst stretches and then painfully dragged themselves up again, taking it in turns to take the lead and thereby directly expose their bodies to the additional strength-sapping force of the raw icy blast and the heightened fear that one slip or loss of concentration would lead to sudden calamity.

Finally, just as total exhaustion threatened to engulf them all, they started to descend and with the peaks now behind them the weather conditions slowly improved. They all began to thaw out and managed to pick up the pace considerably once they could see the safety of farms and villages scattered across the meadows like a patchwork quilt at the foot of the valley, thousands of feet below. The sturdy and steadfast farmer was as good as his word and ten days after leaving his home, battered and bruised, dehydrated, blistered, exhausted and starving hungry, they arrived at their first town in Romania and what an arrival it was!

Poles, thousands of them, mostly military but some civilian, were everywhere and the high level of organisation surprised them all. After the usual bureaucracy and tiresome personal documentation the lieutenant was informed that, provided the exiled Polish diplomats who were negotiating with the host authorities could arrange an orderly transit, they would all be transported to an Adriatic Port and then shipped to France or England. They were ecstatic: it was not just wishful thinking. The Polish army was to be reformed in the west and would fight again. Their sense of relief and exhilaration was intense and much alcohol was consumed over the next few days, as they recovered and toasted their future while feeling safe in the sanctuary of Sighet.

The German Government, suspecting and fearing that these

soldiers would be deployed on the Western front, began to increase diplomatic pressure on Romania to intern the Poles and, in response, internment camps were indeed set up. The Romanians however, perhaps foreseeing their own fate, only paid lip service to the whole question of security. Most Poles, in small groups, just walked out of the camps, often with the tacit approval of the authorities. In fact Jan's military colleagues in Sighet were not properly incarcerated at any stage of their stay. They were permitted to attend the Catholic Church and freely mixed with the locals. They found a vibrant friendly community with a large and thriving Jewish population, which showed great kindness and generosity to the Polish refugees. Little did they or the local inhabitants know that over the next five years this town, even to a greater extent than so many right across war-torn Europe, would see its population decimated at the Nazi extermination camps.

Jan and his colleagues stayed in schools and an old army camp for about ten days and then, after being given the nod by an official from the Mayor's office, simply walked to the railway station and, along with about fifty other Poles, boarded a train for Hungary. The Romanian railway staff never asked them for tickets and every time they heard their Polish voices they simply waved them through. It seemed that most people were very sympathetic and eager to help the troops on their way. The train stopped a couple of miles short of the border and, unseen, they crossed over that night on foot, guided by a local railway guard who also gave them food and cigarettes. They were then supplied with money and clothes from the Polish Government in Exile and told to make for Budapest. This time they had to buy tickets and, although some Hungarians supported Hitler, most were quite prepared to see the Poles safely through their country.

Jerzy and Jan reported as instructed to the Polish embassy in Budapest and were then, after being deloused and bathed, provided with tickets to Yugoslavia. They were warned that German sympathisers and agents near the border would either report them to the local police, who would be within their rights to arrest them, or might even try to harm them. In the event the Hungarians proved extremely helpful, even providing extra carriages on the trains especially for the Poles: but again they had to walk across the border at night. This time, however, they did so with the implicit co-operation of the border guards, who knowingly turned their backs, smoked their cigarettes and talked amongst themselves.

They travelled rapidly by train across Yugoslavia and almost immediately upon their arrival at Split they boarded a boat that offered the chance of liberty at last. As Jan walked up the gangplank he was overcome by an immense sense of relief and gratitude towards Jerzy. He looked up at his friend and with tears in his young eyes said, "Well, we made it and I'm so happy today. I don't know where we will all end up, but for the moment we're free and I know that without you I would have been dead by now. I owe you so much and I thank you for making this possible. I just hope my family have been as lucky and that one day soon I'll be able to introduce you to them."

Jerzy gave him a fatherly hug and ruffled his young friend's curly hair, "I'll do everything I can to make sure you get back to your loved ones and I can promise you that if you're strong enough and determined enough anything is possible. Never lose faith. Although it might take us a while, we'll both get back home in the end. Nazis and Bolsheviks can't stop us now."

Salisbury, Wiltshire: 4th October 2008

I picked up the postcards and examined them, looking for any possible connections, but was surprised by the diversity in both time and location:

An Easter card dated 1950, the greeting in English, but devoid of any message, stamps, date or address on the front or rear.

A picture of the town centre at Osimo in Italy, again no stamp, address or message, just the date: September, 1945.

A photograph of The George Inn, Codford, in Wiltshire, again blank except for a hand written date of January, 1947.

A picture of Edinburgh Castle and in Polish the words, "visited today with the school, reminds me of home! 7th

July, 1941." There was no stamp or postmark to provide any possible leads.

A picture of what appeared to be rows of war graves against a background of a coal slagheap and written on the back - Lens, Pay-de-Calais, 1944.

A picture of Sao Vicente monastery in Lisbon, containing no dates or any other markings.

A picture of The Houses of Parliament and written on the back in Polish "A reminder of the trip down the Thames, June, 1947."

A photograph postcard of several scenes of Breda, the Dutch city which was stamped and franked, dated 14th December, 1946, addressed to Sergeant Wittold Vranek, Camp 170 Pipers Wood, Amersham, Bucks, England. Written on the back in English "Thank you for sending the addresses. We will keep you all in our hearts and once again we express our thanks to you and your men for your actions of 28th October, 1944. We will never forget your sacrifice." It was signed 'the Crutzen family'.

A photograph of the Arc de Triumph in Paris with no date or markings of any kind.

A photograph of Winchester cathedral with no stamps or address but written on the back, again in Polish, "The Stonehenge trip. I didn't realise I was so close! July, 1946."

I considered what I had learnt from this assortment as I sipped my coffee, which was now turning cold, having remained untouched for the fifteen minutes I had already spent studying the cards. I had found another local Wiltshire connection and an indication of travel in Italy, France, Holland, Portugal and the UK, some of which was almost certainly during or at the end of the war: the earliest date being July 1941 and the latest June 1947. There were at least two distinctive sets of handwriting apart from that on the back of the Dutch card, so was I now looking for two people?

At least I had a name, Wittold Vranek, without doubt a Polish soldier who probably fought across Holland and into Germany towards the end of the war. I needed to know more about what happened at Breda, particularly on 28th October, 1944. What was the significance of the other locations and does the handwriting match any of the letters? Could Osimo have something to do with the Italian campaign, as I knew the Poles were at Monte Cassino? How does the other monastery, the one in Portugal, fit into the puzzle?

Perhaps even more relevant and far nearer home, I now had a solid starting point for my enquiries - camp 170, Pipers wood, Amersham. The M.o.D. would hold a mountain of information about military camps and their various uses over the years and they may also be able to provide some background concerning the sergeant who had now most definitely become a potential subject for my enquiries. Could he in fact be the very man I was looking for, but if so, could he have fought in both Holland and Italy? Something in the back of my mind was reminding me that two distinct and separate armies were involved in those campaigns and that their dates of operation overlapped.

Another possibility would be to explore what had become of the Dutch family, but suspecting that this would be more complex and time consuming I decided to put it on hold. I then jotted down a few notes and lists in order to prioritise those leads I felt would potentially reveal the quickest results. Experience had taught me to disregard nothing, and although my aim remained to identify the Polish gent who left the case at The Red Lion Inn, I had a strong feeling that, in order to do so, I might have to reconstruct what had happened to him both before and after his strange disappearance. To that end I sensed that these postcards could play an increasingly significant role and, encouraged that I had taken something positive from my analysis, I decided to translate another letter.

Suddenly my level of interest rocketed, as I saw the name and address on the top of the next letter dated 14th November 1939. Once again I found the language flowery, rather formal in places, yet with a sprinkling of colloquialisms, and these idiomatic phrases caused me to guess their meaning by use of context only. I was not altogether happy with my translation but felt I couldn't improve upon it:

To Henryk Nowaski, No 4, Gniew Street, Pelplin, Pomerania.

Dear Papa and treasured sister Maria,

I'm safe and it's my birthday today but I'm troubled because you are so very far away. We used to be so happy on this day every year because it's Jozef's name day as well, and we always had a lively dinner party, celebrated with all our friends and sang 'Sto Lat' until we were hoarse. It seems that 'the one hundred years' of that lovely tribute has now become an impossible dream because the way things are going many Poles will be lucky if they survive the next few days or weeks at best. So my dearest guardians, as the song also says, you must both 'live for us' until we get back home. You are probably thinking that I should have written before and for my lack of family duty I am truly sorry.

The truth is I have been afraid to tell you that I have lost dear Mama and my brothers and I have no idea what has become of them since I last saw them at the evacuation farm at Luck. I will tell you what little I know but I hope you have heard from them before now. Oh, how I pray for you all every night, I miss you so much and long to be back home. The Russians held Tomek and me prisoner but I escaped and have been helped by our troops. Then we walked for days across the mountains into Romania and now I hope I'm going to France or England where the soldiers are going and they say I'll be safe there. I'm on a boat, a British freighter, which is called 'Lady Luck', perhaps that's a good omen, and we're making for Portugal where the British will arrange another ship for the rest of the journey.

There are hundreds of our soldiers on this boat and I'm told there are many more such craft, all fully loaded, but I am scared of going so far from home and I have heard terrible stories of what is happening in our Poland. Lwow is in ruins and our enemies are once again carving up our country between them. Mama gave me her rosary to keep me safe, but when I see her again I can give it back and tell her it cared for me in her absence. When I hold it I can see Mama's face and hear her voice and I don't feel so alone.

I can't post this letter because my friend Jerzy says there is no longer any post at home as things are so bad, so I'll keep it until I know that it will get through. I will let you both know where I end up and I hope you can give me good news of Mama and our brothers. Jerzy says that the English will help us throw the Russians and Germans out, but I think he only tells me that to make me feel better. If anything happens to me Jerzy will let you know but I'm sure I'll be all right so don't worry about me.

I promise I did all I could to help Mama and Tomek, but we were so powerless against the Russians. I love you all and I hope with all my heart that you are safe and that the family will be reunited back at the home where we were all so happy.

Your loving son and brother, Jan.

So now I knew that Henio in the previous letter was Henryk Nowaski, the father of Jan, the husband of Ewa (Ewka also being a familial diminutive) and the brother of Roman in Warsaw. I had their address in Pelplin and had learnt that Jan had been captured with Tomek, who was probably his brother and that there was at least one other brother. It seems that they also had a sister, Maria who stayed at the Pelplin address. Despite my growing determination to focus on solving the current problem I found myself continually digressing back to the war, visualising how tragic life must have been for this family and how desperately they must have tried to stay together. Why would the Russians capture boys and what had actually happened to them since they left the capital?

After a few minutes I managed to drag myself back to the present. Could it be that Jan was my subject? It looked like he came to France or England, but how old was he? I checked the handwriting against that on the postcards and there were definite similarities with the one of Edinburgh castle, but with so few words to compare I was far from certain that it was a match. Perhaps it was Tomek or could Jerzy have been the man and was he one of the soldiers? Perhaps it was someone I knew nothing of as yet? I quickly did the mathematics in my head and concluded that Henryk would almost certainly be outside the age profile but, apart from him, all options were still wide open.

On the other hand it was progress of a sort, as I had learnt a great deal about the Nowaski family, but questions whirled around in my mind making it difficult to be incisive and it seemed certain on reflection that this letter could never have been posted. Surely it would have been censored if it had passed through the military authorities here, and anyway Pelplin was under German control so it certainly wouldn't have got through if posted in Portugal or anywhere else. It may even have been that Jan didn't reach the UK. It seemed to me that for every fact I uncovered, a host of further questions arose. I was extremely anxious to see what light the other documents would shed on the mystery but experience also told me that in order to make the most of any clues I required sharp eyes and a clear head and so I needed to take a break and stretch my legs.

After lunch I found myself, once again, pondering the events described in the letters and my curiosity quickly drove me back to my desk. It was difficult to detach myself from Jan's predicament and, perhaps because of my own ancestry, I increasingly identified with him and his family. Seldom in my life have I personally considered how the events of history have impacted on particular families caught up in such violent and disastrous events, yet alone imagined the immense desire for survival and reunion that must have driven the displaced individuals who abruptly found themselves refugees in their own country.

I examined the next letter, the only one that had been typed and at first I thought this would make translation easier but then I noticed that an English typewriter had been used and certain amendments then made by hand. The use of an English typewriter complicated matters considerably, making my task problematic, and so, with an audible sigh of resignation, I realised that I would almost certainly be using more guesswork. Accurate translation would now be difficult because there are seven vowels and thirty-five consonants, not to mention the extra digraphs and diacritics in the Polish language, as compared to English.

The paper itself was of a poor quality and was worn through in places where it had been folded: it was dog-eared and grubby at the edges. It had evidently been torn along the whole top and bottom edges but the lines of tear were relatively straight as if it had come from a longer document that had been folded in two places then ripped along the folds thereby extracting a section from the middle. About twenty-five minutes later I was reasonably content with my rough-and-ready translation:

> *The Government of Great Britain has officially welcomed us and Winston Churchill has personally acknowledged the difficulties we have endured and the suffering of our people at home. He invites us to fight alongside the English and their allies to defeat their enemies and in return they will help us all to return home and free our people. This is his personal promise to his Polish friends and the undertaking of his Government. Our Government in exile accepts his invitation and urges all Poles to join the struggle, on land, at sea and in the air, until the victory is ours. Mr Churchill is an honourable man, a man of his word, and his nation too now suffers the exactitudes and deprivations of war. We will fight together with courage, comradeship and resolve, as is our destiny, and we will prevail and then it is the duty of every Pole, military and civilian, to hold Mr Churchill to his word and ensure we all go home.*

I found the following written in longhand on the bottom of the document: -

> *Jan,*
>
> *I will do all in my power to continue to look out for you but my circumstances may change and I may have to go back to the war. With this in mind I send you this excerpt from our company orders of last week. Keep it with you and guard it dearly: it may one-day help you return home. Remember we have been promised much in the past and*

betrayed or let down at every turn, but this time I believe
Mr Churchill will stand with us. I look forward to seeing
you soon as promised.

Your friend Jerzy, 10ᵗʰ September 1941.

I was relieved to know that Jan had made it to England alongside Jerzy, who was obviously then in the army and probably already was at the time he was mentioned in the previous letter. It could therefore follow that they had called at Portugal en route as Jan suggested, and one or other of them obtained the Lisbon postcard there. The only other postcard that fitted into the intervening time period is that of Edinburgh castle so does that infer that they were in Scotland and, if the writing was Jan's, then was he of school age, so did he attend one locally, possibly on an army base or resettlement camp? It certainly appeared that they were living reasonably close to each other.

However, what really stole my attention was the exalted level of respect and trust seemingly bestowed on Winston Churchill by both the Polish Military Authorities and the individual Polish servicemen (if Jerzy was a typical example). I would have expected far more cynicism or at least a healthy degree of scepticism, bearing in mind their historical experiences in general and events of the previous two years in particular, but instead I detected an uncharacteristically naïve acceptance of what were really no more than expedient political promises. Then again, perhaps I was being rather harsh on all those concerned, judging these matters out of context and with the benefit of hindsight. With these thoughts uppermost in my mind I tried to imagine how Jan would have coped with the practicalities of living in the UK presumably without language, family, home or any real possessions and at the mercy of his hosts for everything. Such dependency would have included even the very basics, so necessary for human existence, which my generation and I now take totally for granted.

FOUR

The Gulag Express
12th October 1939

Tomek was shivering from the cold: he was starving, half blinded from the coal dust and had completely lost track of time. He had been left in the coalbunker without food or drink for another two days and then, as he was dragged out on the third day and again doused with ice-cold water, he lost consciousness altogether. Now oblivious to his condition and surroundings he dreamt, but it was no reprieve from grim reality because he was caught in a nightmare kaleidoscope of danger and self-recrimination.

He was assailed by disjointed vignettes of their journey, the hardships, the beatings and the violence; images that switched, repeated and intermingled, until he was distraught with fear and confusion. After what seemed like hours of mental turmoil he slowly started to make some sense of his confused thought patterns and the disconnected and surreal sequences that flashed through his troubled mind. Gradually clarity emerged from the fog as the ambiguous and tantalising elements of his memory coalesced, painting a picture of his many shortcomings and giving him a glimpse into the future. His father appeared and made his displeasure perfectly clear. In front of everyone at the farm he pointed his finger angrily at Tomek and blamed him for letting the whole family down and being solely responsible for Jan's predicament. His mother immediately leapt to his defence but the others looked at him accusingly and, under their disdainful stare, he was forced to examine his conscience.

He listened painfully to the force of their arguments and

reluctantly accepted the contention that it was his bravado and impetuosity with the Russians that had landed them both in dire danger. What if his recklessness had cost his brother's life? His thoughts raced back to other instances in his childhood when his uncontrolled sense of adventure and high spirits had caused trouble, normally for his brothers or friends but rarely for himself. For the first time in his life he felt a deep sense of failure and guilt and an overwhelming motivation to protect his family and make them proud. He prayed that it was not too late and resolved to make amends: to think things through before acting and to consider the consequences for those close to him. He decided that if he was going to survive and find his way home it was time to turn over a new leaf in his life and grow up. He would now take full responsibility for his own actions.

No sooner had these conscientious decisions been made than all such newborn hopes were shattered as his dream suddenly transformed once more and, yet again, he found himself quaking in front of the machine gun. This time he was deafened as it fired and spat but he still screamed out as the bullets ripped into his brother's body, picking him up like a rag doll and throwing his bloody, dismembered corpse back into the wall and then, mercifully, he too was struck down and succumbed to the pain and darkness.

He came to on the floor of a cattle truck, his clothing soaked through in his sweat, as someone was gently washing his face with a water soaked rag that smelt of hay and horses. A bottle was then held to his lips and he managed to swallow a few drops of water that eased his parched and swollen throat and tasted so sweet and refreshing. The soldier holding the bottle said, "Take it steady son, you were having a nightmare, but you're with friends now and safe, at least for the time being. From what we heard of your screams and ramblings and the state you're in, it looks as if you've had an even tougher time than we have."

Tomek tried to speak but the soldier cut in, "Steady on, there's no need to explain anything to us, just lay back and rest. When you're feeling easier you can have some of our bread and smoked sausage. I don't think you're badly hurt, just exhausted and dehydrated. By the way I'm Wladek but everybody calls me 'Doc' because I'm a medical orderly with the Lwow Infantry Division Reserves. I was training to be a doctor in the city before I was called up."

"Where are we and where are we going?" croaked Tomek as he propped himself up on his elbow and took a first look at his surroundings.

"Well, I don't know where we're going other than to Russia, but as you've probably realised we're on a train and it left Lwow this morning. About five hundred of us were loaded into the wagons, forty in each truck and you were put in here by a couple of Russian medics when we stopped at Luck. They didn't tell us anything and you've only just come to."

Tomek said, "Are you all prisoners of war?"

"Nearly all of us. We were captured when Lwow fell but there are a few civilians as well, mostly lads and professionals of military age. It seems that they're already removing the ones most likely to cause them trouble. There's also one wagon containing women but I have no idea where they're from or why they're here. They've also separated us from all our officers and NCOs and they put them on a different train. It doesn't look too good for any of us, but we'll try to stick together and look out for you as well."

Tomek could see that the truck was full but there was just sufficient room for several people to lie down, although most of the soldiers, some in tattered uniforms and without footwear, were sitting against the walls or leaning on each other. Pale sunlight filtered through the cracks in the boards and, although a draught was also blowing in around the doors, it felt warm and dry and he was relieved not to be tasting and swallowing coal dust. Despite the uncertain future and his poor physical condition he felt secure and strangely content for the first time since he had been separated from his brother. As his thoughts returned to Jan and the rest of his family he kept wondering whether they were safe and how they were all coping before he fell into a fitful but nightmare-free sleep.

When he awoke he heard a quiet, almost whispered conversation taking place around him and so he kept his eyes firmly closed while he strained to hear above the noise of the train.

"The next stop for fuel and water for the engine will probably be Pinsk and after that we can't expect any help from the locals as we're into Russia. I think they'll take us as far away from Poland as they can and that means we'll have to be transferred onto the main Warsaw to Moscow line at Minsk. If we're going to make our move and have any real chance of success we've got to act quickly."

"You're right," Tomek recognised Doc's voice, "But a mass breakout is out of the question as they won't hesitate to shoot us. Although the men guarding us are simple infantry soldiers and not politicos, their bosses are ruthless and the guards would much rather kill us than attract the attention of their own political police. Stalin and his cronies have murdered hundreds of thousands of their own people to hang on to power, so a few hundred Poles aren't of any significance."

"Since we were captured and documented, their checks on us have been almost nonexistent. It's quite clear that these guards are reserves and have very little idea of security work. Although they searched us when we were put on the train, it was pretty cursory and they didn't even bother to check our identity against any lists or make a headcount. This could work to our advantage because if just a few of us manage to escape then they probably won't even notice we're gone until the train reaches its destination, perhaps not even then," added a third voice.

By now Tomek was wide-awake and listening intently as Doc summarised their thoughts, "Let's agree then, we look for any opportunity but we also need to find out more about where the guards station themselves when we next stop and how much freedom, if any, we have to move about outside the truck. If we spot any weaknesses in their security we'll make an attempt either there and then if it's a one off chance, or at the following stop. We need to strike the right balance between going before we get too far from help on the outside and trying something without sufficient information or planning."

"Then that's what we'll do," said the first soldier. "Now let's get some sleep!"

Tomek thought that in view of what he had heard he would stick close to these men and, while he only had himself to worry about, if he saw a chance to escape with them he should take it. In line with his new-found sense of responsibility he then also considered all the pros and cons and possible consequences of such an escape and decided that if he was going to be of any practical help to his mother and brothers then he must make every effort to gain some professional help from these soldiers. He also made up his mind that once he was free he would make straight for home as he had a sudden and strong premonition that his brothers would be trying the same thing.

An hour later, after Tomek had eaten twice from Doc's hoard and was beginning to feel stronger, the train pulled into Pinsk and, as predicted, the engine took on coal and water but the prisoners stayed locked inside until this was completed. Then the doors were unbolted and pulled open almost simultaneously, right along the full length of the train. As the light poured in Tomek saw a row of fully armed Russian troops along the far side of the platform and set up between the troops and the cattle trucks were trestle tables each supporting huge metal buckets, full of water with mugs tied to the containers by thick wire. There were also piles of small loaves scattered across the tables but no other food, clothes, blankets or other comforts. On an order the guards took one step forward and cocked their weapons, which were pointed directly at the trucks. No further orders were given and after a few seconds one or two prisoners nervously jumped down onto the platform. As there was no immediate or adverse reaction from the guards the others followed, slowly at first, then almost as a deluge until there was a considerable crush between the tables and the rail trucks.

As he drank and chewed on a lump of stale bread Tomek heard further trucks being added to the rear of the train. He stood on his toes to see above the crowd and as he looked around he noticed about two hundred additional Polish prisoners being marshalled by more troops alongside the tracks, about a hundred yards further down the platform. In the other direction, about twenty yards beyond the engine, stood another body of guards and this time they were gathered either side of a machine gun position. As Tomek was thinking that escape looked impossible they were ordered back onto the train but before the doors were bolted some of the new arrivals were pushed by the guards into each of the trucks so that all were now overcrowded.

Tomek made his way through the crush and found Doc and his two companions deep in conversation in the far corner. He introduced himself and thanked Doc for his kindness and then continued, "I heard you talking about making an escape and I want to come with you, I'd be of great help to you once we get out into the countryside. I can hunt, stalk, trap, fish and if all else fails scrounge and steal all we need to survive."

Doc smiled broadly introducing his comrades as Red (he had bright ginger hair) and Lech and then added, "I'm sure you can do all those things and you would certainly be a real asset to us, but I'm going to have to say no, because it's far too risky. The chances of us all making it back home or across the border into a neutral country are very slim and I'm not going to risk your life in such an enterprise."

Lech reinforced Doc's point and then said, "When we stopped I managed to look between the trucks to the far side of the train and noticed far fewer troops positioned there, perhaps one every twenty-five yards or so. Even so, it's enough to make sure that there's no way we can get to the other side of the trucks without being spotted."

Red joined in, "As we can't get away on either side of the train and, with the guards to the front of the engine and the rear of the trucks, there's no way out there either, so what about getting down onto the tracks and hiding under the train? If we get out last, behind everyone else in the truck, we can drop down alongside the platform onto the track while we're shielded from view. In fact if we take a few people into our confidence, they can hang back on both sides of us so that the guards at the front and rear can't see what's going on either."

Lech appeared doubtful, "How do we know that there's anything to hold onto, let alone somewhere to hide underneath the wagon? There might even be a guard patrolling directly along the tracks on the far side of the train and it would all be over before we got five yards."

Doc deliberated for a moment and then concluded, "We definitely need to minimise the overall risk if we can but there's only one way to find out, so if the system they use at the next stop is the same, I'll drop down on my own and have a quick look. If there are no guards patrolling the track itself and there is something to cling onto underneath I'll let you know and you can join me, but if it's a 'no go' I'll either be caught straight away or I'll climb back up onto the platform and we'll have to think again. We only need something suitable to briefly catch hold of because once the train has travelled a few hundred yards and we're out of sight of the station we can let go and allow the rest of the train to pass above us. We can then make off across country."

Tomek, who had been listening and trying to suppress his disappointment, thought perhaps at last he could be of some use, "I can help cover you from the side when you drop down but much more importantly I can also tell you a great deal about these wagons. I was always playing around the Pelplin goods yards with my brother who is mad about trains and railways and we used to watch the engineers at work and did some carrying and fetching for them."

He went on to explain that the fitters were constantly moaning about repairing the cattle trucks because they got so much use and were nearly always overloaded, not just with cattle but with timber, coal, iron ore and all sorts of unsuitable goods that they were not designed to carry. In order to make them stronger and last longer they reinforced the chassis after they had been in use for about five years or so. He then gave them the good news, "They did it by welding extra metal cross-members to the bogie underneath the timber frame. If this was common practice across the whole railway system then this one could have been done as well, so there will be plenty of places to hold onto. You could even wedge your feet in between the extra supports, for a short distance at least."

"Well thank you young Tomek, I'll find out soon enough and you most certainly can help cover us, so I'll get a few more of our mates to organise it as soon as we're ready." With that Doc turned to his two partners and together they gradually refined their plan for escape.

The train was held in sidings during the hours of darkness and the prisoners remained locked in throughout, forced to relieve themselves into two buckets, one in each corner near the door. By morning the stench was unbearable and the general mood mutinous, but still the doors remained firmly bolted. Shortly after first light they were once again on their journey towards Minsk and the relief offered by way of the intermittent fresh air current that passed through the truck as they gained speed was short lived, because the contents of the buckets soon slopped across the floor leaving the nearest prisoners standing in their own filth and being mocked and jeered at by their companions. They were all rather surprised when the train stopped mid morning and those with their eyes glued to the cracks in the timbers shouted out that it was a small market town well short of Minsk.

Doc was waiting at the side of the door and as it slid open he was glad to see that the system employed for their management seemed to be as before, with the trestles and a similar line of guards. Satisfied, he withdrew around the edge of the door and, with his two friends, was the last to leave. "Cover me," he shouted to make himself heard above the noise of the engine before he jumped down off the side of the platform onto the track bed. Once he had disappeared from sight his friends remained backed up against the wagon to hide his movements as much as possible. Just as they began to feel somewhat exposed as the rest of the prisoners moved to the tables leaving a gap behind them, Red felt a tug on his trouser leg. As he looked down expectantly he saw an extremely excited face and Doc urgently hissed up at him, "Come on then, we can do this." Red was just about to climb down to join him when pandemonium broke out as several shouts of alarm, followed by a stream of barked orders, came from the front of the train. Doc, believing he had been spotted, pulled himself up onto the platform and as he struggled to his feet there was a burst of automatic gunfire and as everyone dived to the floor, further shots rang out and more orders were shouted.

Tomek looked up and to his left, over the prisoners seeking cover on the ground, towards the source of the commotion and there, about fifty yards from the train, sprawled across a small grass embankment were three apparently dead prisoners who had been shot in the back. An officer approached the bodies and suddenly one of the fallen Poles rolled over and sat up clutching his left arm, blood pouring from between his fingers. He said something to the approaching Russian who coldly aimed his already unholstered sidearm and shot the prisoner three times in the chest. He then immediately shot the other two, still unmoving prisoners, turned calmly towards the train and shouted another stream of orders. Before Tomek could properly process what he had witnessed they were all being bundled back onto the train at gunpoint and the doors were then firmly bolted.

They were left hungry and thirsty as they sat reviewing what had happened at the station. "We could have made it," said Doc. "Those other poor sods must have made a bolt for it on the spur of the moment, but what on earth could have possessed them? It was total madness and now they've also ruined our plan. Just when we were so close."

"If only we'd realised what was really happening straight away we could have taken advantage of the noise and confusion. It was an ideal opportunity but we just lay there like schoolboys instead of getting under the wagon while the guards were distracted. They won't be so lax from now on. They're bound to review everything and tighten up all round. I don't think we'll get another chance and that's an end to it. We've got to face up to the fact that we missed our golden opportunity," interjected Lech emphasising the disappointment that they were all feeling.

They remained locked in the stationary train for two hours before moving off and some ten minutes later they passed through Minsk without stopping. A further hour dragged by before the train unexpectedly stopped again. As they stepped onto the platform of another provincial market town the contrast was immediate and dauntingly impressive. All the station name boards had been covered over with thick sacking and there were no civilians or station personnel anywhere to be seen. The guards were from a different regiment, their numbers had doubled, there were several machine-gun positions stationed along the platform and additional guards were climbing onto the roof of the train. The doors of the wagons were being unlocked one at a time, in sequence, starting at the front and there were no tables or other obstructions on the platform.

This time the prisoners were brought to attention, properly lined up and counted. As they stood there a Russian officer moved down the front of the line and singled out every tenth prisoner by touching him on the arm. That individual was then pushed forward by another guard who walked down the back of the line, keeping pace with his senior officer. Those selected were then marched off to the side and put into one of the cattle pens boarded by metal rails that must have been used as a holding yard for the beasts prior to being loaded onto the railway cars. At first the prisoners formed their own individual fears of what was going to happen, right across a whole spectrum of reasons and possible punishments, but as their imaginations worked overtime a collective sense of impending disaster took hold and they all prayed desperately not to be selected.

Tomek, positioned between Doc and Red was doing his best to stand to attention but like everyone else he had already realised the alarming significance of being picked out. As the officer approached he was trying desperately to calculate whether or not he would be chosen as number ten. When the Russian was only a few paces away he risked a glance sideways and counting under his breath, in time with the officer, he confirmed it. He would be number ten! As the Russian reached out with his right arm and looked straight at him, Tomek automatically tensed up, waiting for the inevitable push in the back. He bit down on his lip to stop himself crying out in fear and despite the pain and taste of blood he nearly fainted, but Doc, sensing his plight, held him upright. The outstretched hand paused in mid-air right in front of Tomek's face. Then slowly and deliberately it passed on by before falling heavily on Red's shoulder and he, not Tomek, was pushed forward as the Russian regained his rhythm and carried on counting along the line. Tomek expected Red to shout out, "No, I'm number eleven, the boy is number ten. You know he is. Take him!" but Red marched off without a word of protest or a glance back, and Tomek thought that perhaps Red didn't realise what had happened.

Doc leant down and whispered in Tomek's ear, "Don't worry, you're safe and don't say anything. He knows you were number ten and so did the Russian. We all know, because we were all counting."

Tomek would later reflect that he had witnessed a small degree of compassion from the Russian and typical selfless courage from Red. The compassion didn't last long though as three of the women prisoners were also singled out and put in the pen with the men. The same Russian Officer then came forward and through an interpreter issued his orders, "Prisoners will not attempt escape under pain of death, you will obey orders at all times and you will show respect to your guards. If only one of you disobeys these rules you will all be punished by the state. My men will now carry out the punishment for the escape bid. This time it has to be one in ten, if there is another breach of your proper conduct it will be far worse for you. You will now witness the punishment and see for yourselves that we do not make idle threats."

All eyes turned to the animal pens where some sixty prisoners were standing silent and motionless in the strict confines of their new prison and then, without another word but on the hand signal of the commander, three machine guns opened up. The prisoners were slaughtered, with less mercy than had been shown to the thousands of animals that had stood on the very same spot. They were riddled with literally thousands of rounds and mown down under the haunted and disbelieving gaze of their friends and brothers in arms. Many present, including young Tomek, who was visibly in shock, white as a ghost and unable to move, could not comprehend the enormity of what they had seen.

The carnage caused by the hail of heavy calibre bullets ripping through the flesh and bones of the defenceless prisoners, crammed together in the holding pen like sardines in a can, was sickening. The resulting mutilation, with severed limbs, the spurting of arterial bleeds, the strewn body parts and the many unrecognisable corpses all covered in gore amidst the spreading flood of blood was the shocking but inevitable result of such callous mass-murder. The horror was so great, even to the seasoned professional soldiers, that it felt as if the enemy, entering into an unprecedented level of cruelty and barbarism, had taken a forbidden and irreversible step. It was not surprising that some of the Russian guards were themselves horrified and ashamed of the excesses of their commander, despite the fact that many knew he was himself acting under the direct and unequivocal orders of the local N.K.V.D. chief.

The secret state police had eagerly and ruthlessly assisted Stalin in his infamous purges by identifying, imprisoning, torturing and murdering many millions of Soviet citizens who had arbitrarily been classified as 'enemies of the state'. The whole apparatus of the security and state police system operated in a climate of fear where their power was total, unopposed and frequently exhibited to a terrified population. This proven weapon of the tyrant and terrorist was now to be unleashed on the Poles, both military and civilian.

Back on the train Tomek voiced his fear and confusion, "Are they going to kill us all do you think? If not, what do they really want with us and if they are, why bother to put us back on the train?"

Doc replied in a very measured and authoritative tone, "That cold-blooded execution back there was to teach us a lesson. Make no mistake, they are ruthless, but they won't kill us all because they apparently need us for something. As you suggest we wouldn't be back on the train otherwise. One thing is for certain though, there can be no more escape attempts. It's going to be more difficult anyway as we move further east and we have a duty to each other, and getting your friends shot is not the way to do it."

Lech leaned forward and looked into Tomek's eyes, "We are going to survive. All three of us, because we owe it to Red and to our loved ones. There comes a time to accept your fate with dignity and resignation and Red found that moment, but there is also a time to fight for life with every ounce of your strength and resolve. We've now reached that time in our lives and the way things are going it may last far too long, be far too painful and test us to the limit but, after what we've seen today, not one of us should ever give in to these cruel bastards."

The mention of Red's name and the stoical way he had acted grieved Tomek and he was horrified as he realised that by changing the count many subsequent prisoners who would have previously escaped selection had also been murdered and at first he felt responsible for those deaths as well as Red's, but then he felt a growing determination not to let such a noble act be wasted. As he pondered on his uncertain future he also drew strength from the way Doc and Lech had behaved since they met. "You're right Lech, it's up to us to make the best of it and if we're going to get home again we'll have to depend on each other. I'm so glad that you're both here with me because I've now discovered the hard way that I wouldn't last long on my own!"

Left to their own thoughts they gradually drifted into sleep but frequently awoke with a desperate thirst or pangs of hunger. About five hours later the train stopped but again they remained locked in overnight. In the morning as the door opened they discovered that they were not, as expected, in a station but in the middle of the countryside. They were again well guarded, given water to drink and thrown a small loaf each before being marched off. Lech tried to estimate how far they had come on the train but remained uncertain, "Where are we?" he asked Doc as they marched alongside each other down a muddy track close behind Tomek.

"Judging from the time spent travelling from Minsk I'd say somewhere just short of Smolensk, off the Warsaw to Moscow main line, but I don't have a clue as to where we're heading. I think the general direction is still eastwards but the guards aren't giving anything away."

They spoke very little from fear of the guards and to save their energy, as they were all very weak and frequently stumbled and fell on the rough surface. They all began to suffer further as the day wore on and those without footwear were quickly hobbling, their feet badly lacerated, and had to be supported by their colleagues. They longed for the five-minute rest every hour but dreaded the pain when they started to move off again and the only sustenance they were given was an occasional mug of water and, at mid-day, a ladle of cold potato soup. They presented a forlorn picture; these five hundred bedraggled, half-starved souls as they snaked their way, under heavy escort, across the Russian plain towards a dark and unwelcoming forest on the horizon.

They arrived at the tree line before nightfall and an hour later they were herded into a pre-prepared ten-foot high barbed-wire compound. Its only shelter being a huge marquee-type tent without sides, that sat incongruously right in the centre, like some macabre big-top waiting mockingly for the happy crowds to gather. The only permanent building on the site was some two hundred yards away, set alongside an overgrown forest track and it served as the guards' barracks. They were shown the first act of common decency of their incarceration, when they were all issued with two red-cross blankets and a small square ground sheet. This compound was to become their home for every night of the next two months and every day they toiled, clearing the virgin forest and, under the orders of Russian tradesmen, they constructed a military camp. It comprised of two rows of huts, each row containing five buildings. Most of the raw materials came from the forest, with all the additional supplies being trucked in from the railway line.

Throughout this time they received just sufficient nourishment to work and survive but, despite the best efforts of Doc, his fellow medics and the handful of doctors within their ranks, their overall health deteriorated. The civilians, not used to such harsh and demanding circumstances, suffered the most and several became so desperate that they committed suicide. The worst problem however was caused by the total lack of medical supplies, which meant that wounds and injuries, both those suffered in the war and now from accidents on the construction site, soon became infected. Over twenty men and two women died during those weeks and the Russian commander, in the face of repeated pleas, resolutely refused to provide any medicines.

Administration, kitchen, barrack and toilet buildings were all erected, until the result was a large self-contained camp in an isolated and concealed site, deep in the forest and far from prying eyes. Finally, a ditch and perimeter fences were added and then, after generators and endless quantities of equipment were trucked in, the camp was ready for business.

"Well, let's hope all our hard work was worth it and we can have at least some small degree of comfort when we move into the new camp. Even as prisoners of these slave drivers it'll be comforting to have a proper roof over our heads at night and some decent food from a proper kitchen," stated Tomek echoing the thoughts of most of the prisoners who, now that the heavy snows had arrived, were eager to move into the camp.

"This is the last place on earth I'd choose to be, but as I've got no say in it at all, there is a certain attraction to sitting in there all snug and seeing the war out." added Doc who could already see himself inside a warm hut, eating a half-decent meal.

"When do you think we'll move in?" asked Tomek.

"I thought it would have been several days ago, but as they keep finding us extra things to do it could still be a week or so. As normal, the guards aren't giving anything away. It's a job to get even a couple of words out of the friendliest ones and there aren't many of those about." replied Lech as he rolled over to get some sleep.

The following morning as they stood on parade for roll-call they were astonished to see a convoy of ten trucks arrive with a large military escort of about a hundred guards, consisting entirely of NKVD personnel. Suddenly a huge, spontaneous and raucous cheer went up from the prisoners as they saw Polish troops start to disembark from the central vehicles and line up in an orderly and practised manner at the entrance to the new camp. The cheering stopped immediately as one of the guards, now positioned in a watchtower, fired off a burst into the air.

"Look, they're nearly all officers and NCOs, there's hardly an ordinary ranker amongst them," shouted Lech.

The truth suddenly dawned on Doc and he explained to Tomek, "The camp isn't for us. I should have realised, it's never really looked big enough to take us all anyway. No, we've built it for the NKVD. It's obvious that they wouldn't use such a large number of their own staff just for guard duty so it must be some sort of processing or interrogation centre for our captured officers and now they've started moving them through. I suspect that now we've finished here it will be time for us to be moved on to the next job where they are short of a labour battalion or two. This bastard war gets worse by the day."

Tomek could hardly hide his disappointment at losing the promise of better living conditions. Nevertheless, he was also pleased to see the Polish officers, as their discipline and bearing reminded him of the pride and patriotism he had felt before the war but was now no longer evident amongst his own companions since they had been so badly treated as prisoners. After being captured and living entirely with the troops he had come to understand their frustration at being overrun so quickly by both the Germans and Russians. Almost to a man they were convinced the fault was entirely that of the Government, which included the most senior military officers. Consequently they had lost their respect for the entire military high command. They believed these individuals were incompetent, old-fashioned and over-confident to such an extent that they had been criminally reckless with their country's future and were also directly responsible for their own current and precarious predicament.

The following day they remained behind the barbed wire in their 'circus', as it had become known, watching as another convoy arrived, depositing more Polish officers, NCOs, civilians and even boy scouts who were then all marched into the new camp. The Russians went to extraordinary lengths to keep the two sets of prisoners and their respective guards apart, and to prevent any form of communication between them. A line of sentries was permanently placed between the two camps and only the NKVD contingent was permitted inside the new facility. Those few enterprising individuals who tried to shout across to the officers as they arrived were severely beaten by the guards and the attempts to communicate soon ceased. Such behaviour became a major talking point within Tomek's group but they could find no logical reason for it other than the camp commander must be power mad, as well as an enthusiastic and cruel disciplinarian.

The next day they were formed up for roll call, made to dismantle their own camp and then marched out of the forest, again under heavy escort, back towards the railway lines. Just before they left the tree line Tomek looked back at a sign recently erected on the side of the track but he couldn't read the Russian script. He turned to Lech, "What does it say?"

Lech repeated the question to those closest to him and someone immediately replied, "Transit camp - Military personnel only – Katyn." This was then repeated by several others who had all laboured so hard to construct the NKVD camp in what would eventually become infamously known as a site of mass murder, 'Katyn Forest.'

Over the next few minutes Tomek, disturbed by the arrival of so many prisoners under the control of the feared NKVD, their own sudden departure and the uncertain future for them all, asked a stream of nervous questions, "How many of our troops have they captured for God's sake? Why bring them here into the middle of nowhere? Why are they guarded exclusively by the NKVD? Where are we going now?"

He was left with his troubled thoughts as no one answered his questions, simply because none of the prisoners knew any of the answers.

They boarded another train, again herded into cattle trucks, and were soon heading east towards Moscow but most of them were too dispirited to debate or care about their likely destination and were content to welcome the temporary escape of sleep. It was as well that they were blissfully unaware that they had just embarked on a 1,750 mile rail journey, joining the Trans-Siberian Railroad at the capital, which would take them to a camp half way between Novosibirsk (New Siberia) and Krasnoyarsk, east of the Urals and deep into the harsh environment of Siberia.

A number of vital armament works, industrial factories and chemical plants were being built there and others moved lock, stock and barrel from eastern Poland and the Ukraine. These seizures were not restricted directly to the Soviets' preparations for war or their manufacturing effort: there were also prizes of status. For instance at the outbreak of war a new state-of-the-art radio station had just been opened at Luck and following the Russian invasion it was immediately dismantled and transported to Russia, together with its key personnel and engineers. In the following months dozens of factories and ten thousand inhabitants who had been rounded up from this one small city alone were transported east.

Moving elements of the production and armaments' infrastructure such massive distances was a logistical and organisational nightmare but it was a valuable rehearsal for events later in the war when the Red Army became convinced that it was necessary to move everything further east out of range of the Luftwaffe if they were to have any hope of driving the invading Germans out. Like Hitler, Stalin had no compunction about using slave labour to achieve maximum output and considered all prisoners, including prisoners of war, expendable in the process.

The Poles on the train were destined for the Siberian forests to help supply wartime industry's insatiable demand for timber. The journey took three weeks and as they travelled east the winter enveloped them with a vengeance and, despite another issue of blankets, the prisoners continued to die, both from the intense cold and malnutrition. At every stop bodies were removed and the Poles, even in their weakened state, many with frostbite and gangrene, were forced to bury their dead friends in ground so frozen that it had to be broken with pickaxes. After a while the permafrost made it totally impossible to dig into the soil and so the train then stopped every day and the bodies were simply thrown from the wagons. The corpses either rolled down the embankment or lay where they fell, just clear of the tracks.

Finally the prisoners left the train and were marched along another track that had been cleared of snow and ice, towards their new home, which came into view two hours later, and Tomek could not believe his tired and watering eyes. "It's massive and it looks as if it's been here for years," he exclaimed, "Surely it's not just for us, look at the watch towers, there are dozens of them and the buildings must stretch for miles, what sort of camp is this?"

Lech replied, "It's a proper prison and it must hold thousands. It's the size of a small village and look over there," pointing towards a large compound at the centre of the complex. "Those must be prisoners and they don't look military to me and they certainly aren't Poles, but they're starving, just like us. We definitely aren't going to be any better off here."

Doc, who managed to keep a sense of perspective no matter

what the circumstances added, "I suspect you're right but there's no point in jumping to conclusions. We'll find out soon enough. Anyway, we've survived up to now and I for one don't intend to let the bastards have the satisfaction of seeing me off, at least not yet!"

As he finished speaking they marched through the front gate of what was to be a hell on earth for these Poles and the many thousands of prisoners who had preceded and would follow them over the years. They were then paraded and following roll-call divided up and billeted in three rectangular half-brick, half-timber barrack-like buildings. Each one held about two hundred prisoners and the Poles discovered that there were already about seventy-five Russian inmates in each of the buildings. There was a mutual atmosphere of suspicion between the two groups and this was exacerbated when one of the Russians, who appeared rather fitter and less emaciated than the others, addressed Tomek and his companions in passable Polish. "I'm a prisoner like all of you, but I'm in charge of this hut and whether you survive or not largely depends on me. I'm the supervisor and you must do what I say without argument or hesitation, if you don't you will be punished and there is only the one punishment here and that is death. The guards will be doing their best to work you or starve you to death anyway so you don't need me as an enemy as well. Don't speak in the presence of, or try to address, a guard as all communication with the authorities must come through me. Until the spring you will be engaged on snow clearing and tree felling, but when the thaw arrives you will be building the new canal and railway spur into the camp. Now get some sleep. We start early."

As he finished one of the Poles asked, "How long are we here for and what's happening in the war?"

The supervisor shook his head, spat on the floor and replied with a dismissive hiss, "You'll be here until you die and any mention of the war is forbidden." He then went to his customary position by the door and bedded down.

Over the next week or so they acclimatised themselves to their new surroundings. Work started in the dark at 6 am and finished at 8 pm when they were given the only meal of the day, usually stale bread and watery soup. The Poles worked alongside the Russians and the guards appeared not to make any obvious distinctions between the two groups who remained wary of one another.

They slept on the floor of the block wrapped in their blankets and anything else they could find or scrounge from each other. The only heating came from a wood-burning stove in the centre and, although it barely raised the temperature above freezing, without it they would all have frozen to death on the first night.

On many occasions Doc noticed one of the Russians, a wizened old man with grey hair and a long white beard, watching him intently and finally, that night, finding the gaze increasingly unnerving, he approached him. "I don't know if you can understand me but I…" The Russian interrupted and in perfect Polish , said, "I have been watching the way you look after the boy, thinking that you seem to be a decent enough fellow who may listen to some advice from a simple soul who has, against all the odds, survived here for nearly ten years."

Doc sat on the floor beside him, "I'd welcome advice from any quarter and you're certainly not a normal prisoner. You're well educated, well spoken and I suspect, like me, a long way from home."

"Yes, my name is Boris Zansky and I come from Moscow where I was a successful, and although I say it myself, a respected playwright but at the height of my success…," he then dropped his voice to a barely audible whisper, "…Mr Stalin decided to introduce me to this establishment."

"What did you do to deserve such a punishment?" asked Doc already finding it difficult to comprehend how this man could commit any serious crime.

"You need a short history lesson on our Russian ways! This camp and hundreds like it are managed by the 'Chief Administration of Corrective Labour Camps' in Russian it is abbreviated to GULAG and so the camps themselves have become known as the Gulag. They were founded in the 20's and are now used as a place for the Government to detain, torture and annihilate its enemies, both real and imagined. There are a few common criminals and real offenders in here but nearly all, like you I suspect, have done nothing other than try to prosper in an increasingly dangerous world. There are over five million people in these camps and although some did criticise our leaders, most like me followed a profession that Stalin thought was a threat in itself."

He explained that millions of teachers, military officers,

poets, writers, philosophers, scientists, mathematicians and other powerless victims of Stalin's purges had lived, suffered and died in similar camps. He believed his real sin had been learning of their existence, purpose and cruelty through his literary friends and so the NKVD arrested him in the middle of the night. "As usual in my country today, there was no charge, no court, no trial and no sentence. In effect, I disappeared and to the entire world I exist no longer."

Doc instinctively believed Boris and, stunned by the enormity of the situation, he could only think of one question, "How have you managed to survive for so long?"

Boris moved closer and continued to whisper, "You need help, without it you will die. The food we are given is insufficient to sustain our levels of work and so we need to obtain more. Without it your fate is sealed. In the free world men who falsely think they are superior can only thrive if nurtured and supported by women. In this place, where all is alien, paradoxically this truth remains valid and they hold the key to our wellbeing. They live in a separate camp close by, but some of them are employed here, either in the kitchens or at the guards' quarters, as housekeepers, nurses, nannies and general servants. No doubt many are abused but some have become useful to their bosses and are granted certain privileges in return. One or two of these women risk their lives for some of us and I have been fortunate enough to be close to one of those involved."

"Are you saying you'll help us?" asked Doc not sure of Boris's motivation.

The amiable Russian smiled and shook his head slightly, "I can only do so much, the supplies are limited and you really need to cultivate your own sources but I will do what I can. During my forty years on this earth I have learnt that the resourceful tend to rise to the top. We must extend both our ingenuity and our limited circle of friends."

Doc was stunned to hear the Russian's true age as he looked like an old man, at least twenty years older, and he then realised that this camp would slowly suck the very life force from each and every one of them, regardless of the amount of help they could procure. Doc explained what he had heard to his two friends and over the next few days they learnt more about the machinations within their prison. The supervisor was known as 'Genghis', an obvious reference to his extreme ruthlessness: they learnt not to antagonise or oppose him, and for the most part he picked on less resilient prey. In order to give the spies no cause to become interested in them Doc's group kept their own counsel and avoided anything that could be considered political or anti-establishment. In short, as best they could, they kept a low profile.

Food was the only currency. It was smuggled, hidden, stolen and hoarded and it bought the guards sexual favours and information. It was also traded by the supervisors and the NKVD spies, who occupied every building, to recruit, retain and reward their informers. As the trust between Boris and Doc grew the Russian revealed that his lifesaver was an old friend and drama student called Anna whose husband, a dentist, had been arrested by the state simply because of his education and intellect. When questioned he had refused to denounce his friends as traitors or incriminate them as common criminals as suggested by the interrogators. For this 'crime' he was summarily executed and she was sent to the Gulag.

Doc, feeling slightly guilty that he still retained a lingering doubt about Boris, and wondering whether he could be setting them up asked, "Why are you telling me all this, how do you know you can trust me or my friends? You seem to be breaking your own rules, those very precautions that have probably kept you alive for so long."

Boris considered for a moment and then replied, "I'm nearing the end. I'm totally exhausted both mentally and physically and close to giving up. Since I arrived here I have been contaminated by the treacherous and cruel atmosphere into trusting no one, other than Anna who was already a friend and at first, to my shame, I even thought she was setting a trap. When I first saw the way you and Lech cared for young Tomek and each other I decided I did not want to die with a twisted and malignant view of the world. The way you have behaved since reminds me of what I used to believe in and, bearing in mind my relationship with the communists, whom better to trust than an honourable, catholic, Polish soldier who has also lost the country he loves. I want you and your two friends to survive and I intend to do all I can to make sure that happens. Anna will help."

Over the years Anna had developed numerous ways to smuggle food using all her wiles, skill and ingenuity but the key to her success was a clear understanding of the mindset of the guards. They knew that escape from the camp was pointless, as an inmate would receive no help from the outside, the population being petrified of the prison authorities and the NKVD. Local party members and the native community leaders also received large rewards if they gave information leading to the recapture of a prisoner, dead or alive. The camp also had its own tracker dogs and the guards were encouraged to take any action necessary to prevent a successful break out, including shooting an escapee on sight. Their incentive was simple: if they failed and a prisoner escaped 'on their watch' they were stripped of all rank, property and income and immediately imprisoned in their own camp. In these circumstances their prospects for survival were nonexistent. If, on the other hand, they shot the prisoner dead then at worst they were fined up to two week's wages. In any case the land was so inhospitable, the distances between settlements so vast and the weather so inclement that any fleeing prisoner would be dead within a few days from starvation or the cold.

Furthermore, spies and informants were planted in every works, hamlet, village and town and in any case the inmates were in such a weakened condition that most never even contemplated an escape attempt. Well aware of these circumstances the guards concentrated their efforts on forcing as much work out of every prisoner as possible and they were consummate slave masters, driving each person to the very edge of collapse every day. Neither were they overly concerned by the deaths within the workforce because more prisoners arrived every week and after all, this establishment was referred to by both guards and inmates alike as the 'death camp.' There were some eight thousand men and women in the camp and on average over two thousand died every year.

Inside the compounds the prisoners were pretty much left to their own devices under the control of supervisory prisoners and the NKVD spies. Certain pathways, those to the kitchen, the work sites, the guards' quarters and the log piles for example were often used by both male and female inmates and the guards rarely entered the compounds as they were fearful of contamination.

Tuberculosis, dysentery, scarlet fever and other contagious diseases, not to mention pneumonia, influenza and enteric conditions were commonplace, accounting for nearly half the deaths. This reticence by the guards to closely supervise their charges inside the camp created many opportunities for Anna to discover hiding places and develop supply routes for the transfer of smuggled, stolen and gifted food. It also enabled them to smuggle messages and, very infrequently, to meet each other. She employed every conceivable means to supply Boris and his friends, including hiding items in her own body and the bodies of the many dead. The corpses were removed daily and both sexes were buried in huge pits and trenches that were dug by the prisoners every summer. Boris, Tomek, Doc and Lech all found the mental strength and resolve to regularly recover hidden food from the bodies.

Anna also managed to recruit one of the Polish girls, Halina, an attractive seventeen-year-old who arrived in the same intake as Tomek. The older woman recognised a physical and psychological strength within the girl, combined with a resourceful and practical appreciation of how to survive in such a hostile place. She was mature beyond her years and Anna took her into her confidence and secured her a job as a house servant to the wife of a colonel of the Guard regiment. By risking their own lives and taking every chance to obtain extra food they were, between them, able to keep Tomek and his friends alive throughout the long, harsh winter months.

During this time Tomek often thought of home, he dreamt of it at night, he imagined it during the day and on occasions, when past the point of complete exhaustion, he even hallucinated: clearly seeing his home, his school and the landscape he loved, a verdant, vibrant reality right in front of him. He always felt that he could just reach out and touch it but before he could grasp hold of his enticing memories they scornfully evaporated to be replaced by the grim reality of starvation and brutality. It was the simple things that he had previously taken for granted that he missed the most. A walk down the country lanes he knew so well, the birds singing in the hedgerows, the scent of summer flowers, seeing the squirrels feeding in the orchard or the young storks noisily poking their heads over the nests on the chimney. He longed for the warmth of the spring sunshine on his face, the sound of children playing in the street, a fishing rod in his hand and most of all a proper meal on the table. Surprisingly, he was not tortured by such constant thoughts: on the contrary, they drove him on, gave him the strength to resist the hunger and oppression and provided hope for a future. He also dreamt of Halina. Even in such a wretched place they were falling in love and snatched a few precious minutes of time together whenever possible. Halina told Anna how she felt towards Tomek very early on in their relationship and she did all she could to help and protect them.

As the thaw set in they were put to work building a new section of canal to carry the lumber between an existing canal and a tributary of the river Yenisey. This was heavy, debilitating and sometimes dangerous work as the banks, over fifteen feet high in places, frequently collapsed trapping those working nearby. Boris and Lech were buried under one such fall. Tomek, Doc and others toiled unceasingly for over an hour in an effort to save them with an urgency that surprised the impassive guards. The rescuers removed boulders, soil and rubble until their fingers bled and their backs were breaking, but it was to no avail and eventually their friend's bodies, that had been abused by so many in life, were thrown by strangers into an anonymous pit in Siberia. No services or words over graves were permitted here, after all, the state assumed you were dead when you arrived.

"Doc, why did Genghis stop us from taking the bodies to the pit ourselves, what harm could it have done?" asked Tomek that night, as they lay awake on the barrack floor, unable to sleep.

Doc, who had seen too much suffering and cruelty lately found it difficult to gather his thoughts or give the lad any comfort but he tried to explain, "The system is designed to remove all our dignity, to strip us of our self-respect and to make us accept brutality as normal. They set out to break us and then kill us, and today they knew that if we had been able to stand at a graveside, no matter how brutal or basic, and pay tribute to the men who we loved as brothers then we would have grown in strength and resolve. That would have been an unacceptable threat to them but we can still honour our friends by carrying on and, when we're free, we'll tell the world of this place. Speak of the monsters who created it but also of the thousands of true Russian patriots and the foreign innocents who died here."

Tomek's next comment gave Doc some real hope for the future.

"If you're right and we do get out of here we've got to take Halina with us because I like her a great deal," then, realising he might have revealed too much, he added, "and Anna too of course."

Over the next few months their loss drove Tomek and Doc even closer together and they became inseparable and even more determined to survive. This tenacity was reinforced after Anna made it clear that she would continue to provide food and help in any way she could and Halina swore to save the life of her love and his friend.

Back in the Katyn Forest near the transit camp, at about the same time as Tomek mourned his friends, the NKVD was conducting further mass-murder. Determined that the captured Polish officers should never be allowed to return home, and in any way threaten to hinder their occupation plans for Poland, the Soviet Politburo devised a plot for their liquidation and a subsequent cover-up. The Poles were taken in groups deep into the forest and there, near the NKVD buildings, alongside an earth and gravel track, they were shot in the back of the head, piled into heaps and then buried in mass-graves. 4,443 murdered souls would later be recovered from this one site. The corpses were found stacked in the pits like discarded logs of wood: broken, wedged and haphazard. This was not a crime of hatred by a few war weary soldiers but a cold, calculated mass-murder by the Soviet State. Stalin himself signed the order for their execution and specially selected NKVD thugs were trained to carry it out with frightening efficiency. The Katyn forest had been used by the NKVD for mass-executions for years before these dreadful war crimes took place and they were well schooled in the practice of deceit and denial. A similar fate befell another fifteen thousand missing Polish Officers, NCO's and civilians who were also held in Soviet prisons.

Life and death in the Gulag continued but during the spring hardly any Polish soldiers arrived, with progressively more civilians taking their place, until in the summer all new arrivals were ethnic Poles. Their stories soon spread throughout the camp and it became clear that the Polish inhabitants of the Russian occupied section were now being imprisoned en masse and Soviet citizens moved into their homes to replace them. Ethnic cleansing on a grand scale had been introduced and the Soviets were making the most of its by-product: slave labour.

FIVE

Flight of Anguish
20th October 1939

Ewa had become frantic over the disappearance of Jan and Tomek. She knew intuitively that Jan was alive but she also sensed that he was in mortal danger. She was unable to shake off a mood of growing despondency and desperation. The pain of separation was eating away at her ever shrinking reserve of resilience and, as her imagination provided ever more horrifying possibilities of what might befall her precious sons, she developed a gnawing and unrelenting ache deep inside her soul. As she paced the room her heart raced, she gasped for breath and despite the cold she was beset by a series of immobilising hot flushes with the beads of sweat forming on her forehead and face mixing with her tears of anger and impotency. Irrespective of whether these physical symptoms were real or psychosomatic she was utterly convinced that her two boys were being physically ripped away from her and, whatever the danger and risk to the rest of her family, she must go to their aid.

That very morning, as she was plucking up the courage to confront the Russians, Jacek told her of the talk at the camp between the labourers. Rumour had it that his brothers had been arrested and transported. She flew from the farmhouse and ran headlong to the Russian camp and at the gates she screamed out for answers. In response to her questions and demands, which she suspected were not even understood by the sentry, she was driven off at gunpoint, poked with his rifle, threatened with being shot and then physically pushed and prodded back down the track towards the farm. Reluctant to give up, she returned to the gate once the sentries had changed over, but again she was forcibly refused entry. When in desperation she remonstrated with the two new guards she was pushed over backwards and then kicked about the legs and body until, battered and bleeding, she lay whimpering on the ground. As she slowly crawled away into a nearby drainage ditch one of the guards lifted his greatcoat, unbuttoned his fly and urinated over her head and down her face, neck and shoulders. As they walked away the other soldier turned to her and said in broken Polish, "If you ever show your ugly Polak face around here again then you'll have more to worry about than a couple of missing kids and the stink of piss. Now clear off while you still can." They laughed and joked in Russian as they walked back towards the camp gates.

Try as she might she could not stand up but she was more demoralised, flabbergasted and stunned into immobility by the realisation that one of the guards understood everything she had been saying and chose to ignore the frenetic pleas of a terrified mother, than by the beating or being urinated on. She curled up into a ball and, nursing her bruised ribs and aching back, she felt total despair and abandonment overwhelm her. For the first time on their journey she completely broke down and wept and whimpered until she was physically exhausted and mentally drained of hope. She would willingly have given her life for any of her children but now, in this alien and hostile environment, she found herself totally unable to intervene and powerless to protect any of them. An hour later, as she slowly recovered a degree of self-control, she briefly considered returning to the camp gate for one final attempt at action but, as she painfully picked herself up, she found she no longer had the courage within her. Disconsolate, she reluctantly returned to the farm and after bathing and tending her injuries she discussed the situation with Dominik and Bogdana.

"What do you think I should do now? I know that even if I manage to find some different guards they're not going to be interested in helping me and I'll probably get another beating or worse. It might even provoke them into taking it out on the rest of you here at the farm."

She wondered whether the rumours were right and the boys had been caught stealing food. All the notices made it clear that they would shoot everyone they caught pilfering. Her heart told her that they were still alive but her head warned her to face up to the fact that they could already be dead, "Oh God! I'll never forgive myself if anything has happened to them. I just wish we had stayed at home."

Dominik was the first to make a suggestion, "I've been ordered back to work at the rail yard by our new lords and masters, why don't I see if I can arrange to hide you on a goods train going west from Luck? It might get you back as far as the German controlled area. My neighbour has connections to the resistance movement and should be able to smuggle you into the city. If you want to risk it?"

"I can't leave without knowing what's happened."

"I think we both know that you're not going to find out anything, but with any luck you could make it home, especially if you get some help from the underground. It's certainly better than waiting here, not knowing, and I'm sure that if the boys have managed to escape or talk their way out of it they'll make for home and not risk coming back here into the same situation as before. We both know that's all they've wanted to do ever since they arrived. That's your best bet."

"Do you think we could make it back?"

"It's chaos in the towns, there are refugees everywhere and the Russians have got their hands full with the underground and all the prisoners they've captured. If you're going to go, you won't have a better opportunity than now. With just the three of you, you might well make it."

They called the boys in, explained their reasoning and asked for their thoughts.

Jacek chipped in first, "We can't really stay here anyway, the food is all but gone and I'm sick of eating raw potatoes from the fields and those mangels that we keep digging out of the heap. They're frozen solid, woody and tasteless and how the cattle ever managed to eat them is beyond me. Let's try to get back to father before we all die of starvation."

Jozef agreed and addressed Dominik, "I don't think it's fair to stay here either because if our brothers have been caught, then, just by being here, we put your family in even greater danger and you stand a far better chance of surviving if you stop sharing the little food you have. We can fend for ourselves on the journey and when we get home father will look after us, he'll know what to do."

They mulled it over again and discussed how they might travel back home and, about an hour later, they had agreed a bare bones plan and a preferred route, which heavily depended on the collaboration of the resistance movement.

At 8.30am two days later they bade farewell to their host family and left for their neighbour's farm. He was another ex-soldier and Polish patriot whose eldest son was already fighting with the underground movement. After being briefed by the farmer on the final arrangements, they found themselves on the road to Luck. They were hidden at the bottom of a horse drawn cart, covered in old wooden planks, logs and coal: all three protected in a small hollow next to the three foot high timber side of the ancient vehicle. The farmer had created their hiding place after the invasion and had used it on a regular basis to smuggle goods, food and cash past the Russian checkpoints. He was making a tidy black-market profit from the population trapped in the town and was now also in the process of legally selling off his large hoards of coal and timber. He also obtained information on troop movements and deployments in the area and passed it on to the resistance movement operating in the surrounding countryside.

After agreeing to help his neighbour he had quickly enlarged the hardwood frame that supported the weight of the load above so that the family could be accommodated in the void with minimal discomfort. Small holes had been roughly drilled into the side of the cart and then disguised by smearing them with manure and mud: this made breathing easier and also allowed one of the occupants to have a very limited degree of vision. Ever the opportunist, if this trip proved successful, he intended, for a suitable reward, to use the system again to smuggle weapons and perhaps even resistance fighters into the town. Despite these modifications the atmosphere inside was fetid and claustrophobic and all three were curled up tight and crammed into each other with hardly any room to move or stretch.

Jozef felt as if he was being kicked all over his body as the trailer bounced and jolted its way along the rough road, the shocks being intensified by the rigid floor. A sudden spasm of pain shot up his spine as he unsuccessfully tried to shift his weight off of the metal reinforcing bar screwed to the rough boards under his left hip. "How much further? I feel as if I've been buried alive and I can't stand it much longer," he whispered to his mother who was up against the side of the cart and had access to the spy holes.

"I've no idea, I can't see anything at the moment but you'll be alright, just keep your nerve. We're perfectly safe here and the farmer knows what he's about so try to relax and take your mind off the discomfort. You should set an example for your younger brother."

Jacek decided he could not let that pass, "I wish you wouldn't talk about me as if I'm not here and nobody needs to show me how to behave. I'm the one suffering in silence and anyway it's not so bad if you concentrate on something else. I play music in my head over and over again, trying to improve each time, and it definitely works."

Ewa was just about to suggest that they should keep quiet, as ordered by the farmer before they set off, when a sudden challenge was shouted and the cart came to a halt at a checkpoint about five miles from Luck. She tensed up and quietly covered the spy holes with a small piece of bark, which had been fixed to the inside for this purpose and could be slid across and then held in place until the danger passed. The farmer produced his identity and travel documents, which had been granted for the purpose of delivering fuel, and one of the four soldiers carried out a visual check by walking slowly right around the cart. He appeared satisfied, took about a dozen logs and two bucketful's of coal off the back of the cart, pointed to the brazier they had burning alongside their tent, smiled knowingly and then waved them on. Ewa now realised where they were and having informed the boys they all remained silent, anxious and alert as they continued on towards the town

They joined a queue at the town's outskirts and the farmer became concerned when he saw several individuals and their vehicles being pulled off to the side of the road and searched. As he watched he saw people arrested and marched off to a nearby building that used to be a police outstation. He also realised that he would have to take his chances ahead because if he turned around now he would certainly draw attention to himself and invite further suspicion. After about ten minutes they were at the head of the queue and the Russian guards' interpreter ordered him off the cart. His papers were checked again and after explaining the supposed purpose of his trip he was shepherded to the side. A group of labourers were then ordered forward and told to unload the cart. The farmer was undecided whether they were specifically targeting him or whether it was just a random search but in either case he knew he was in serious trouble.

Ewa and the boys were terrified when they heard and felt the cart being unloaded and in a matter of minutes their fears were realised as they were dragged, along with the farmer, into the old police station. A cover story had been prepared for just such an event and the farmer was ready to respond when the Polish interpreter demanded, "Explain yourself and make sure there are no lies, because you're already deep in the shit and believe you me, you don't want to make it worse."

The farmer handed over his papers and in a confident voice said, "My son Jozef is sick and we've brought him to see the doctor. I'm the only one permitted travel papers because they're not issued to anyone of school age and my wife refused to stay at home. You must understand that we've lost two sons to this war already and she won't allow the two that are left to be separated from her. So you see, Sir, I had no choice but to bring her with me and so I hid them all in the cart. I'm authorised to bring logs and coal into town and I was going to use the money from this trip to pay the doctor."

A conversation then followed between the interpreter and the Russian sergeant who appeared to be in charge. They both came forward and inspected Jozef who did indeed look ill: despite the cold he was sweating, but he was also shaking from fear and between the streaks of coal dust on his face his complexion was pallid. "What's wrong with you lad?" demanded the interpreter.

Jozef felt his mouth go dry and his voice croaked as he replied, "I don't know, Sir, I've got a fever and diarrhoea and a blinding headache. Our neighbours have all had it recently and they couldn't get rid of it without a potion from the doctor."

"We are not barbarians. I'm sure you could have got a travel document for your son as he is so ill. You should have tried harder. Now where are their identity papers?" asked the guard.

The farmer knew this was the really weak part of the plan and he had to force himself to remain confident, "I know from previous visits to the town that things have become difficult with many thieves and profiteers, my misguided countrymen, trying to take advantage of the situation. Papers and passes are often stolen and used by the saboteurs and those running the black market, so I decided that the family should leave their identity cards safe at home."

The interpreter had heard every excuse possible over the last few weeks, "You bloody fool!"

"I know it was stupid now but I thought that as they were hiding they wouldn't need them anyway and as soon as we had seen the doctor we would have been on our way back home with no harm done and no one the wiser. I'm very sorry for not thinking this through properly. I've been a proper idiot, but I was very worried about my son and although we're now quite rightly all in trouble, I still need to get him to a doctor. It's not his fault that his father's witless."

On hearing the translation, the sergeant thought for a moment and seeing an ideal opportunity to profit said, "You really have been very irresponsible and just asking for trouble, but I don't think you are criminals and your son is obviously ill. I will, however, need some security for your safe conduct if I'm to overlook this serious breach of regulations and give you a second chance. What can you provide? "

The farmer handed over his small pile of notes and Ewa took off her silver St Christopher, a confirmation present, from around her neck and gave it to the sergeant who then grabbed her left arm and pointed to her watch and gold wedding ring. She handed them over and, although saddened at the loss of such treasured and sentimentally valuable items, she considered their loss a small price to pay for their release. She was therefore elated as they were issued with temporary passes, escorted back to the cart and told to go and visit the doctor. The wooden framework that had formed their hiding place had been smashed but everything else was in a heap on the ground just as they had left it. After reloading the cart themselves they carried on into the town, mightily relieved that their plan and the guard's greed had saved them from far worse consequences.

As they approached their destination and Jozef started to regain his composure he couldn't help but be impressed by the beauty, grandeur and architecture of the Old Town area. He stopped in the square opposite the imposing belfry and stared up at the solid, three towered stone edifice of the 14th century Castle of Lyubert, known as the pearl of Luck. Standing deep in its shadow, contemplating its long existence, he turned and looked across at the majesty of the Cathedral of St Peter and St Paul. He felt that if he had been transported back into the Middle Ages he would have been completely at ease, being totally familiar with his surroundings. For a moment or two he thought that the horror, turmoil and danger of the war was of no significance whatsoever when set against the peace, history and permanence of this backdrop. He was quickly brought back down to earth by his mother who shouted at him sharply to catch up.

When the farmer dropped them off at his contact's address he immediately dismissed them from his mind and concentrated on his own future. Before he had walked fifty yards towards a different exit on the other side of town he was already thinking of how he might first recoup his losses from this trip, and then construct a new hiding place so as to continue to profit from the contraband business.

Ewa and the boys sat in a warm, nondescript office in the business district and she explained her circumstances to her contact, a Jewish jeweller and engraver who was now virtually without work and devoted most of his time to the underground resistance movement where he acted as a messenger and forger. He was a small, thin, mousy haired and generally dull looking individual: a grey man in his early sixties who would definitely not draw attention to himself or last long in the memory of casual acquaintances. He spoke in a very quiet voice with a local working class accent and had a pair of spectacles dangling on a piece of cord around his neck. He was shoddily dressed, sported a small but untidy beard and was the total opposite of what Ewa imagined a well-off city professional gentleman to be. She concluded that he had probably been recruited by the insurgents as much for his appearance and demeanour as for any other skills he might possess.

He took Ewa's hands in his in a paternal gesture of support and explained his thoughts, "I'm known as Tadeusz and you are all most welcome here in the heart of the city of my birth. I think we can be of benefit to each other in these difficult and dangerous times and your arrival is most opportune."

"I can't imagine that we can do anything for you. It's us that need the help."

"Well, you want to get across into the German controlled area and it so happens that we desperately need to get the priests out because the Russians are hunting for the ones we have managed to hide. Over half of them have already been deported or shot and the only way we can save the rest is to get them out of the Russians' grasp before it's too late. The Godless enemy are becoming more organised by the day and are rounding up both Jewish and Christian leaders and seem determined to stamp out the whole church organisation in an attempt to demoralise us."

Half the population of Luck were Jewish and throughout the region it was considered to be a Jewish city and a fine example of peaceful and productive co-existence. Tadeusz explained, "We mix well and have a very good trading and social relationship with our Christian neighbours. I would go so far as to say that until recently we had a model life of happiness and contentment, but now the war has arrived and everything's changed. The Russians have started by persecuting the Poles but I know our turn will surely come, so I have chosen to stand up and fight in the only way I know how. We need to show the whole population that together we are capable of achieving some quick success by getting the clergy to safety and giving them some hope for the future."

Jozef spoke up as soon as Tadeusz had finished, "Of course we must do all we can to help you and the priests, it's our duty to them and to God, but I don't see what we can do in a practical sense as we aren't soldiers or partisans. Our brothers have already been captured, or worse, and we only just made it past the guards to get here which shows that we are hardly capable of looking after ourselves let alone taking responsibility for someone else."

Tadeusz stood up, went to his coat hanging on the door and took a small photograph from the pocket and then returned to the table saying, "You are of most use to us because of the very fact that you are a normal family and like thousands of others you are simply trying to get back home." He then placed the photograph on the table, "This is the priest and, as he is only slightly older than your mother, we intend that he should pose as your father. I will provide you all with false papers and travel permits that will get you to Brest. You will be given a contact there who will help and, once you cross the river Bug, you will have escaped the Russians. I will not hide the truth, so you should know that the dangers to your family may be just as bad under the Germans, but the priest should be safe and we are trying to make further plans for him once you've crossed over."

They were all unaware that the Germans would also persecute the priests. In Pomerania alone only twenty of its six hundred Priests survived the war. Over two hundred were murdered in Warsaw and, nationally, by the end of the conflict, a total of nearly three thousand had been arrested and shot or sent to their death at Dachau.

The three of them studied the photograph of the priest in plain clothes, commented on his kindly face and neat moustache but couldn't help comparing him to Henryk and they all felt uncomfortable doing so. Any such feelings were soon dismissed the next day when they met Father Antoni Chepek. They were all blindfolded and Tadeusz and two members of the underground army carefully led them through several back alleys, into an apartment block and then down into the cellar. They were lowered through a trap door before their blindfolds were removed and they found themselves in a very large tunnel, which was dimly lit with oil lamps and stretched for several hundred yards ahead with numerous side tunnels and doors leading off in all directions.

Tadeusz made a grand sweeping gesture with his arm, "Isn't it magnificent: we have our own underground city with literally miles of tunnels, caverns and secret entrances. It's an intricate maze and a partisan's dream because we can fight above and hide below. We just melt away whenever the Russians get too close. We keep weapons, stores and fighters down here and it's also where we hide the priests, but it's becoming a battle against time because knowledge of the tunnels has always been pretty commonplace amongst the town's population and, as living conditions deteriorate, the collaborators are more likely to betray us. Some would already sell their own mothers for a few zlotys or a decent meal and we can't watch all of them. The sooner we get the priests out the better."

"What is this place? How was it built?" asked Jozef staring around in genuine awe at the size and scale of the tunnel system.

"Salt mines. They're now mostly obsolete but they run right underneath a large part of the old town area and legend has it that they're also connected to some of the local villages, but we haven't found any proof of that so far. Originally they must have taken hundreds of workers decades to construct but now just a few dozen of us are all working flat out in the process of connecting some of the main tunnels and caverns with our own network, giving access into the sewers and many of the cellars. This will give us scores of escape points and, if necessary, we will fight the Russians down here as well. We will booby-trap every junction and every tunnel we give up and they will have to pay a heavy price for every yard they manage to take from us," explained Tadeusz.

They were shown into a side chamber where they met the priest, a kindly and cheerful forty-four year old who had been born and brought up in Warsaw and joined the priesthood straight from university where he had studied philosophy and German. He had a clear but fatalistic understanding of the risks facing him, but was far more concerned about the welfare and prospects of the mother and her children and was therefore extremely reticent to further endanger them by agreeing to the plan. It took some time and the combined efforts of the whole family, reinforced by Tadeusz's forceful arguments, to convince him that it was the best option for all concerned.

They spent the next two days underground waiting for their false documents, learning their cover story and building up trust and friendship. Jozef and the priest hit it off straight away, drawn together by their strong faith and detailed theological knowledge, which kept them up until the early hours, deeply engaged in enthusiastic discussion and debate. At first Antoni found the domestic side of the arrangement, being so close and informal with the family and particularly around Ewa, far more difficult and frequently embarrassing. He put this down to the fact that he had over the years become very comfortable with the life of a celibate bachelor and her closeness and friendly disposition reawakened feelings he had long since pushed from his mind. She on the other hand was very light-hearted and dismissive in her approach, always managing to laugh off such encounters, treating them as the inevitable consequence of their living and learning together in such confined quarters.

Gradually they began to relax into their assumed identities and both adults were able to act, at least in public, in accordance with the broad demands of their roles without undue awkwardness or hesitation. Then on the third day, armed with their new identity documents and travel permits, they somewhat nervously and reluctantly emerged into the streets and headed for the railway station and the first stage of their trip west.

They had no trouble purchasing the tickets or boarding the train and as they sat down Ewa, for the benefit of anyone in earshot, said, "I hope our house is alright and the neighbours safe, perhaps the school and college are open again and the boys can get back to their education. If things aren't too bad maybe you can get back to work as well."

"Don't worry dear, we'll find out soon enough, at least the boys are safe and that's the most important thing, now please don't fret so or you'll make yourself ill," replied Antoni, hoping he had struck the right tone between the caring father and the not so patient husband.

The priest took a look at the other passengers in the carriage and although most seemed to be locals, there were several Russian soldiers and one smart, official looking man in a suit who was about fifty years old. Although he pretended to be reading a book his eyes were everywhere and he closely examined all new arrivals. The priest decided that he would keep an eye on him as he suspected him to be a railway official or even a transport policeman. He then turned to Ewa and they chatted quietly about everyday matters and the difficult conditions, engrossed in their own domestic problems, as were most of the passengers around them. As the journey progressed and passengers came and went they became more confident and relaxed and when, about four hours later, they pulled into the station at Brest they were mightily relieved.

Things then changed quickly as soldiers and police poured into the carriages before anyone could get off: all the passengers were forced back into their seats. "Everyone pay attention, this is a full security check. Have your papers and tickets ready for immediate inspection and open up your bags and luggage so that they can be searched. You must then remain in your seats until you have been processed and released," shouted one of the police officers.

As they waited their turn Jacek became increasingly nervous: he started to sweat and felt nauseous as he tried to ignore the frightening images of discovery and capture that flooded into his mind. He tried to drive such thoughts away by breathing deeply and silently, rehearsing what he had been told to say if spoken to. Despite this diversion, he felt as if their very survival depended entirely on him and he wondered if he was up to it but then, as he looked out the window for inspiration, he finally gained some control over his errant emotions and realised that of all the family he was the one with the good memory, the rigorous self-discipline and singular mental application. His self-confidence grew as he sternly assured himself that he was the best equipped to deal with any situation that required a clear head and some convincing acting.

"Why have you come to Brest?" demanded the police officer as Antoni handed over their documents.

"We were in Luck visiting my sick mother-in-law when the hostilities broke out and this has been the first chance to come back home. It's taken us quite a while to obtain the necessary permissions and we are now trying to get back to normal," replied the priest remembering to stick strictly to their rehearsed script and to keep his replies as short as possible. As he spoke one of the Russian soldiers was sorting through their suitcase, which had been packed by Tadeusz, ensuring that everything was exactly what you would expect to find with a family in their circumstances.

After looking at the soldier who in response shook his head, indicating that nothing untoward had been discovered, the police officer said in broken Polish, "That's fine, you may go on your way now." Jozef managed to hold back a sigh of relief and reached out for the suitcase as the group of officials started to move on to the next passengers.

"Not so fast, stay where you are!" commanded the man whom Antoni had suspected of being a railway bureaucrat or policeman. He then spoke to the military group in Russian and they all turned their attention back to the Nowaskis. "I have been watching you and I am not at all comfortable with you. You are going nowhere until you explain yourselves to MY satisfaction." He then looked at Jacek who he had noticed sweating and looking distinctly uncomfortable and in his experience such nervousness was definitely a sign of guilt and so he demanded, "Where is your Grandmother now my lad?"

"She's back at home, her bronchitis is much better and her neighbour, Mrs Lipska is keeping an eye on her for us, Sir." replied the boy with some confidence after only a moment's hesitation, although a few beads of sweat remained on his brow and his hands felt clammy.

The official was in fact an NKVD officer and, still mightily suspicious, he decided to change tack. Slowly and deliberately enunciating every word he threatened, "You are a lying Polish pig and I suspect your parents are saboteurs. Enemies of the state and they can be shot. Taken from this train and executed on the platform, here, right now, immediately upon my order and my order alone. I will give you one more chance to save yourselves. What are you really up to?"

Antoni could see that the secret policeman was trying to break what he saw as their weakest link and he was tempted to jump in to defend the boy, but as the words formed on his lips he realised that if he did, it would only serve to extend the interrogation and encourage their inquisitor. Things were going badly enough as it was and he concluded that the longer it went on the greater their chance of being caught out.

Jacek did not react to the intimidation but replied as calmly as his nerves would allow, "Sir, I have been brought up to always tell the truth and I will continue to do so now. We are on our way home and we would not, under any circumstances, break the law and it would not be possible for my family to put people in danger as you suggest. You should come home with us, it's not far and you could speak to the neighbours who will vouch for us and tell you all about our dear grandma in Luck. I must also apologise to you for not answering promptly but I have always suffered very badly from travel sickness and I have only just started to feel better since we have now been stopped for a while." The boy was conscious of the fact that he had strayed from his practised responses but felt he had done the best under the circumstances.

The NKVD officer remained quiet for a moment or two, then leaned forward and stared at the boy intently, at first looking directly into his eyes to distress and perturb, and then slowly and deliberately he searched his face for the telltale signs of guilt or panic. He used the unnerving silence and his close physical presence to intimidate the boy and through him his whole family as he considered their veracity and potential for trouble. Then, with a click of his fingers towards the soldiers and a slight nod of the head to the family, he

114

made up his mind, "You can let them go now. They're of no further interest to me," he ordered as he strode away down the corridor, now convinced that the boy was being honest and looking for his next suspect.

As they walked along the wide platform towards the exit Jacek was totally self absorbed, unaware of his surroundings and feeling drained and numb from the delayed shock. The tension slowly began to subside and then the relief and euphoria flooded in and with it the sounds and sights of the outside world returned, and once more he became fully sentient of his surroundings. He couldn't help but be struck by the ostentatiously grand and imposing nature of the massive building that enveloped them like a cathedral: such a contrast to the more modern, utilitarian stations in his own home area. Once outside, his curiosity having been tweaked, he lingered to look back at the somewhat Gothic building and was not altogether surprised to see that the facade looked much more like a castle or fortress than a railway junction. He was wondering if the rest of the town lived up to the opulence and status of the station when Ewa turned to him and with real emotion in her voice said, "I'm so proud of you my son and so will your father be when I tell him what you did. After your brilliant performance back there, I'm absolutely convinced that our reunion isn't that far off."

Jozef added his appreciation, "I thought we were all going to be arrested and I don't know where that train-sickness business came from, but it certainly did the trick. He totally lost interest at that point. Well done little brother!"

Antoni could not contain his relief either and he unashamedly gave all three of his adopted family an enthusiastic hug and kiss right there in the street, oblivious to the inquisitive stares of passers-by. None of them, not for one minute, could have imagined him to be an ordained and devoted priest.

They met the contact as arranged that night. Breaking the curfew he took advantage of the fog and darkness to smuggle them back across the river Bug, again in a rowing boat, and they were mightily relieved that this time they were shrouded in darkness and they neither saw nor bumped into any bodies or carcasses. By morning they were safe in a small farm, three miles inside that part of Poland controlled by the Germans and designated as the area of 'General Government'. Still in the hands of the resistance movement Ewa arranged for a message to be sent to Henryk at Pelplin station by telegraph from the nearest railway station at Biata Podlaska, informing him that they were safe and on their way home. The following day their contact was ready to hand Antoni over to another messenger for the next leg of his journey to Warsaw, but before he left he said a tearful goodbye to the Nowaskis. He now considered them to be close and honoured friends and after he had solemnly blessed them he said, "If you should ever need any help do not hesitate to come to me, I will always be in your debt and you will always be in my prayers. I don't know where I'll be but I'll make sure that I can be located through my childhood parish church, The Holy Cross. You'll find it easily enough."

The church was a beautiful, large and imposing twin-towered Baroque edifice next to the monument of Copernicus on the northern stretch of the Royal Route, known throughout Warsaw as the Polish Champs Elysees. "Thank you for being my family and good luck to you all. I truly hope we will meet again."

The contact informed Ewa that the message to her husband had been sent but it could take some time to arrive because many of the telegraph lines had been destroyed in the war and as fast as they were repaired the underground were doing their best to blow them up again. He added that another contact at Biata Podlaska would also provide them with railway warrants and passes for Pelplin, under their real names. He was however, uncertain whether the Germans would allow them, without further documentation, to cross into the western part of Poland that had now been incorporated into the Reich. Even with the correct paperwork it was still possible that as Poles they would be refused permission to return to their home, but being German-speaking would at least give them a chance. Like so many well-educated families brought up in western Poland, with its turbulent history of conflict and occupation by its neighbour, the whole family and most of their neighbours were fluently bilingual.

The next day they boarded an almost empty train without any difficulties from the authorities but within a few stops it was full to capacity and they then experienced the first of a string of lengthy delays and diversions. They spent hours waiting at signals and were frequently forced onto branch lines or temporary sections of newly laid track to avoid destroyed bridges, yards and junctions. On three occasions they had to leave the train at the entrance to a badly damaged station and then walk a mile or so to the other side where they then boarded another train to continue on their way. The further west they travelled the more frequent and longer were the hold-ups and when they arrived at Lodz, where they were due to change trains for Torun, the bomb damage was so extensive that the whole station was still out of commission. Temporary buildings had been erected on the site of the old marshalling yards, but despite the best organisational efforts of the Germans, who were everywhere, chaos was the order of the day. After two hours of constantly searching and asking for their connection they finally found the right train but, as they were about to board, the ubiquitous German military official stopped them and demanded their papers and tickets.

"Poles are not permitted to pass into the Reich without special sector approval: this is as far west as you can go, so I'm afraid these tickets are of no use to you," he added as he examined the documents without any overt hostility but in a routine, neutral and definitive tone.

Ewa was in no mood to accept any hindrance, she was tired, desperately worried about her missing sons, bitter and irritable, "My husband is the telegraphist at Pelplin and is performing a valuable service for the Reich. It is not our fault that we were unfortunate enough to have been born in this cultureless backwater of poverty and ignorance. My family has a proud German heritage that goes back centuries and we would not be in this position now if our parents' generation had held onto these lands, as they should have done. If you want to blame someone then blame those at Versailles and our fathers who were too weak and war-weary to prevent the break-up. Unfortunately there may be some Polish blood way back in my ancestry but that's because they weren't thrown out when we had the chance. We are German patriots so don't you dare tell me where I can go and where I can't. What's more, you are fighting this war so that decent families like mine can assume their proper place in the world and not be dominated by these barbarians and forced to work at their behest. The Fuhrer has now rightly claimed this land back so that *WE* can become German citizens again. How dare you interfere with his wishes? It's been done specifically for us. You, as an ambassador and agent of our great leader, should know better than intimidate his most loyal and long suffering citizens. Now, either you let us board our train or you will fetch your commanding officer immediately and we will both see what he has got to say." She said this in faultless German with passion and rising anger and looked him in the eye throughout: by the time she had finished the soldier had heard enough. After a click of the heels and a bow of the head he initialled, dated and stamped her travel permits and as he handed the documents back he simply said, "Heil Hitler," saluted smartly and walked off shaking his head in amusement or bewilderment.

Once on the train she turned to the boys and said, "From now on whenever we are near other people that we don't know we'll talk in German and never let an official see you are nervous or agitated. No matter how you may feel inside always appear confident and sure of yourself. Remember, most of their soldiers are just ordinary young men used to discipline and doing as people in authority tell them. We can use that to our advantage but always be alert as they, like the Russians, also have a secret police force and they certainly can't be fooled easily. They are cunning, devious and totally ruthless."

"What are we going to do when we get home, it looks to me as if these Germans intend to stay forever and, if they do, surely it's our duty to join the underground and help to fight back?" asked Jacek as he settled into his seat feeling generally far more self-assured and certain for the first time in weeks that they would now make it back home.

Before Ewa could answer Jozef shook his head, tut-tutted and said, "Little brother, how can you be so keen to get involved in this bloodshed and put mother and father through more anguish after all we've witnessed these last weeks? I would be happy just getting back to college, seeing Jan and Tomek again and forgetting all about the war, the underground, the secret police and all the rest of this horrible nightmare." This seemed to say it all and so they settled down for the rest of the journey absorbed by their own private and anxious thoughts.

Their papers were checked once more at Torun station where they spent the night unhindered and they finally arrived at Pelplin station early the next day. Ewa headed straight to the telegraph office, eagerly anticipating her husband's greeting but as she approached she saw that it was occupied by a German army

118

officer and several officials she did not recognise. About twenty yards further on, beyond the freight office, she saw a porter; a sixteenyear-old lad she recognised who was frantically beckoning at her. As she approached he reached out to take her case and as he bent down he spoke quietly into her ear, "Don't say anything and just follow me. I've got to get you out without them checking your documents. I'll explain everything once you're safe outside." He took her by the arm and ushered them all into the main building, through the general office and then into the postal sorting area and finally out into the street through the loading bay. As there was no guard immediately outside he quickly crossed over the street, turned the corner and entered the church.

They sat in a rear pew as the porter explained what had happened, "I'm sorry to drag you in here under these circumstances but you are all in danger now, especially if the Germans identify you. It is with deep regret that I must tell you that Mr. Nowaski has been killed and many of our friends and neighbours have been arrested and taken away. I'm so sorry."

Ewa thought she had misheard him at first, but as he continued speaking the full impact of his words hit home and she fell to her knees sobbing uncontrollably. All her resolve, bravery and defiance of the previous weeks fell away in that one moment of realisation, as the very thing she had struggled and fought for was taken from her. She collapsed into the arms of her sons and they cried together until their abject sorrow drained their strength and they were left numb with grief. Comforting each other as they were, in the house of God, their thoughts inevitably turned to their maker. The porter, humbled and rendered helpless by the palpable sense of loss and sorrow, joined them in praying for the repose of Henryk's soul.

After what seemed like hours but was really only a matter of minutes, Ewa having recovered sufficiently to speak asked, "Please tell me what happened?"

The porter gathered his thoughts, chose his words carefully in an effort to minimise any further distress, and carried on in a quiet and respectful voice, "Mr. Nowaski had been helping the underground by sending Morse code messages between units and also, while you were away, he was hiding our escaping soldiers at your home. Just one or two at a time before they were smuggled on into Warsaw, where some continued to fight and others looked for their families. To tell the truth most of us have been helping in one way or another, but about a week ago the Germans started rounding people up. Sometimes they would just pick people up on the street and occasionally they would do a house sweep and arrest everyone in a particular area. When it first started they only took Jews away, so we started to smuggle them out as well but then they brought in whole fleets of trucks and took away all the people they had arrested, whatever their religion or background. We never saw them again and there were all sorts of rumours flying about saying they were being tortured and murdered but no one really knows what's happened to them."

Ewa saw a flicker of hope, "So Henryk may be alive even though they have taken him away. He may not be dead after all."

The porter realised how foolish he had been and felt ashamed that he had given this disconsolate yet dignified woman such a false hope and he immediately tried to correct his error. "I'm so sorry, but your husband is already dead. The Germans shot him right here in the square. They raided your house while he was at work and found two soldiers there. They came straight to the station and the SS took him and the stationmaster out into the street in front of the station. We were all made to stand and wait as they rounded up people from the Market Square and brought them round to the station. There were twelve men in all lined up and the SS captain read out a proclamation saying that every person found sheltering fugitives, Poles or Jews, would be executed and so would their families and, in addition, ten other people would be selected at random and executed alongside the culprits. They were all shot in front of us and the stationmaster was killed as well because the Germans believed he was involved and they wanted to fully control the station and all communications in and out of the town. A German civilian is now in charge and soldiers are permanently stationed there to ensure we always obey their rules and toe the line. It was lucky I spotted you first."

Ewa asked. "Where are they buried? I would like to see my husband's grave."

"I'm sorry, Mrs. Nowaski, but there are no graves: the Germans took the bodies away and we don't know what they did with them."

Ewa sobbed as she finally asked the question that she now

dreaded, because the implications terrified her. "What has happened to Maria, did she perish with her father?"

The porter immediately reassured her, "No, as far as I know, she was at the hospital when the shootings took place. I haven't seen her since and she definitely hasn't been anywhere near the station but news would have travelled fast and the staff at the hospital would have known what had happened shortly after, so she could well have gone into hiding to avoid being picked up. I'm certain she is all right but why don't you try the hospital, she might even be staying with a colleague. I don't think she would have chanced going back home."

Ewa nodded in understanding, wiped her tears and said, "Thank you for taking such a risk to warn us. I'm grateful to you for telling me the truth of what has happened here and if my dear husband was still alive I know he would be proud of you. Run along now and get back to work before you are missed."

Although Ewa was anxious to get to the hospital and find out what had happened to Maria, she was equally concerned about the safety of her sons and as she pondered what she had been told she found the burden of responsibility almost unbearable. She feared that the family was disintegrating around her whilst she was powerless to influence events or even prevent their suffering. She again prayed with the boys and gradually, as she gained strength from the comforting and familiar words, her confidence and self-belief returned and she resolved to visit the hospital as soon as darkness fell.

When they left she was surprised to find the streets almost deserted and they arrived without further incident, but a German infantry soldier was standing guard at the main hospital entrance. Unwilling to risk having their identities discovered they carefully worked their way round to the rear staff entrance and were relieved to find it unguarded. Once inside Ewa approached a porter and after mentioning her daughter's name they were taken to the Senior Nurse's office. Ewa explained her plight and implored, "Where is Maria?"

The nurse smiled reassuringly and said, "I'm sure she is safe. She left with Doctor Puzak on the same day as the men were shot at the station. The doctor's wife is Jewish and he was terrified that the Germans would find out so he was going to take her to Warsaw where it will be easier to hide. He had confided in us and so, when your husband was shot, Maria felt she couldn't stay and asked him to take her as well. He brought his plans forward and they left that afternoon."

Ewa thanked the nurse effusively and asked, "Has anyone heard from them since?"

"No. I don't think so, but we didn't expect to because Doctor Puzak said he was making a clean break and keeping his exact plans secret so as not to put any of us in danger. He is a very intelligent and resourceful man, and thinks a great deal of your daughter both professionally and personally, so much so that he has taken her under his wing. Try not to worry too much as I'm sure he will treat her as he would his own daughter, so she couldn't be in safer hands"

As they had nowhere else to go they took a risk and quickly made their way back to their home, each deep in their own private thoughts, trying to make sense of all that had happened to them, and desperate to find peace and safety. It felt strange as they entered the now empty and damp house by the back door, having retrieved the key from its hiding place by the well. They soon discovered that the couple who rented the basement had left and Ewa assumed that they had not been forcefully taken as all their possessions had also gone. She rebuked herself however, because even in her distressed state she felt that she should have checked on their welfare with the porter. The house had not been ransacked and Henryk's cash tin was found in its usual place behind the loose brick at the side of the fireplace. It contained a tidy sum of cash that should enable Ewa to obtain some supplies the next day. They decided it would be safer to spend the evening in the back room of the basement where no candlelight could show through the windows. At first the boys were inconsolable, but as the evening wore on they both realised that they would need to be strong for their mother and so they began to comfort her. They sat and talked about their father and sister, their missing brothers and their life together before the war. They discussed what their father would want them to do in their current position now that he had been taken away and what advice he would give about their future plans. As the evening wore on they all realised that they were destined to battle through another troubled and sleepless night.

First thing in the morning they all sat together and again discussed what they should do next and it was decided that their options were severely limited. Ewa explained the position as she saw it to the boys, "Although he didn't like to talk about his life in Gdansk your father told me when we met that both his parents were dead and his oldest brother went missing during the Great War. Apart from Roman in Warsaw he has no other living relatives. I think it would now be far too dangerous for us to try and travel back there without help from the resistance. Our best option is to contact my family in Gniew: I'm sure they will find us somewhere to hide and we can then make some proper plans for the future. I've also realised that if our telegraph message got through, the Germans will know we're coming home so it's far too dangerous to stay in this house. We'll leave this morning as soon as we have some supplies."

It was also agreed that in the meantime they would be safer hiding inside and not attracting any attention from their neighbours or the authorities and they would only venture out if absolutely necessary. Whilst Jacek conducted a thorough search around the house, collecting candles, crockery and kitchen utensils for future use he discovered, tucked behind the mantel clock, the letter his mother had sent home from his uncle's in Warsaw. He read his mother's words, smiled to himself as he imagined his father and sister reading it over and over again and put it in his pocket to show his mother at a more suitable time. The contents made him fully appreciate, probably for the first time, the immense burden of responsibility that his mother was carrying.

Her plight made him consider his future role within the family and he decided he must now do his fair share and come out of his shell by being more practical and taking on ever more responsibility. As a first step he volunteered to fetch the supplies while Jozef and his mother packed what they could carry and prepared for the walk to Gniew. Ewa thought about going shopping herself but decided that if the Germans were actively looking for them she would be more recognisable and would certainly stand out more than the boys. She had noticed in her recent travels that despite the war or perhaps because of it, the streets, when in use at all, seemed full of boys.

Jacek was able to purchase some bread, sausage, ham and

pickle but was amazed at how the prices had gone up and as he made for home, avoiding the army and police patrols, he wondered where they would get any more money from. He thought he had left home with a small fortune, but there was little left in his pocket after his few meagre purchases.

Jacek had only been gone for about ten minutes when, in a flurry of activity, the street was sealed off at both ends by military police and then a small convoy of army vehicles disgorged their troops who sprinted along the road to their allocated buildings and immediately started banging on doors and systematically searching all the houses. Orders were barked out and windows, doors and personal property smashed as the residents were bullied, beaten and driven from their homes. All was done with overt hostility and at a breakneck pace and if there was no immediate response from a home the front door was immediately battered down and the soldiers poured in, pushing, shoving and terrifying those inside. The staccato, brash authority of their commands, the menacing sounds of their boots on the cobbles and floorboards and the metallic clanking of their equipment and weaponry all added to the psychological atmosphere of intimidation and contempt.

In a matter of minutes the occupants were forced out into the street, roughly searched for weapons, stripped of jewellery and cash and then ordered into the backs of the trucks. Anyone who faltered, slipped, resisted or protested in any way was beaten, kicked and literally thrown onto the transports. Children wailed, women screamed and an old couple spat defiance and hatred at the soldiers until they were silenced by gunshots. Ewa heard the commotion outside, realised what was happening, grabbed Jozef and ran to hide in the cellar.

No sooner had they concealed themselves behind their old broken piano than the front door burst open and a soldier started shouting, "Come on out, all occupants are under arrest so come out immediately or risk being shot on the spot." Several other voices then joined in, "Show yourselves, hurry up and come out now, hurry, hurry!"

They stayed where they were, huddled together until they heard the sound of dogs growling and snarling at the top of the cellar steps. "Come on out or I'll let the dogs go and they'll tear you to ribbons. Once they're loose there's nothing I can do, so you've only got the

124

one chance," shouted the handler as he struggled to keep the two leashed security dogs under control. With the scent of prey washing into their nostrils they barked and yelped for the opportunity to attack and win the praise and reward of their master.

Ewa felt humiliated by the fact that her home, the one place in the world that she had always felt safe and unthreatened, had been violated in such a brutal, abusive and oppressive manner and all her resistance just crumbled away. The advice she had so sincerely given her boys just a couple of days ago echoed in her mind but now those words seemed so hollow and pompous. Any vestige of self-belief had been shattered when these men savagely burst through her door, quite prepared to shoot anyone they encountered and furthermore, did so as a matter of simple right and routine. Ewa stood up and shielding Jozef with her body she put her hands in the air and walked towards the steps, "We've done nothing, it's only me and my son here," she shouted standing just clear of the reach of the ferocious, straining and slavering animals.

"There's no use denying it. You're the wife of the telegraphist and we knew you would be back sooner or later. You will both now answer to us for your crimes," said the SS dog handler as two other soldiers tied their hands and dragged them away to the parked trucks. Twenty minutes later, with about eighty prisoners on board, the army vehicles pulled away heading towards the local Gestapo Headquarters.

Jacek turned the corner leading to his street just as the first lorry was leaving and he immediately dived for cover through a boundary hedge and lay there watching through the shrubs as the vehicles drove by. He saw his mother and brother in the back of the second lorry and his heart sank to his boots as he was overwhelmed by an indescribable and total loneliness. He lay on the cold ground and for the second consecutive day, despite his recent resolve to toughen up and be a man, he broke down in a flood of tears, his ability to resist any further destroyed by a combination of despair, anger, hatred and frustration. He finally cried himself out then somehow managed to dredge up the last vestige of perseverance that was hidden deep inside his character and rationally accepted that he could do nothing more for his mother and Jozef. The shock of their loss hit him like a sledgehammer but also made him determined to avoid capture himself. He realised it would be difficult seeing that he was now entirely on his own, but he felt it was his duty to his parents and his country.

Throughout his short life he had always felt somewhat inferior to his siblings. To make up for his lack of physical ability and practical skills he worked even harder at school and always studied at home. He had constantly felt disappointed and frustrated that his academic success never brought him the popularity, confidence and easygoing cheerfulness that they naturally possessed and he so admired. Over the last few weeks however, he had come to realise that these things were no longer of any relevance whatsoever. Although he felt relieved that he had managed to save the day on the train at Brest, it now dawned on him that as far as everybody else was concerned he never really had anything to prove in the first place, either to his family or himself. He was loved and cherished for what he was and now, perhaps too late, he realised that he had never been seen by others as he once saw himself.

All that mattered to him now was his survival and he needed to decide what to do next. He slowly took firm control of his emotions and as he calmed down he started to think logically and analytically, examining his limited options. He realised that from now on he would have to stop feeling sorry for himself, rely on his own abilities and resources and take responsibility for his own fate. Once he had reached this conclusion he was not so daunted by the uncertain future and felt he was perfectly capable of putting together a reasonable plan of action. Where could he go? He immediately decided that it would now be too dangerous to contact his family in Gniew, for their sake as well as his own. Who could he trust to help? The only person who sprang to mind was the priest and, knowing that his sister was also heading for the capital, he decided to make for Warsaw.

The more he thought it through the more difficult the practicalities seemed to become and he knew he stood no real chance of reaching his goal without someone in Pelplin giving him a decent start. He also considered that his quickest solution was to use the railway and thought who better than the porter to help once more, so he headed for the station, keeping to the back streets, alleys and gardens. He knew every inch of this area of town, his own neighbourhood, and managed to reach the sidings without being detected and then hid amongst piles of sleepers where he could watch the station exit in relative safety. As he laid there he suddenly wondered if it was the porter who had betrayed them, and could it happen again; but then, remembering how he had initially warned them at the station, he dismissed the possibility as most unlikely.

Shortly after 6pm he saw the porter leave work and followed him home. He challenged him as he entered the front door and after a brief exchange he was invited in and ushered straight to the porter's room. "Please be as quiet as you can, I don't want my parents finding out you're here. The least they know the better, as I'm not too sure how they would react. What do you want?"

He told the porter what had happened since they left the church, what he intended and asked for any help the porter could offer. The lad promised to do what he could but made it perfectly clear that this was the last time he was prepared to take such risks, as the Germans were looking for any excuse to transport the locals and he had his parents' welfare to worry about. Jacek spent a restless night on the bedroom floor and early in the morning, dressed in an ill-fitting spare railway uniform, he crept downstairs with the porter and they silently left by the back door and headed for the station. He was in hiding, back in the sleepers, shortly afterwards. A strict condition of the porter's help had been that Jacek destroy his identity papers and so they were thrown on the fire along with his few other personal items that might connect him to Pelplin and subsequently the porter. He could not, however, bring himself to destroy his mother's letter, the only tangible thing he had left to remind him of home and his family. After much discussion and argument the porter finally relented and he placed it in an envelope and they sewed it into the lining of the uniform jacket.

At lunchtime he was collected by the porter and taken to one of a number of goods' trucks being shunted into the sidings and there hidden amongst a consignment of scrap metal. As he turned to leave the porter said, "These carriages are going to Plock, it's not Warsaw I know, but it's the best I can do as I can't risk you staying here any longer. If we're caught together we'll both be shot so the sooner you leave the better and at least you're going a fair way in the right direction. I'm truly sorry about your family. Your father was the best teacher and colleague I've ever had and I can assure you he will never be forgotten around here. Now, remember that the train won't go right into the station at Plock but into the goods yards so, if you're careful, you should have a decent chance of getting clear of the security police. The rest of the journey is down to you. Good luck."

Three and a half hours later Jacek jumped down onto the rails at Plock, took a quick look around, stretched his stiff legs and, keeping low, ran for the road just beyond the ten foot high boundary fence. He couldn't see a gate, either to left or right, so he started to climb over the wire mesh but, just as he reached the top, a soldier appeared around the corner of the building on the opposite side of the road. He saw Jacek straight away and shouted, "Halt, don't move or I'll fire," and he aimed his rifle directly at Jacek only twenty yards away. Jacek had no choice, he was a sitting target astride the top of the fence, and as he looked down into the approaching soldier's eyes he knew that he would not hesitate to shoot him.

Jacek was surprised at how calm he felt even though he was in a precarious position and staring down the barrel of a rifle. He had never been reckless in his short life and it certainly wasn't a feeling of bravado on his part but nevertheless, he was no longer frightened. Something had changed since he set out on his own and he felt strangely calm, detached and confident of his ability to survive whatever was thrown at him. In a perfectly conversational and controlled tone, aimed at reassuring the soldier Jacek said, "I'll come down slowly. There really is no need to be hasty. You've got me covered so there's nothing I can do. I know when the game is up."

At that point another soldier ran round the corner and Jacek immediately lost any lingering hope of further escape. He was marched off to the railway police station and the soldiers, convinced that they had captured a young saboteur, were not surprised to discover that he had no identity papers. When interviewed he gave a false name and told the German military police that he was trying to get back to Warsaw having been stranded in Lwow when the war started. He kept his story as close to the truth as possible without putting at risk any of the people who had provided help. He maintained that he had acted alone and by necessity had become adept at stowing away on goods trains and stealing to survive. A thorough search of the yards had been made and nothing untoward had been found, but they did discover his hiding place on the goods wagon, exactly where he said it was. His account, told in great and vivid detail with the aplomb of a seasoned actor, seemed credible even probable and the police officer who interviewed him concluded that the lad was indeed a petty criminal, not a saboteur or a political threat. He was sent to the local lock-up where he escaped the attentions of the SS and Gestapo but in a matter of days he was designated, along with other common criminals, men of military age and the homeless, as fit for allocation to a labour battalion. Shortly after Christmas, along with several hundred other local Poles, many of them in their teens and some even younger, he was transported to work in the coalmines of the Ruhr.

Jozef and his mother sat on the floor of the cold cell they shared with a dozen other prisoners. They had been punched and kicked by the SS guards when they had arrived and many of the other prisoners also had bloody and painful injuries. Ewa put her arm around her son, pulled him closer and whispered, "When they question us make sure you tell the truth because the more we lie the easier it will be for them to catch us out. Tell them where we've been but don't mention any of the contacts, the priest or the porter. If they ask about any of your brothers simply say they were separated from us at Luck and we don't know what has happened to them. We mustn't endanger those that have helped us and in any case nothing we tell them will make it any easier for us. They've already decided what they're going to do and when they're going to do it and nothing we say will alter that fact."

"Are they going to kill us then, the same as they did to father? Is that what you really think?" asked Jozef, already suspecting that he knew the answer.

"I really don't know son, we've been in difficult situations before and managed to come through it, so perhaps with God's help we will again, but I won't lie to you, things are bleak and a prayer or two would certainly help," replied Ewa before they held hands and quietly began to recite the Hail Mary. As they did so others joined in, slowly at first, one or two at a time, until all the prisoners were praying out loud and as one in perfect Latin, as if they were at Sunday Mass and not incarcerated in a torture cell.

They spent a week in the cells, were frequently separated, interrogated, assaulted, stripped naked, abused and threatened with the firing squad. They had little sleep, kept awake by the screams of those being beaten, and the moans and shouts from their own cellmates and other prisoners throughout the building. Ewa was repeatedly mocked, ridiculed and indecently assaulted and although she was regularly taunted and threatened with rape (and lived in constant fear of it happening) she was spared that particular brutal humiliation. Jozef prayed constantly and derived great strength, courage and resolve from his unshakable faith. The guards and interrogators tried to use this against him, constantly asking such questions as, "Why has your God abandoned you? He doesn't care about you or your pitiful country. He can't stop the pain or save your family. We decide what happens to all of you. It's us and nobody else with the absolute power of life and death."

Jozef never rose to the bait, not once did he respond to the provocation or blasphemous jibes, but simply maintained that he had nothing to do with the resistance movement. Unconvinced, his interrogator persevered, "Now tell us who helped you to get back home? What organisation did your father belong to? Where are your brothers? Where is your sister? Where are the soldiers being hidden now? Who is in charge of the local activists?"

He answered as best he could when he could, but the questions were incessant and every time he hesitated or said he didn't know he was punched in the face or beaten across the legs with a length of rubber hosepipe. In his heart he knew he was being tested and he was driven by an overriding and burning passion to stand by his beliefs and do his duty to God Almighty, the Church and his mother. This quiet determination and passive resistance in one so young confounded and annoyed his guards. As they became increasingly frustrated their treatment of him grew ever more hostile and brutal. His response was to draw ever deeper on his spiritual resolve and he actually grew in mental strength and developed an iron will that would, for a time at least, ensure his survival.

They told their tormentors their story over and over again but eventually, as Ewa's resistance was beaten from her, she admitted they had received help and gave up the code names of their contacts. Once this had happened they told Jozef that she would be shot in front of him unless he corroborated her account in full and so, knowing it was no idle threat, he acquiesced immediately. Despite all the intimidation and pain, neither ever mentioned the priest or the porter.

They were eventually forced to sign written confessions admitting that they were agents for the underground movement and had assisted escaping soldiers. The interrogator told them that they would be taken to a proper prison and made to work until the authorities decided their fate. Two days later, with about twenty other prisoners, they were marched under guard through a deserted town centre to the railway station and there loaded into a cattle truck and locked in. They were heading for a labour camp at the massive rail junction at Tarnow in the south of the country where they would be worked from dawn to dusk. Here they loaded gravel and rubble onto the railway system for transport west, to support the massive construction programme that the Germans had introduced across the Third Reich. Ironically this included the huge swathe of Poland that was now being incorporated into Germany proper. Nothing was wasted: even the bricks, from bombed-out buildings and the destroyed houses of suspected saboteurs, were loaded onto railway transports by labour gangs and then taken to Germany for reuse.

At first they were relieved to find themselves alive and not separated, but as the weeks passed and summer approached, more and more prisoners arrived and frightening rumours started to spread throughout the camp. It was suggested that their establishment was to close and all the prisoners were to be moved en masse to a camp for political prisoners. Trustees had been told that it was to be a new punishment camp with an experimental regime under the complete control of the SS and that it would be far harsher than anything that had gone before. At first Ewa told Jozef not to worry because rumours were always circulating and few had real substance, but as they persisted she began to feel very uneasy. In June the whole camp was indeed shut down and every prisoner was loaded onto railway cars, crammed inside and this time, as predicted, they headed for another home. The next day they arrived at a newly established camp at an old Polish army barracks outside of Oswiecim in Galicia. On 14th June, 1940, Jozef and his mother were on the first transport of Polish prisoners to arrive at Auschwitz concentration camp. As they were herded through the imposing entrance gates Jozef, for the benefit of the old Polish gypsy beside him, translated the now infamous and mocking German words on the metal archway above their heads, "Arbeit macht frei - work brings freedom."

SIX

The Written Word
Salisbury, Wiltshire 5th October 2008

I picked up the next letter, written on both sides of a very thin piece of waxy paper, almost brown in colour and obviously intended for a totally different purpose. The texture was similar to that of tissue paper but stronger, coarser and less malleable to the touch and the ink had run slightly, creating a feathery appearance to the letters. The ink itself was a very dark blue with a brown tinge, but I wasn't sure whether its discoloration was due to the ageing process or whether the ink had been diluted or adulterated. The strange combination of the paper and ink and the resemblance of the handwriting to that in the first letter added to my already heightened level of anticipation. Because of the poor quality of the materials the words were not as legible as before but the style, old Polish phraseology and archaic vocabulary, told me it was certainly by the same author. I translated it as follows:

> *To Father Antoni Chepek, care of the Holy Cross Church, Warsaw.*
>
> *My Dear Father Chepek,*
>
> *If you are reading this then my darling son Jozef is alive and my dying prayers have been answered. You once, not so long ago in normal times, offered your help if I ever found myself in real difficulty and I have to say*

that we have long passed that time. I am sorry this letter is not brief but it is my last communication, in effect my only testament to the world I leave behind, and there are things which must be said.

I hope you can forgive and believe me when I tell you that I have found hell and it is here, not only here on this earth, but here in our raped and ruined Poland. Jozef and I were captured and two years ago (it seems like a whole lifetime has passed since) we were sent to a camp near Osweicim where we have been forced to work, alongside hundreds of Russian prisoners of war, building another camp nearby. Unlike the poor Russians we have survived despite the starvation, abuse and hardship, but time is now running out. The other camp has been in use since August and as God is my witness thousands of Jews, Gypsies and Poles are being murdered here every day in vast gas chambers. I have witnessed cruelty beyond human imagination and I have cried out for the intervention of the Almighty, but we have been abandoned by the world and the Holy Trinity. The bodies are stacked as high as the fence and then they are incinerated in massive ovens. My heart and my body are now broken and the Kapo, to whom we owe our lives, tells me that I am on the list for extermination next week. I ask you to tell the Pope and the whole world of what is happening here but not for my sake, as I am so diminished that I will truly welcome death now. Despite what I have said I have made my peace with God and in my tortured heart I know he will forgive my weakness.

I beg you to take care of my son who has always wanted to join the church and that event would make me so proud. Although his faith has been tested beyond endurance, unlike mine it has not broken, but his soul needs time to repair itself and I saw enough of your Christian spirit to know you can help. I don't know when this war will end but with my dearest Henryk gone and me to join him shortly it is vital to me that our first-born son should survive. The Kapo will smuggle this to Jozef and he will be instructed that my final wish is that he delivers it to you personally and in an unopened condition. Although I am no longer

certain of anything in this malevolent world, as a mother
I desire with every fibre of my being that Jozef will safely
make it to you and what happens to him then is now your
responsibility and I beseech you as a priest and a friend,
do not let me die in vain.

Please pray for all the souls tormented in this
shameful place and may God bless them and in death
have compassion upon them. I can only wish that one day
those responsible for such evil will be brought to justice in
this world and the next.

In respect, friendship and even hope,

Ewa Nowaska
October, 1942

Despite my knowledge of the Holocaust and my somewhat cynical
outlook on life, brought about by spending so long in the police, I
found myself overcome with emotion and had to break off several
times during the translation as I struggled to imagine what the
author had endured and the total helplessness of her situation. As
usual when I needed to clear my head I had a cup of coffee and then
went for a walk. I strolled in the warm autumn sunshine around the
quintessentially English setting of the cathedral close, and then on
along the river Avon and considered calling a halt to the search.
The painful contrast between my free and contented lifestyle,
played out in such beautiful surroundings when compared with
the inhuman treatment and naked hatred heaped upon these decent
and caring people living in perdition, was suddenly all too clear.
It made me feel uneasy about the depth of my intrusion into the
lives of such desperate folk and I dreaded causing the survivors or
their descendants any further heartache. The letters in themselves
were heart-rending, so how much more painful would they be to
those closely related to the actual events. On the other hand I also
felt a professional sense of responsibility to give such a person or
persons the opportunity to make their own decision as to how much
they might want to know. In the end I decided to carry on and see
just how far my enquiries could take me and then decide whether
or not to approach anyone I should trace.

Back at my desk I still couldn't bring myself to dwell on Ewa's letter or yet analyse what it told me, so I decided to sort through the photographs again to see what information they might provide. I divided them into piles based on size, shape, type of border and content and found that a group of six appeared to come from the same roll of film. They all showed four uniformed soldiers accompanied by three young women taken at various rural locations that appeared continental. The uniforms were of the desert variety and all the girls wore light summer dresses. Another batch showed a group of young men and women, all in civilian clothes, taken outside a line of English council houses. There were also three, taken during the winter, of a young soldier in full Polish army uniform alongside a wooden single story building by a small lake, surrounded by silver birch trees. The building could well have been a barrack hut and the location appeared to be British. The remaining photographs were of babies, family groups and wedding parties but I could see no obvious connections. I examined the Polish soldier through a magnifying glass and although I could make out the word 'Poland' on the shoulder flash I could not distinguish any other identifying badges or insignia. The shoulder flash did tell me that he was a member of The Free Polish Forces serving with the wartime British army. I made a note to have the photograph enlarged if I drew a blank elsewhere.

Having thumbed through the English/Polish dictionary and found no marks, insertions, highlighted words or other useful information, I decided it was time to tackle the penultimate letter, the one written in German. I walked the hundred yards to see my neighbour who was German/ Swiss in origin and had kindly agreed to translate it for me. His German was far better than my Polish and although he experienced the same problem of the language used being old fashioned and heavily regionalised, he quickly produced a written translation:

Mazingarbe mine, July, 1941
To father Antoni Chepek, The church of the Holy Cross,
Warsaw

Dear father Chepek,
*   I am sorry to write in German but I was instructed to*

136

do so by my contact as it attracts less attention here and I also remember you saying that you studied it at university. I hope you are well. I am writing this letter in the hope that you remember my family after all that must have happened to you in these strange and fateful times. You once offered my family your help when we were together at Brest and only now have I had the chance to contact you. The Germans shot my father and then both my mother and Jozef were captured. My sister Maria escaped to Warsaw but I have no idea what has happened to her since. I have been wondering if you have heard from mother or Jozef and whether they have heard anything at all from Maria or my other brothers Jan and Tomek. As for me I was on my way to see you when I was arrested and I am now in a labour battalion working for the Germans. Things have been a lot worse and I am resigned to seeing the war out as a captive. When I was first caught I was sent down the mines in Germany and had a terrible time but six months ago we were all moved to the Pas-de-Calais and put to work down the mines here. It seems so strange for me to see massive black slagheaps surrounded by row upon row of graves in the military cemeteries from the Great War. Apparently Europe has learnt nothing since those days and so we all suffer again.

I am learning French and being helped in every way possible by a few friends from the very large Polish community living in the town here. Their families settled here in the last century and most of them are bilingual and many work in the pit. Our guards are not as severe as they once were, with one or two being quite friendly, so it is relatively easy to slip away unnoticed for an hour or two and there are no reprisals as long as we parade for work. It is not worth trying to escape because they control the whole of Europe with a fist of iron and it is no longer possible to get to England without a great deal of help.

Since we have become proficient miners we seem to be more valuable to them and we receive sufficient food and, although we are guarded, we live in barracks rather than a prison camp. I have slowly recovered from the cruelty and hard labour of Germany and grown tall, fit and strong. It's strange how I have changed so much in such a relatively short time but to survive I've had to adapt, grow up quickly and learn to stand up for myself.

It is now possible for me to smuggle a letter out and I am told that if you get this it will have been via friends in France to England and then through a courier to Warsaw. If you have a reply then I hope it can come back safely the same way. It is only when you experience such harsh times that you appreciate what is really valuable in life and I have had endless hours to ponder such things. I have concluded that only family and friends make life worth living and I now long to see my family and little else matters to me. I know you will help me if you can,

Yours in respect and gratitude,
Jacek

Finally a turn for the better, only a small one admittedly, but nevertheless, I allowed myself the hope that it would signify an end to the catastrophic downward spiral of misfortune that had beset this family. I reviewed what I had learnt from the latest letters and although Jacek was definitely alive, with improved prospects in mid 1941, there was no guarantee he survived the war, but his location directly corresponded with the postcard of the war graves dated 1945. Both his parents had probably perished and, despite his mother's hopes, the signs were not good for Jozef. A new name had also been added, that of the priest Father Antoni Chepek of the church of the Holy Cross, Warsaw.

I decided that before I started active enquiries I should review all the recent information I had gathered, compare that to my existing notes and lists and then summarise all the important leads into a single working document. This is what I came up with:

1) Ewa and Henryk Nowaski had at least five children, their sons being Jan, Jozef, Tomek and Jacek and their daughter Maria. In September/October 1939 (when Warsaw was being bombed) they lived at 4, Gniew Street, Pelplin, Pomerania. The Germans shot Henryk.

138

2) In September 1941 Jan (school age?) was somewhere in the UK (possibly Scotland) with a soldier called Jerzy.

3) In October 1942 Ewa and Jozef were at Auschwitz concentration camp and Ewa was shortly to be murdered. She was hopeful that Jozef would contact a priest, Father Antoni Chepek, at the Holy Cross Church in Warsaw. Did mother and son both perish or did Jozef survive and if so, how? It seems so unlikely that he would have been able to contact anyone on the outside.

4) In July 1941 Jacek was in a labour battalion working as a miner at Mazingarbe in the Pas-de-Calais and he was also trying to make contact with the same priest. His sister Maria had been in Warsaw.

5) Henryk had a brother called Roman who lived in Warsaw and he was definitely alive sometime before the city fell to the Germans.

6) Tomek was a prisoner of the Russians (along with Jan, before Jan escaped) but I knew nothing further of him.

7) On 14th December 1946, Sergeant Wittold Vranek, a soldier at camp 170 Pipers Wood, Amersham Bucks, was sent a post card from the Crutzen family in Breda Holland. The sender mentions the date 29th October 1944.

8) There was an Italian connection with the postcards and the photographs, but its relevance or otherwise is not yet clear.

9) The photographs of the Polish soldier are surely key pieces of evidence and he could be my subject, but it is far too early to be sure. Perhaps they were taken at Camp 170.

If I had still been a police officer I would have had access to a huge variety of search facilities, systems and resources but I was now entirely on my own so it was back to basics. I picked up the telephone and made my first call to the Headquarters of the Polish Ex-serviceman's Association at Hammersmith in London. I explained what I was trying to achieve and the very helpful secretary agreed to search their computer system for my list of names and call me back. I then telephoned the Amersham Library and museum and they provided me with the name of a local historian. In turn he explained that there had been a number of army camps around the old town area during the war and that between 1945 and 1947 several were used as resettlement camps where Polish soldiers were demobilised. He added that some ten thousand such soldiers passed through those camps, with many settling in the locality and that a sizeable Polish community still existed with its own Social Club and he kindly provided me with its telephone number.

That evening I called the Polish club at Amersham and spoke to the steward who was most helpful and he explained that more than sixty years after the war they are still regularly being contacted by people searching for relatives or colleagues, and also by family history enthusiasts tracing Polish family lines. He agreed to post my names on their noticeboard seeking help from their members and undertook to call me back in about two weeks.

Four days later the secretary from Hammersmith called back with the news that she had found no matches against my names when compared to their computerised membership list. She was, however, very interested in what I was doing and said she would discuss it with the other members of staff to see if they could offer any suggestions. She promised to get back to me and I then telephoned an old associate in the Royal Military Police and asked for any suggestions that might help in the search and within the hour he was back in touch. He provided me with the details of a Polish section at The Ministry of Defence, which is still responsible for the records of all Polish servicemen who fought alongside the British.

I was now getting used to the fact that, once I had explained my objective, everyone seemed so eager to help and were prepared to significantly put themselves out to do so. This was in pleasant contrast to many people that I contacted in the course of everyday life and business who appeared too wrapped up in their own problems and office policies to worry about really helping 'the customer'. The girl in the MoD office listened to my request with interest and gladly put my names through their system and immediately had three hits, and what a surprise it was for me!

The first was Tomek Nowaski, the brother who Jan said had also been captured by the Russians and who I knew the least about, and yet I was being told that he had definitely served with the Polish Free Forces.

The second name was that of Jacek and yet he had been in occupied France in a German labour battalion!

The third was that of Sergeant Vranek who also had a record on file. There was however no record of Jan, the very one that I knew had been safe in the UK and the one that I suspected was most likely to have been on record. She did, however, caution me that many files had been lost over the years and others misfiled, so the fact that a name was not on the computer did not mean that they had not served. Eager as she was to help she would not release any further personal details because of their strict confidentiality rules. She also told me that although the names' index had now been computerised, the only detailed records were the original hardcopy files and these were stored elsewhere and would have to be ordered. She agreed to request the files for scrutiny and offered to write to the subject if they were still alive or their next of kin if the subject had died. I would be permitted to enclose my own letter with that communication and it would then be up to them if they wished to respond or not. If the subject was dead and there was no next of kin listed then, only under those circumstances, would she release the full record to me. She confirmed that camp 170 was one of the resettlement camps at Amersham and members of the Polish 2nd Corps, many of whom had seen action in Africa and Italy, had passed through it. She also pointed out that many units from the 1st Polish Armoured Division that had been fighting in France, Holland and Germany were demobilised at a resettlement camp at Codford in Wiltshire. This could tie in with the postcards of the George Inn at Codford and that of Stonehenge only nine miles away.

I agreed to confirm my requests in writing and did so the very next day, enclosing a verbatim copy of my latest summary. I would now have to wait for the files to arrive and be thoroughly examined before she could contact me. I also had to wait and see if my other enquiries would throw anything up. Having set the ball in motion I now had plenty to think about and the time to decide where to go next.

SEVEN

Growing up in Scotland
25th February 1942

Jan sat on his bed in the school dormitory and thumbed through Dominik's diary. It had been in his pocket when he left the farm and, although initially he had felt pangs of guilt about keeping it, he was glad of its powerful link back to Poland and those he loved. He had always kept it close and had read it many times since his escape. He then picked up his rosary and held it tight and one at a time, as he moved his fingers across the familiar beads, he pictured the faces of his parents, his brothers, his sister and his friends. These actions had become almost a daily ritual and he had convinced himself that as long as he did this, they would be alive and stay safe.

He had heard so much bad news from Poland through his army friends and in the papers that he felt that he could no longer be just a passive, far removed, protected and irrelevant witness to events. He believed he had seen the brutal reality of all-out conflict, heard the language of hatred, persecution and bigotry and tasted the heart breaking loneliness of separation and statelessness. War held no romantic or adventurous connotations for him, it was just a means to an end and with every fibre of his being he knew that Poland must fight back, but what could he do? He had been forced to grow up quickly and, as he thought of his parents and wondered where they were, he decided that he could no longer act like a boy and expect or depend on others to look after him indefinitely. He could not imagine a future for himself without returning to his family in

Poland and now, as a young man, he had a duty to do something about it. He realised that his options were very limited but with a deep sigh he laid back on his pillow and, staring at the hundreds of cracks in the ceiling, he thought about the possibilities for a long time until finally, he decided what he would do.

That evening he was so excited to see Jerzy for the first time in twelve months and admired his friend's new uniform, asking question after question about the badges, the corporal's stripes and the progress of the war. Jerzy's promotion, his responsibilities and the general details of army training intrigued him greatly. Jerzy in turn was surprised by how much Jan had changed since they last met. He had grown in height, filled out and matured from an insecure, undernourished adolescent in a strange country into a confident, handsome young man who seemed completely at ease in his surroundings. Finally Jerzy asked, "It's time we talked about you and things at school, how would you sum up your progress so far?"

"Fine, I don't think there's any problem there, the English is pretty good and I keep up with everyone else alright, but I need to talk to you about something far more important. That's: where do we go from here? I'll tell you exactly what I think and I hope you'll support me. I've decided that it's about time I left school and joined the army."

His friend was taken aback, coughed to create some thinking time and countered, "Yes, I think you should join up as we're always looking for more recruits, but it's far too early for you yet and anyway you're not old enough."

Jan expected this response and was ready, "I've given this a great deal of thought and I'm determined to leave school and join the army like you. I can say I'm seventeen and no one will know that I've added a year on, because I had no written record of my birthday when I arrived and I look old enough anyway. I'll tell them that they made a mistake on the identification card they gave me when we left Liverpool. There's so much chaos with the records and they know the information is unreliable, so I'm sure they won't argue over it. Even if they do, they can't prove how old I am one way or the other and if you help me out I'm sure I'll get in."

Jerzy did not look too happy with this pronouncement and voiced his concern, "I think you should finish your education here first: they told you that you can stay until the summer and you can think about what you want to do then. As you say, your English is pretty good now so I'm sure you could get some work and earn yourself some money. There will be plenty of time for you to join up later on, if that's what you still want to do then. Anyway, from what you told me last time you seem to be hitting it off with the local girls and you might change your mind and decide to settle down before too long and make a permanent home here. If I was you I wouldn't rush into it straight away, you should take every opportunity to learn as much as you can about this country because we may all be here for some time yet."

Jan had to admit that he had grown to like his current home, after the initial shock as the boat docked at Liverpool when he had been so amazed at how green and unfamiliar everything appeared and it felt like he had arrived on a different planet. The locals were very inquisitive about the new arrivals and always seemed to want to approach them, ask questions that were not understood and prod and poke as if they were examining a different species. It was not hostile or unfriendly, just a genuine sense of heightened curiosity that was particularly directed at the few children amongst the group of about five hundred. They were first encamped in Cheshire and, as refugees, found themselves being documented, deloused again, questioned and issued with identification and ration cards, but the difference this time was that they were welcomed as equals and treated with respect and affection. After about three weeks they were taken by train to Scotland where Jerzy and his regiment were immediately given the task of defending the Scottish East Coast around Fife from an expected Nazi invasion from Norway. Jan was sent to school with the few other children in the party. Over the next two years Jan had settled into a routine and he had grown in strength and confidence and being a quick learner, he rapidly mastered the basics of his third language. He had even grown accustomed to the local diet but he had the advantage over Jerzy because local cooks prepared the school meals, whereas in his friend's regiment the cooks were Polish. Try as they might they were unable to learn how to prepare the local food and ended up with Polish meals cooked with the most unsuitable English ingredients. The results literally looked like a dog's breakfast and tasted little better. It took weeks of raucous, but good-humoured, complaints from the troops and exasperated experimentation by the cooks before a reasonably appetising compromise was reached. During this time Jerzy had been moved from camp to camp all over Scotland and the Polish army was being constantly reorganised and increased in size.

Jan, having made his decision, was now totally resolute and wanted to make it clear to his mentor that he considered his future aim in life, and his duty, should be to help free Poland and fight alongside his own countrymen. His ultimate aim was to be reunited with his family. He was not about to be persuaded, even by his best friend, that he should delay the first step towards achieving this. "I know you're only looking out for me and I appreciate that what you say makes sense, but this is something that I must do and, the sooner the better, because I've got to be trained and equipped and I need to be ready. There is already talk, since the attack on Pearl Harbour just before Christmas, that the Americans will help the British to open a western front by invading France. I really can't wait any longer."

Jerzy knew that Jan was stubborn and unlikely to change his mind. He also accepted that if their positions were reversed he would feel exactly the same as his young friend. He accepted defeat, shook his head in mock frustration and advised, "Just make sure that you take the training seriously and continue to study hard, because it's also our duty to prepare for life after the war. There will come a time and it could be quicker than we think, when all these hundreds of thousands of soldiers will be looking for jobs in civilian life and only the best qualified will succeed."

They continued to discuss their future and the progress of the war and Jan was delighted to hear that General Anders was trying to arrange the release of imprisoned Polish soldiers in Russia, following inter-government agreements that a whole new army could be formed from these men. They discussed the implications of these proposals and the war in general until it was time for Jerzy to catch the bus back to his barracks some ten miles away, leaving Jan to plan his immediate future.

He signed up the very next day, insisting that he was seventeen and commenced his basic training the following week with other recruits to the various units of the 1st Polish Armoured Division currently being formed in Scotland by General Stanislaw Maczek under the auspices of the Polish Government in Exile.

During his first few days at the training camp Jan met another recruit from a neighbouring hut called Barry Reigal, who spoke Polish with the strangest accent that Jan had ever heard. After a couple of days Jan could contain his curiosity no longer and so struck up a conversation with the stranger and was astounded to discover that Barry was not only English but hailed from the East End of London. He explained that his great-great-grandfather was also a Polish refugee, who had arrived at the port of London in 1831 after he had been captured and banished during one of the many Polish uprisings against the Russian occupation. In the early years he was helped by the Association of the Friends of Poland, which had just been founded in London by the Scottish poet Thomas Campbell who had so eloquently championed their cause against Russian oppression in his famous work 'The Pleasures of Hope'. The Pole became a market trader, married a local girl, had a family and settled down to a quiet life.

Three generations later the Great War intervened and Barry's father joined up, he fought at Ypres until he was wounded and sent home to recuperate but he never fully recovered. Barry went on to explain that there was now a sizeable community of exiled Poles in his neighbourhood and he spoke Polish on a regular basis, only with a Cockney accent! He had volunteered on his eighteenth birthday and was surprised when his request to join the Free Polish Army had been granted because, as a British subject, he thought he would be debarred. Evidently, although a trickle of Polish volunteers were arriving from around the world, more were needed to build up both Corps and the authorities were also keen to accept as many English speakers as possible, to help ease the inevitable communication difficulties.

As they talked about their history and the progress of the war they formed a mutual respect and understanding that, over the next few weeks, against a demanding background of endless drill, weapons training and combat exercises, developed into a close and firm friendship.

With basic training complete Jan was not surprised to discover that Jerzy had pulled some strings and both he and Barry were posted to the 3rd Battalion of the 1st Rifle Brigade and on arrival they were also allocated to his company where he planned to keep a watchful, paternal eye on them both. Whenever possible they spoke in English and this helped to improve Jan's pronunciation and vocabulary to such an extent that he found himself able to think in English. For this reason Barry and Jan were asked to provide help to an English woman, Isabel Muriel Surtees (Lady Napier) who had been setting up canteens, regimental shops and other facilities all across Scotland to assist the Poles in their settlement and rehabilitation. What had started on a very small scale was rapidly becoming a major enterprise and she explained to them that in order to help the whole Polish community in every way possible, she wished to learn their language. Over the months Jan and Barry helped her become fluent in Polish and she went on to broadcast to the Poles in their native tongue on the BBC. In recognition of her selfless charitable work she was unofficially accepted into the Polish army, allowed to wear their insignia and work directly under the Polish Ministry of Defence.

For the Poles, life became a mixture of long periods of intensive training and short periods of leave, much of which Jan spent in London with Barry. On these trips Jerzy often accompanied him and they both grew to know and admire the Londoners, with their chirpy sense of humour, their resilient community spirit and the warmth of the welcome they extended to the visitors. It was on one such trip that they were invited to a wedding, that of a Polish spitfire pilot and his English fiancée who worked as a typist at his airfield just outside London. Jan and Barry were in uniform and, not unnaturally, the pilot made a beeline for them during the reception at an East End pub. He was already well under the influence as he introduced himself, "Well, I didn't expect to see two of my fellow countryman from the army here, I thought it would just be us Brylcreem boys but you are most welcome. Have you heard the latest about General Anders?"

"We know that Sikorski and Churchill are trying to get the rest of his army out of Russia, but Stalin is making problems because he says they are cowards having refused to fight with the Red Army on the eastern front," replied Barry who followed events just as closely as Jan.

The pilot frowned as he listened to Barry's accent but held back from commenting and added, "We were told yesterday that a second large contingent has left Russia and they're also going to the Middle East on the pretext of releasing more Soviet divisions on occupation duty alongside the English in Iran and Iraq. Apparently the Russians can't or won't equip our men, but Churchill will and he wants them deployed in the west. The diplomat who told us said that there could be a total of a hundred thousand men coming out of Russia. What a day for Poland! Come on, let me introduce you both to my wife and we can drink a toast to her, another to you, one to Poland and another to Anders' army."

Jan looked at the pilot with a very serious expression and replied, "I'd be proud to drink to your wife and the others but only on condition that I propose a toast afterwards." The pilot agreed, but despite his euphoric state he was a little concerned as to what this young man and his strange speaking friend might have in mind. As it turned out he had no cause for alarm because the toast proposed by Jan was, "To the beautiful bride, the Royal Air Force, The King, Anders' army, Maczek's Army, the allied victory and last but certainly not least, a free Poland." To the pilot's surprise every single one of the wedding party repeated word perfect what must have been a contender for the longest toast ever and immediately afterwards burst into spontaneous applause. Jan was left wondering whether this was a true reflection of how the British felt towards the Poles in general or whether they were making the most of an ideal opportunity to show their appreciation and admiration for the outstanding performance of the Polish pilots during the Battle of Britain. He decided that in either case the sentiments were heartfelt and, despite the hardships, he was glad he had been given the opportunity to live and work alongside such hospitable and honourable working-class people.

As the evening progressed Jan also spent time talking to the Groom's colleagues and soon learnt that the pilot was to be awarded a medal by the RAF for his bravery in a recent dog-fight over France where, despite a severely damaged plane, he disregarded his own safety and continued to engage the enemy until forcefully and repeatedly ordered to break off by his Polish commander. Jan was told that now that the Poles had their own squadrons with their own officers they were more inclined to obey orders; in stark contrast to when they flew in English squadrons and blatantly disregarded any instructions which in any way prevented them from attacking the enemy at each and every opportunity. The groom himself

148

had, during the Battle of Britain, whilst in an English squadron stationed at Middle Wallop in Hampshire, been threatened with Court Martial when he had deliberately disobeyed standing orders and the verbal commands of his superiors when alongside another equally reckless Polish pilot he had taken off in thick fog to engage German bombers who were attacking their base. Once above the fog they had successfully closed with the enemy, shot down one aircraft and drove off the rest.

Having listened to the account given in such a matter-of-fact manner without any bragging or grandiose embellishment, Jan felt very proud of his countrymen but this was tempered with a great sense of sadness that so many similar young men were losing their lives so far from home. He understood that they were not by nature disrespectful or insubordinate men, but were driven to ignore certain commands by a deep hatred of the Nazi regime and in England the Luftwaffe were the only visible and confrontational representation of all that had been done to destroy their country and murder its people. They could not in all honour turn down any opportunity, no matter what the risk, to use their training and their skills to attack, again and again and again.

The following year Jan's division was reorganised as more and more recruits joined and Jan's whole company was transferred to bolster up a new unit, the 8th rifle battalion of the 3rd Rifle Brigade and with new comrades, under the command of Lt. Colonel Aleksander Nowaczyski, they began major combat manoeuvres in Scotland. All sorts of rumours about their own deployment circulated throughout the camp and there was great celebration when it was confirmed that the Polish 2nd Corps (Anders' army) was to become an independent part of the British Eighth Army. Although significant components of the Free Polish forces had fought with distinction in France, in Egypt, at Narvik in Norway, and at Tobruk, many had been waiting in England and Scotland since Dunkirk when, along with their British and French allies, some thirty-five thousand Poles were evacuated from all over France. In fact many Polish units unable to reach Dunkirk fought their way out to other French ports as French units alongside them were surrendering or suddenly becoming civilians again! Churchill sent ships to collect them and on their arrival in England he was delighted to discover that, despite their frantic and often solitary rearguard actions, most of them had managed to escape in good order with their weapons and equipment intact.

Jan and his colleagues felt that, at last, the complete army in exile was going to be used as a major front-line force in the fight against the Germans. They now, for the first time, had good reason to believe that they would soon get their chance to throw the Nazis out of Poland. It was this objective that had sustained and motivated them all for years and finally it was much more than a distant or forlorn hope. They went about their training with a renewed vigour and purpose.

EIGHT

Escape to Judgment
8th November 1942

Jozef, shivering from the cold, sat on the floor in the secrecy of darkness and in whispered tones conspired with his friend Zenon the Kapo, who had proudly served in the 18th Lancers (18th Pomeranian Uhlans Regiment) under the famous Colonel Mastalerz. Zenon was with the two squadrons of cavalry led by Commander Swiesciak when they charged an exposed German infantry battalion in a Tuchola forest clearing in the Polish Corridor on the first day of the war. The terrain through which the Germans were pouring tens of thousands of men and columns of armour support consisted of dense spruce and pine woodland and tracts of ancient yews and broadleaf trees, one of the largest and most beautiful forests in central Europe, interspersed with peat bogs, small hills, glades, narrow roads and almost a thousand lakes.

The Poles had caught the enemy infantry unawares, as they swept out of the woods, and totally overwhelmed them with hardly any casualties on their own side. As the Germans scattered into the forest the Poles withdrew to reform for another attack when they themselves were suddenly caught in a curtain of 20mm cannon and machine-gun fire from enemy armoured cars, which had been sent to investigate the noise of battle. As the Poles galloped for the cover of a nearby hill the Kapo's horse was shot from under him and Swiesciak and most of the Poles were slaughtered by the unrelenting rate of enemy fire. Mastalerz, waiting with a small reserve, witnessed what was happening from the start and immediately charged into the field of battle in a suicidal attempt to save his subordinate Swiesciak but was almost immediately struck down by the machine-guns. Zenon, who was trapped underneath his horse, was captured and taken prisoner along with the few Polish survivors. The action did nothing to stop the relentless German advance into Poland but slowed down the push through the forest for a day or two and provided an opportunity for the successful withdrawal of two hard-pressed Polish infantry battalions.

The Germans, aware that the early success of Polish lancers charging against their lines and overpowering a whole battalion could embarrass them internationally and boost the defenders' morale, attempted to limit the spread of the news by treating all the captured Poles as political prisoners, suitable for forced labour and extermination and so, like Jozef and his mother, Zenon was one of the first to arrive at Auschwitz. Their action however, was of little value as word inevitably did spread across Poland, was then further embellished, and out of this one early skirmish at the start of the war, grew countless fictional stories of brave and defiant Polish Lancers fearlessly charging into the German lines and putting them all to the sword!

These legends started when the Germans were showing journalists around the battlefield the following day and an Italian press reporter, seeing the dead horses and machine-gunned Poles lying alongside German tanks that had later arrived at the scene, drew his own conclusions. In the interests of a good story he wrote of 'heroic Polish Lancers charging Panzer tanks in a desperate attempt to defend their homes'. At this moment the myth, which is still repeated today, was born. In fact all sides used this particular battle for their own propaganda purposes. To the Poles it was proof of their tenacious fighting spirit and their determination to secure freedom at almost any cost and, once made public, the Germans turned it to their advantage to show the immense superiority of their armaments and the invincibility of their army. The Russians used it later to illustrate the stupidity of the Poles in general and their lack of proper military leadership and tactical awareness in particular.

As political prisoners held in 'protective custody' Zenon and Jozef wore a red triangle of cloth on the left breast of their striped uniform, but this categorisation did not prevent a number being tattooed on their left breast by the Nazi bureaucrats to identify them as cattle not humans (it was only later that the tattoos were placed on the left forearm instead) or having their heads shaved bald. At first they were put to work in one of the factories inside the camp but Zenon was soon 'promoted' to supervisor (Kapo). A rank made up from Poles, Ukrainians, Czechs and many German prisoners; the latter unlike the other national groups included many convicted criminals (who wore a green triangle on their uniform and were particularly feared by the prisoners). The Germans formed the largest category amongst those titled Kapo (which included both Jews and Gentiles). Fair proportions from all categories were sadistic, brutal and hateful just like the SS guards who held the gift of life or death within the concentration camps. The majority were just out for their own ends and would do whatever they were ordered, including informing on, beating and abusing other prisoners, just to maintain their extra food ration and other basic 'privileges'.

A few like Zenon, although trying to prolong their own survival, did whatever they could, within their limited authority, to help their fellow inmates. It made little difference in the end as all, privileged or otherwise, were destined to be murdered eventually; but such small gestures of help proved, that even in such an evil place, it was impossible to eradicate all traces of the human spirit. Nevertheless, every Kapo did things in the camp that would have been unimaginable to them before the war and all, without exception, had blood on their hands. A few were callously indifferent to the torment, some felt shame, guilt and dishonour, others were immune to suffering as they had been desensitised by the repetitive horrors and were themselves bereft of emotion, simply functioning as automatons. They wore a uniform of civilian jacket and trousers and carried a heavy wooden club or a whip and answered to a Senior Kapo who in turn would have them beaten or killed if they were unfortunate enough to earn his displeasure.

So desperate was the situation inside the camp that some women and girls volunteered to work in the camp brothel in Block 24 to avoid death and others were specially selected for this purpose and they considered themselves fortunate. All life hung by a very thin thread indeed but for some the pain and anguish was too much and suicides were common. Many threw themselves against the electrified fence.

Jozef had witnessed the murder of his fellow inmates by beatings, firing squad and hanging and he was aware of the gas chambers and crematoria and had heard rumours of medical experiments being conducted on women by Dr Clauberg to develop a simple injection that could be administered to Slavic races to render them infertile. Zenon had additionally seen the 'standing cells' where prisoners were left for days in a cell so small that they had to be forced inside, crammed in like sardines, and once the door was shut they remained wedged upright, unable to move until released. Many were left to die in this position. He had cleared the bodies out of the 'starvation cells' where prisoners were left without food or water until they were dead. He knew of the 'dark cells', which were virtually devoid of light and airtight, where prisoners were left to suffocate as they used up the oxygen. If it was taking too long the guards would light a candle hidden behind a protective screen inside.

He had helped to bury the victims when the first prisoners were gassed in the basement of Block 11. Eight hundred and fifty Russian and Polish prisoners of war were the subject of the first experiment with Zyklon B, a cyanide based insecticide, in September 1941. Since his capture he had by deed and omission helped maintain the regime of dehumanisation, ethnic cleansing and mass-murder that was being waged predominantly against Europe's Jews but which also significantly targeted other so called 'degenerate' nations and groups.

The two friends had seen the charade of normality, which cloaked every stage of the transportation to death that the Nazis had implemented as their 'final solution'. The victims were told they were being moved (resettled) to a safer place where they could start a new life and they were encouraged to pack their prized and valued possessions. They were told that new schools and housing had been built especially for them and many were shown propaganda films filled with happy and contented Jews working and playing in their new towns and villages surrounded by culture and abundance. Little did they know that all the 'actors' were murdered shortly after their performance; which had also been procured by deception and coercion. Even at the point of extermination the fraudulent pretence of familiarity was upheld. When their personal property was taken from them it was meticulously listed and bagged, giving the impression that it would be returned after they had been deloused and 'showered' and they were each given a neatly folded towel and a bar of soap before they were ordered to strip.

The Nazis feared that if the victims knew that they were being transported to a killing factory they would have become unmanageable. They dreaded the inevitable prospect of demonstrations, revolts and riots at every station and camp and went to extraordinary lengths to maintain the massive subterfuge. Periodically they even kept small batches of prisoners in isolation from the general camp population and made sure they were well clothed, well fed and healthy so they could be inspected by German charities and even the Red Cross. Thousands were told to write postcards home just before they were shot or gassed so that their relatives and the politicians back home would not believe any rumours of their true fate or the terrible conditions of confinement.

Jozef and Zenon had witnessed the relentless development of a technology of accelerated death within their camp. At first the beatings, shootings and hangings were considered by the SS hierarchy to be too slow and conspicuous, the carbon monoxide poisoning in mobile trucks too time consuming and, at only about forty deaths at a time, far too inefficient. Hitler, his henchmen, their scientists, engineers and policy makers then worked ceaselessly to design and implement a system that could quickly and efficiently kill and dispossess millions. They created a vast pan-European industrialised process that dealt only in death and nothing, other than life itself, was wasted. The wholesale art and property theft, the raping of women and girls, the desecration of bodies for gold and hair, the gas chambers, crematoria and human experimentation, including Mengele's torture and murder of twins, were the results of their sick and evil machinations.

Those at the railhead who were spared immediate selection for death fared little better. Even the crime of genocide was in itself not sufficient to slake the thirst for violence that drove the German supremacists. They needed to destroy the very personality, self worth and dignity of every single individual they judged to be 'inferior'. Their victims were therefore deliberately and consistently treated in such a way that it became inevitable that their existence in captivity would directly mirror the Nazis perverted and prejudiced caricature of the typical Jew or other 'sub human' nationality or group. This would, they believed, then justify to the whole German nation their own travesty of an argument that demanded such extreme measures. To this end those unfortunate Jews (and the Poles, Russians and other groups incarcerated alongside them) were kept in pitiful squalor and unsanitary conditions that made them 'filthy, degenerate and diseased'. Being systematically abused and intentionally starved some would understandably steal from the guards, the Kapos and their fellow inmates or inform on others for food, thus becoming 'greedy, disloyal, untrustworthy and dishonest'. The Nazi camp regimes were purposely designed to prove, by repeated illustration and example, this ruinous self-fulfilling prophecy and thereby eliminate any remaining trace of German resistance to the final solution.

Zenon and Jozef, constantly breathing in the haunting, cloying smell of death that rained down from the crematoria chimneys and impregnated the very walls of the barrack huts were also surrounded by mass-starvation, routine torture and the hateful duplicity of this monstrous regime. Living the Holocaust every minute of every day they were all too aware of their own certain and impending fate.

The Kapo had given Jozef his mother's letter with her instructions the day after she was murdered. Although he had managed to save them both from the gas chambers for over a year by allocating them to special work details, he knew the time would come when his own health would deteriorate to such an extent that he too would become of little use to the SS guards. In fact his little influence was already deserting him and he had been unable to prevent Ewa from being 'selected'.

As the bitter chill of Auschwitz crept deep into their bones Jozef implored Zenon, "We can't leave it any longer, both of us could be put on the list tomorrow and we certainly won't make it through another winter, we've got to go now or it will be too late."

"We're not ready yet. The plan isn't finalised and we have to wait until there are some SS visitors that the guards won't recognise. If we try to go out now it will be suicide. After all we've been through I don't want to be caught and brought back here to be beaten, humiliated and then strung up in front of the whole camp. I'd rather come back dead and be put in the seat." Those who were killed trying to escape were exhibited on a chair at the main gate and left there to rot holding a malicious sign saying 'Here I am' as a warning to the rest. Anyone captured alive was hung in front of the paraded prisoners. "So be patient for just a bit longer and then we'll have the best chance of success. The top brass always bring an entourage of hangers-on and that will provide us with the opportunity we need."

Jozef pulled his worn blanket tighter around his shoulders and tucked his legs underneath in an effort to retain as much body heat as he could and asked, "I know you'll have to drive but your poor German creates a major problem. The guards will automatically speak to the driver and you wouldn't last five seconds with your accent and lack of vocabulary. I've had an idea for how we can deal with it, so I'm going to teach you a few critical words and you're going to practise and practise until you say them in perfect and arrogant German. Repeat after me, *I am only the driver and I have been instructed never to speak unless the colonel orders me to do so.*"

The Kapo started to practise this one sentence and Jozef cringed at the dreadful result, gave him a few pointers and then the whole process was repeated over and over again before Jozef asked, "Have you decided which vehicle you're going to take?"

"The Commandant's of course, because no one would dream of stopping us in that and if we're going to get out of this hellhole we deserve to do it in style and can you imagine the commotion when it's discovered? It will be a full scale witch-hunt and I wouldn't be surprised if one or two of the mighty SS are singled out and shot," replied Zenon with a wide grin.

Jozef suspected that his friend was joking but he could never really be sure as he found his idiosyncratic and perverse sense of humour difficult to fathom. In fact he couldn't understand how anyone could retain even a vestige of amusement in such a cruel and evil place. "Surely it would be madness to take his staff car, he's the only man that every guard would instantly recognise and we would be discovered before we even reached the gates?"

"Yes, you're probably right. Perhaps I'll take one of the pool cars that are used by all the support personnel. They're always in and out and we can pretend that we're members of the visiting party going for a tour of the locality, you know - trying to get a flavour of how the locals are coping now that they're protected by the benevolent Reich," said Zenon before he set out on another rehearsal of his German lines.

As he listened and again winced at the dreadful pronunciation, Jozef was still undecided whether or not the Kapo was having him on about the Commandant's car but decided to press on in an effort to finalise their plan, "What about the uniforms, is everything set?"

"They're still there and have been since I finished them a week ago. I don't think that's going to be a problem and neither is the vehicle so don't worry about that, but as I said, everything hinges on visitors arriving soon," replied Zenon before yet again practising his German phrase.

Prior to joining the army Zenon, like his father before him, was a tailor by trade and because such skills were much in demand in the camp he was moved out of the factory fairly early on and appointed as the Kapo in the stores where the prisoners' flimsy uniforms were made and the clothes of the dead were recycled. Twelve months ago when the Staff tailor had been sent to face the firing squad at 'the wall of death' for stealing gold braid and silver buttons, he had been 'promoted' again and in consequence was now also required to alter and repair many of the guards' uniforms. Zenon had then used his influence to arrange for Jozef to be moved from the factory and appointed to a less physically demanding job as a messenger where, amongst his varied duties, he was responsible for delivering parts and supplies from the warehouse to the workshop where the camp's vehicles, including the staff cars, were kept and maintained.

On his visits Jozef noticed that some of the mechanics were prisoners and in the course of speaking to them he had watched as vehicles were delivered and collected. He noticed that whenever a vehicle was collected by a driver or N.C.O. they had to sign for it and hand over some sort of requisition docket that was checked against a record held by the workshop supervisor. He remembered thinking at the time that it was yet another example of the bureaucratic German mentality, but was surprised when the first vehicle to be collected by an officer was simply handed over without any checks whatsoever. He watched several more such transactions just to make sure it wasn't a mistake or oversight but the same pattern emerged: any senior officer who asked was simply given the key to the next available staff car. This had given them the foundation of their escape plan and they had been plotting ever since.

Over the weeks Zenon had been able to make copies of an SS senior officer's badges and insignia and he had also managed to steal two basic uniforms, an item at a time. From these he had completed a Standartenfuhrer's (Colonel's) together with SD insignia and a Scharfuhrer's (Sergeant's) complete dress that, although not perfect, would pass a cursory inspection.

It was a week later when a group of senior civilians, SS officers and their Aides arrived at the camp by train and were escorted to the Commandant's block. They then embarked on a tour of the camp, which always included a specially arranged mass-gassing. The visitors would watch through a special window in the gas chamber door as the victims inside choked and died. Jozef and the Kapo waited until the VIPs all disappeared back inside to enjoy their lunch with the camp's senior officers. They knew from camp gossip that it would be a wine fuelled, leisurely and sumptuous meal and this gave them their ideal opportunity to act. They quickly recovered the uniforms from the hiding place in the cloth storeroom and dressed up as the enemy. As they admired each other's new appearance it was clear, that because of their considerable weight loss, the uniforms would need filling out if they were to look realistic. They each donned several prisoners' uniforms underneath, adding extra padding with each layer, and having achieved the desired result walked together out into the compound. They made straight for the garage building and Jozef whispered in Polish, "Remember, I'm the Colonel and leave all the talking to me." Although Jozef was only twenty-years-old the rigours of the last three years had taken their toll and he would pass for ten years older, too young for a Colonel probably but they had no choice as he spoke German like a native.

They approached the supervisor and although Jozef was frightened he had decided that he would not show any apprehension whatever happened. He knew he would not get another chance and he firmly believed that God had a purpose for him and it was not to die in such a heathen place. "I need a car immediately for urgent business on the Commandant's behalf and I have to report back this evening so there's no time to lose." Jozef was pleased with his effort, which was forceful and urgent without being rude or overstated.

"Certainly Colonel, as you wish," replied the supervisor as he took a key from the hooks on the office wall and handed it over to Zenon. "It's the one parked on the left and it's just been washed and refuelled."

They drove away towards the main gates with an SS car but no weapons or papers of any sort and they both realised that it was far too late to turn back. Zenon looked across at his Colonel and said, "Within the next five minutes we will either be free or we will be dead, so you make sure you give the best performance of your young life."

"Well, my friend, if I'm going to God today I'm glad it's in your company and it's not going to happen until I have thanked you for all you have done for mother and me. In spite of the terrible circumstances we've had to endure it's been a privilege to know you and it would even be an honour to die with you, but let's try to put it off for another fifty years or so and whatever you do please don't forget your German. Everything hinges on it," added Jozef as he nervously and repeatedly brushed his hand across the front of his uniform tunic trying to remove phantom specks of fluff.

As they approached the barrier at the gates, one of the guards stepped forward and signalled them to stop and Zenon smoothly slowed down allowing the guard to approach the vehicle, as they had suspected, on the driver's side. "Who are you and where are you going?" asked the guard as Zenon wound down the window.

The Kapo looked straight at the guard and in an even tone replied, "I'm only the driver and I have been instructed never to speak unless the Colonel orders me to do so." His German was passable and showed that he had practised until the words flowed naturally.

The guard was somewhat taken aback by the reply and looked across at the Colonel and explained, "I'm sorry Sir, but we must always enter these full details on the gate log. Perhaps if you show me your papers I can take what I need from them."

The Colonel immediately responded, "Let me explain and listen very carefully because I am not in the habit of repeating myself. I expect instant obedience and complete security from everyone who works for me. None of my staff are permitted to speak of my work, my plans or my schedule without express permission. Any fraternisation with those outside my inner circle is completely forbidden under pain of death. That should tell you how important and secret my work is, now open that gate before I am forced to take your name for causing unnecessary delay to the Fuhrer's personal representative. By his direct order I am The Officer in Command of The Inspectorate of Compliance and Loyalty of the Sicherheitsdienst (Security Agency) and I am charged to report on any and all acts of obstruction, interference or perfidy. You have my permission to enter that, word for word, in your precious log. You will not be told who I am or given details of my mission. Your job is to obey me without question and to open that gate - now." As he spoke Jozef kept looking straight ahead as though he had already dismissed this interference and he gradually raised his voice until the last few words were almost shouted.

Another guard, curious as to what was happening, started to walk forward and the Colonel then shouted, "That's enough - How much more of this blatant disrespect and hindrance am I expected to take? Heads will roll and yours will be the first!" and he then reached into his top pocket. As he did so the first guard, realising his name was about to be taken, needed no further incentive to step back, come to attention and salute, "Heil Hitler."

Jozef slowly raised his right hand in more of a wave of dismissal than a formal response and the driver, sensing the moment of opportunity, started to pull forward. Two of the remaining guards saluted whilst the one who had moved towards them waved them on through the barrier and out the gates past the electrified fence and the watchtowers with their searchlights and machine guns. The chastened guard looked across at his colleagues and spat towards the receding car and said, "What an arrogant, pretentious asshole. What's it coming to when we're bossed around and treated like shit by his sort. I bet he's never even seen any action." His colleagues didn't reply: they had learnt to keep their opinions to themselves.

They were free! Like royalty on a visit to the shires they swept unhindered across the railway track and onto the main road and Zenon went through the gears as the powerful car rapidly picked up speed. Jozef had never experienced such a feeling of exhilaration as the adrenaline pumped through his veins and all sense of fear was temporarily masked. The Kapo was already thinking of what to do next because what happened once they were outside the gates had never figured in their detailed planning. They had superstitiously felt that to be definitive or even prioritise their choices once they were outside would be to assume success and tempt fate, thus inviting certain disaster whilst still within the camp. In any case the car and uniforms opened up all the options and they could now make all their decisions based on the circumstances at the time. As he looked down at the control panel he exclaimed, "Can you believe it, they've actually filled the tank right up for us. What do you think we should do now, stay with the car for as long as we can or dump it and get some civilian clothes?"

"We should try and get as far away as we can while we have the protection of the uniforms, it may well be that they won't miss us for hours yet, probably not until roll-call tonight. I've got a letter to deliver so I think we should make straight for Warsaw, so let's get as close as we can before we have to dump the car. If we're caught we'll be executed anyway so having the vehicle won't make a scrap of difference on that account, but the further we get the less likely that the local troops and police will be actively looking for it," replied Jozef as he settled down in his seat and began to examine his mental map of Poland, already contemplating the alternatives.

"Warsaw it is then. Once there I intend to join the underground, tell them what's going on in these camps and get some revenge on the bastards. It's our turn now and they can have some of their own medicine," said the Kapo with an uncharacteristic vehemence and finality.

Jozef, although deeply religious, had mentally arrived at a similar position and he now believed that his faith had in fact been strengthened by his experiences in the camp. It was not therefore with any sense of regret that he said, "You won't hear any argument from me, we have to fight back and I would even go as far as to say that God expects us to. Hitler's regime is a grotesque affront to all of us and I owe it to my mother, and all the others who have perished simply because they were considered inferior, to stand up and do my bit to confront this brutality and hate. I'll be glad to join you and anyone else who believes it's better to die fighting than to be shipped off to your death in places like Auschwitz."

Zenon looked across and frowned, "That's a fine flowery speech for such a youngster and although many Poles might agree with you I think you've forgotten that you're in the presence of a highly trained, ruthless and disciplined SS soldier!" and in his best mock German, "I will now have you shot!"

They both burst into laughter and through his hysteria Zenon managed to add, "We did it, we got out and not only that, we made them look like fools and incompetents in the process, but please no more moral rhetoric."

They drove on in silence and passed several military convoys but they were not challenged, on the contrary, most vehicles moved off to the side to let them through. They made it safely through the towns of Trzebinia, Sosnowiec and Dabrowa Gornicza but as they approached Czestochowa darkness was closing in and they decided to go to ground overnight and found a barn in which to hide the car. They took the opportunity to thoroughly search the vehicle and, attached to metal clips in the boot, they found a heavy-duty army issue torch with flat batteries, a small tool-kit and the spare wheel but no extra fuel, not even an empty petrol can. The glove compartment and various pockets in the interior revealed nothing and so they took the largest screwdriver with them as some sort of protection and decided to turn in. Though it was cold they both quickly fell asleep and had the best nights rest since they had been taken prisoner. When Jozef awoke at about 6.30am he was surprised to find that his freedom was a firm reality and not the fleeting, illusionary kind, of which he had so frequently dreamed whilst in captivity. After smashing the ice on the horse trough in the field alongside the barn they cleaned themselves up as best they could and were back on the road within the hour. About ten miles short of Radomsko on the river bridge they were stopped at a mobile checkpoint manned by two military police officers with a motorcycle and sidecar.

They pulled in behind a horse and cart and as they waited Jozef said, "I'll deal with this," and got out of the car strutting forwards with a swagger that Zenon thought too exaggerated. As he watched from the driver's seat, with the engine running, he heard Jozef raise his voice and start to gesticulate towards Radomsko. Zenon couldn't understand a word that was being said but he could see that one of the officers was becoming very red in the face and was pointing towards the motorcycle combination.

Just as the Kapo was beginning to worry the Colonel turned

smartly, walked back and climbed back in. As he sat down he said, "Just follow them, they'll provide an escort through Radomsko and see us safely onto the Lodz road that joins the main Warsaw highway about ten miles further on. I told them that we had been held up by local traffic and that before we left this morning we had received a report that saboteurs were active in the town area and I am carrying a vital dispatch that must get through at all costs. I told them I was authorised to commandeer any resources I deemed necessary and, for the next fifteen miles or so, that meant them."

"Why take such a risk?"

"It seemed the ideal solution at the time but you're right, there is a problem. One of them said that the motorcycle offered little protection but he could arrange a proper armoured escort from their base and I think he became suspicious when I turned his offer down by saying that my mission wasn't to be advertised to everyone but only revealed to those I chose as suitable. I may have temporarily assuaged his fears but we shouldn't take any more chances, so once they leave us we'll dump the car and find some civilian clothes."

As they drove through the town with the motorcycle police clearing the way, Zenon, still feeling very uneasy, reached a decision, glanced across at the Colonel and said, "We can't afford to let them tell their base about us, you know we were lucky at the checkpoint as they don't have a radio or field telephone, but our luck won't hold forever. We're going to get rid of them and hide the motorcycle and sidecar. We also need their weapons so when we clear the town I'll pull over and we'll kill them. The SS have probably missed the car by now but they'll probably assume that we've dumped it and might not be looking for us this far north, but if these two report back they are bound to make the connection."

The colour drained from Jozef's face and he admitted, "I don't think I can do that. I know I was feeling and acting tough during the excitement yesterday but this morning things seem so different. I'm not sure I could kill anybody in cold blood and these two aren't the same as those monsters back at the camp."

Zenon responded immediately but in a sympathetic voice, "Look Jozef, you've got to listen to me. Back in the camp you did what you had to do to survive and it's no different now. You have never acted before but yesterday your performance was superb, well, I'm afraid that today is no different and if you don't help me, make no mistake, we will both die. You have no choice my friend. If it could be done any other way then I would be the first to sign up to it." They then talked through a plan and Jozef silently prayed that he would have the mental strength and physical courage to complete his task.

Once they were back in the countryside Zenon flashed his headlights at the motorcycle ahead and pulled off the road onto the wide verge. He took another look around to make sure that the coast was clear and then they both got out and Jozef went around to the boot of the car. The military policemen, having turned the motorcycle around, pulled in front of the car as Jozef opened the boot lid and called out, "You can leave us now and return to your duties, but I have letters of commendation here for you both and a sealed note of gratitude for your commanding officer's attention. I appreciate efficient and prompt assistance and so it is my custom to reward unquestioned obedience, I just need to fill in your details on these papers so could you please step forward one at a time."

As he spoke the motorcyclists had moved to the front of the car and as the rider took off his helmet and walked along the side of the car towards Jozef, Zenon sidled up to the passenger and stood on his left side smiling in a reassuring manner. As the rider approached, Jozef took a deep breath and said, "Could you take my case from the boot? " and as the soldier turned the corner and looked down into the empty compartment Jozef hit him across the side of the head with the metal torch. He deliberately aimed the blow just above the right ear using every ounce of strength that he could muster. Without even a groan the soldier slumped to the floor and Jozef hit him again on the back of the head with such force that the torch bent almost double and was forced from his grasp.

Both Zenon and the second military police officer heard the first impact and the sound of the man falling and the police officer immediately realised something was seriously wrong and he turned towards Zenon searching for a logical explanation, but was sufficiently alarmed to be reaching for the safety catch on the sub-machine-gun strapped across his chest. Zenon was quick to react, took a half step to his right and stabbed him with the screwdriver he had hidden up his sleeve, right handed in the left side just under the ribs. He used immense force to ensure that it penetrated the gabardine coat and uniform jacket and with some relief he felt blood spurt over his hand and body as the blade of the makeshift weapon went to the hilt as he drove it upwards towards the heart. Even so, the soldier was still struggling and screaming in pain as Zenon released his grip on the screwdriver and pulled the strap from the machine-gun tight around his enemy's throat and slowly lowered him to the ground, strangling and silencing him as he did so. Once he was obviously dead Zenon took the Lugar pistol from his belt and ran to the rear of the car.

He found Jozef in a daze, standing over the rider who was on the ground with a pool of blood quickly spreading from his shattered skull. Zenon shook his friend by the shoulders and stared directly into his eyes to get his full attention, "Come on Jozef, snap out of it, we've got to get this mess cleaned up before someone else comes along. I know it's hard but you must accept that it really is us or them and this has only just started. I can't promise it will get any easier but you're a soldier now and kill we must."

"Just give me a minute, please! I'll do what I have to but I feel sick at heart just thinking about what I've already become."

They threw the bodies into the ditch and covered them with clods of earth and grass, branches from the nearby copse and finally a thick layer of leaves from the carpet along both sides of the road. They drove the car off the road into the copse and then pushed the motorcycle even deeper in and made a not altogether successful effort to hide it with branches, but they were satisfied that it could not be easily seen from the road. A search of the combination had revealed several maps of the area, a first-aid kit, a full water bottle and some bread and cheese, which they immediately consumed with gusto. A search of the bodies had provided a watch each, two sets of identification documents, photographs, paper and pencils, a small quantity of German coins and notes, plus the weaponry. They took a map, the watches, the money, a pistol each and the sub machine gun, together with three clips of spare ammunition. Zenon showed Jozef how the guns worked, gave him a quick rundown on weapon safety and allowed him to dry-fire the pistol. They could not afford to stay any longer and so returned to the car and drove off towards Lodz.

Jozef was quiet as they drove and his friend suspected that he was in shock and trying to come to terms with what he had done. Zenon knew from his own experience that the killing and the guilt

166

would not get any easier, but he would come to accept its necessity at a time when normal morality was turned on its head. He decided to engage Jozef in the problem that had been troubling him since he had studied the German maps. "As you said before, if we stay with the car for much longer we're bound to run into trouble so I suggest that we should quickly put some distance between us and the motorcycle. When they discover what has happened there they'll probably assume that we're making for Warsaw where it's easier to hide out and hopefully they will concentrate their search for the car on the routes into the capital. I think we would increase our chances of evading them if we carry on towards Lodz and then ditch the car somewhere just south of the city. In any case we haven't enough petrol to get to Warsaw because it's drinking the stuff. By my reckoning we've only travelled about a hundred miles and have already used well over half a tank."

Jozef looked across, sighed deeply and said, "I agree that the car is bound to become a liability but it's hard to decide at what point we're definitely better off without it. Once we start walking we'll be taking on a whole new set of problems and dangers and they're going to be just as real as now, but we won't have the element of surprise that these uniforms and the car have given us. What we really need is some local help from the underground, especially when we try to get into Warsaw."

They discussed the matter further as they headed north and when the military traffic became thicker, and they were stuck in the middle of a convoy of about twenty army trucks, they found themselves approaching another checkpoint. They could see a group of at least ten soldiers manning the post about half a mile ahead on a sharp bend at the bottom of the valley and they feared the worse as they had nowhere to go because the convoy had now reduced speed and closed up. Much to their surprise the leading vehicles, now just crawling along, were not stopped but waved through as was the whole convoy, including their own car. As they cleared the bend and breathed a huge sigh of relief, they looked at one another knowing full well that the time had now come to get rid of the car. The map showed they were six miles south of the city when they signalled and pulled off the road, allowing the rest of the convoy to pass on by. They followed on slowly and after about half a mile found a track, alongside a small stream, leading into a wood. When the road was clear in both directions they drove down the track and after a few hundred yards on a sharp left hand bend they found another track leading further uphill into a large area of pine forest.

They drove the car as far as they could and finally abandoned it when it became firmly stuck in the deep muddy ruts of the track. As they carried on up the track on foot the car was soon lost from sight and they were satisfied that it would not be easily or quickly found. They agreed that their priority now was to avoid the military, find civilian clothes and make contact with the underground, but they were both conscious of the considerable risks in attempting the latter, despite the fact that they were now armed.

They walked for about three miles before they came to the edge of the forest where they settled down in the tree line to take a long look at what lay ahead. They were at the top of a small escarpment that fell away into a valley about two miles east of Lodz and they saw the Warsaw road spread out below them like a ribbon threading its way north-east. About half way down the slope on their right, nestled in a small sheltered depression was a farm with several outbuildings and a few livestock wandering in the yard. They worked their way east along the tree line until they were directly above the farm and again they settled down to watch. For the next two hours they saw nothing other than a middle-aged woman who left the farmhouse, milked the single cow and fed the rest of the animals before returning indoors. Once the first signs of darkness began to fall the Kapo decided it was time to make a move and he stood up, put his weapons on the ground, ripped off the insignia on his uniform and turned to Jozef, "I'll go down alone and see what I can find out, you stay here and don't approach unless I signal you, then come on down and bring the weapons."

Jozef did not relish being left alone and asked, "How long do you think you're going to be?"

"Not too long, this is normally a very loyal part of the country and they may well help us or tell us of someone who will. If they can't, I'll try to arrange for us to sleep in an outbuilding and then we can come back to the tree line in the morning and keep working east until we find someone who will help. All you have to do is stay here, keep alert and ensure that no one can approach the buildings and surprise me," replied Zenon who then set off down the slope.

168

Jozef settled down once more and watched as his friend disappeared into the dip and it wasn't long before his mind was drifting back to his happy childhood before the war. Then slowly and chronologically he remembered how it had all remorselessly fallen apart, how one disaster led straight to another until nothing remained under his control. He relived everything that had happened since and he was puzzled as to why he had survived when so many others, who were stronger, more gifted and far more deserving, had perished. He felt guilty and unworthy and thought that even if God had spared him for some purpose, he was poorly prepared for it and such a challenge gave him absolutely no satisfaction or solace. The more he pondered on events the more melancholy and pessimistic he became until sometime later he finally came back to the present and was left with a vivid and painful realisation of how desperately he missed his parents, his sister and his younger brothers. About an hour later, just as he was beginning to think about ignoring Zenon's instructions and moving down to the farm anyway, he heard the Kapo's loud whistle from below. He moved carefully downhill and, having to fully concentrate on his footing, his thoughts refocused and he started to hope that his mood would improve greatly if only they were able to eat a proper meal and rest for the night.

Inside he was introduced to the woman he had seen earlier and her father, a frail and arthritic semi-invalid who found it difficult to stand, let alone walk. His daughter, Krystyna was much younger than he had first thought, probably in her late thirties and she had already explained to Zenon that her husband was missing after being called up in August 1939. When she last heard from him, a few days before the war started, he was stationed just outside Krakow. As they sat down Krystyna laid out a meal of bread, dried fruit, pickles and salted pork and invited them to eat, "I'm afraid that it's not much but you're welcome to share what we can spare from the cellar and you must tell us what's going on in the rest of Europe because we hear so very little from our few visitors."

Zenon thanked them both and then updated Jozef with all that their hosts had already told him explaining that the underground seemed to be well organised in the area and Krystyna could get a message to them via her neighbour. She suspected he was actively involved as a messenger because he had the necessary German travel documents to deliver logs and charcoal around the whole area. He had become a familiar figure to the troops who manned the local checkpoints and was known by sight to most of the local Garrison because he was also allowed to make frequent trips into the city to deliver fuel to the German Officers billeted there. Krystyna was prepared to see him the next day but she insisted that once they had eaten they would have to hide in a disused stable and keep out of sight during the day. Jozef told her why he knew so little of the wider war and then asked, "How often do you see any Germans up here or in this area generally?"

She finally sat down herself after carrying a tray to her father's chair and replied, "They've only been to the farm three times since the war started. Twice it was just normal soldiers, checking who lived where and for how long, just throwing their weight about and seeing if we had anything worth stealing, but about three months ago their police came. They searched the place from top to bottom, checked our names against a list and asked us questions about our relatives and friends. They asked us who the local Jews were but we only knew one family along the valley and they moved out last year. They said they were looking for weapons and fugitives and threatened to come back if they found out that we had lied. They haven't been back to the farm since but I've seen the odd patrol travelling back and forwards along the valley road. Their nearest camp is about three miles to the north but they seem to spend most of their time inside the city."

Once they had eaten she took them to the stable where she raked away several inches of straw and leaves from the floor revealing a wooden trap door. "It's where we used to store and over-winter the beet and other root crops for the animals but we haven't used it at all this year since nearly all of them have now been slaughtered. I'm afraid it's very damp and uncomfortable down there but if you keep quiet and stay put you should be safe. I'll bring you some more food tomorrow."

Throughout the night they took it in turns to stay awake and listen out. Although it was claustrophobic and pitch black inside their small underground lair it was reasonably warm, free of vermin and deathly quiet. Despite this Jozef could not sleep or even relax as he felt trapped, blind, jittery and very vulnerable. He worried about betrayal and discovery and the longer he thought about

170

it the more real this possibility became. As the endless minutes ticked by ever more slowly it seemed to him that even time itself was taunting and deceiving him and he became totally fixated on capture: after all, he had seen so much treachery in the camp. He sat there sweating in the darkness as his imagination ran riot and he even visualised Krystyna leading the Germans straight to them and smiling as she pointed out the trap door and asked for her payment. She said nothing and showed no emotion as they were dragged out, beaten with rifle butts, forced up against the barn wall and then shot. As he breathed his last breath the image that burned into his now sightless eyes was that of Krystyna smiling with delight as she counted out her money.

He screwed his eyes shut tight and breathed in deeply to try to clear his mind and shake off the lingering images but new, equally irrational and frightening thoughts came rushing in and caused instant panic. He couldn't stay where he was: he had just breathed in the last vestige of oxygen and now he was suffocating. He had to get out of the hole. He needed light and fresh air or he really was going to die. He moved towards the trap door but Zenon was blocking his way and with a vice like grip pulled him back down into a bear hug and held him close, whispering reassurances until he regained control and started breathing normally.

He was tortured with similar, though less graphic, thoughts all through the next day and his fear was again heightened when Krystyna did not show up with the promised food. He told Zenon how he was feeling and added, "We've got to get out of here and put some distance between us and this farm before it's too late: she could be leading them here right now!"

His friend had no such concerns, "Just calm down, there will be a good reason why she couldn't bring the food and I'm certain that she's a nationalist and won't betray us. I spent a long time talking to her and I know beyond any doubt that she's reliable. Trust me and not your imagination. You've been through a great deal but you're not a trained soldier and because of the recent stress and the years of trauma your mind is playing tricks on you. Being stuck in this hole for so long you've had time to dwell on our predicament and worry yourself sick. I'm convinced that all we have to do is sit tight and wait for the underground to contact us. Just keep it together for a little while longer."

Jozef trusted his friend's judgement and, although he tried to rationalise his fear, he was still left with a nagging doubt and he was mightily relieved when, at about ten in the evening, Krystyna quietly announced the arrival of the underground and then opened the trap door. Two armed men in their twenties were introduced as 'local fighters' and no names were used. Krystyna explained that she had been at her neighbour's house awaiting contact since dawn and was not allowed to return home until the escort had arrived that evening. They thanked her profusely and Jozef felt ashamed and disloyal because he had doubted her integrity so easily. Once she had left, the visitors took possession of their captured weapons and ammunition and then all four of them sat on the stable floor and Zenon told their story in great detail: neither of the partisans interrupted at any stage. When he finished they both asked many questions about the camp, the mass-murders, and the organisation and deployment of the SS guards. It was almost midnight when seemingly satisfied they led the way out eastwards, along the escarpment ridge.

Their guides were obviously familiar with the area as they moved sure-footedly and quickly across ground that frequently caused the escapees to stumble and trip despite their total concentration. About two hours later they came to a small village and were guided over a very large and boggy patch of waste ground and then through back gardens until they entered a small house through a guarded side door.

They were held in a room by an armed guard whilst their escorts disappeared and after about two hours they were taken, through more back gardens and a small orchard, into another house where they were greeted by the local commander of the Home Army. His physical appearance surprised Jozef, as it did not fit with his preconceived stereotype of a young Herculean-type freedom fighter. He was about 45 years old, of very small build and only about five feet six inches tall with grey black hair, piercing blue eyes, a grey goatee beard and a surprisingly deep gravelly voice. "I'm satisfied with your credentials and we'll now get you some suitable civilian clothes so that your weapons and uniforms can be put to good use against our enemies. We already had a pretty good idea of what was going on at the camps from our own intelligence network and local 'watchers'. You must admit it's hard to believe, but now your horrific personal testimony has finally put paid to any lingering doubts and confirms our worse fears. Unfortunately such places exist all over the country and knowing how the Nazis like to export their domination, probably all over occupied Europe as well. We'll get you to the capital where our envoys can take your story to the west, if nothing else it should ensure that they continue to provide us with ammunition, weapons and explosives, as miserly as they are. I know you've suffered a great deal but you're safe here so get some rest and build up your strength. It will probably take a few days to get the necessary papers prepared, so please be patient and in the meantime I'll get a message to Warsaw so that they'll be expecting you."

It was a week later when they eventually left, dressed and properly documented as railway employees and escorted by an engine driver to Lodz station. He explained that the Germans had claimed the city as a part of the Reich and that the Poles were being systematically deported and replaced by German families. Only those in 'essential' occupations or those needed to train their German replacements were being retained and it was becoming increasingly difficult for the resistance to operate anywhere inside the urban area. They helped load a train bound for the capital with huge bundles of cloth from the local mills and only four hours later, after unloading at the other end, the same driver escorted them out of the station yards at Warsaw to a pre-arranged rendezvous.

Over the next three days they were both debriefed separately by an intelligence officer from the Home Army, written statements were taken and they were also given a full medical examination. Their photographs were taken, they were given new identities, found lodgings and set to work for the organisation. At first they were only employed to carry messages, deal with low-level intelligence work and smuggle food and supplies across the city. Over the weeks they learnt to safely find their way about above ground, and also became more familiar with the network of tunnels and sewers used to secretly criss-cross the city. They were both amazed at the level of organisation, sophistication and discipline within the Home Army and surprised at how well armed the small fighting units were. As with any professional army they had their Operational Units and Headquarters and Divisional Commands with Support Units that included Intelligence, Propaganda, Publishing,

Communications, Medical and Engineering. They also brought themselves up to date with the progress of the war by listening to radio broadcasts from the BBC in London and reading the Home Army's own Daily Bulletin Sheet (which in addition to general news also included details of promotions, acts of bravery and punishments and sentences issued). They also attended briefings from senior officers and returning couriers, who regularly travelled to London to liaise with the Government in Exile.

As time passed by they were progressively given more responsibility and Zenon, because of his experience, became heavily involved in the training of the large number of recruits that ranged in age from ten to sixty. The Germans, by attempting to control the population by total fear, terror and reprisals became the best recruiting Sergeant Major possible. They caused so much resentment, hatred and bitterness that they created the most perfect conditions for the birth, sustenance and rapid expansion of organised armed resistance. So much so that the Polish underground movement became the largest in any of the occupied countries and, although the Germans had some minor success in disrupting its activities, it was virtually ineffective in its battle against the relentless progress and effectiveness of the organisation. Jozef had become involved in the intelligence gathering section and on his trips across the city, identifying targets and establishing smuggling routes for the arms and supplies dropped by the allies, he began to forge wide-ranging links with the Jews trapped inside their Ghetto.

Sat in a command bunker deep inside the Jewish quarter Jozef was watching his Jewish counterpart Simon devouring the sausage that Zenon had supplied. As he waited Jozef reflected on the contrast between the almost military air of order and efficiency within the command post and the total desolation and despair he had seen above ground when he had entered the Ghetto for the very first time. The streets had been littered with corpses, some covered with newspaper or sacking held down by bricks or rubble. Most had died from starvation or disease as thousands of Jews from across the countryside were driven into the Ghetto where there was no food or accommodation for them. Many of these newcomers lived on the streets, walking past or stepping over the corpses, mostly the young and the old, the weak and the lonely, without even looking at them. Life was so cheap and to survive for one more day was the most they could hope for. It reminded Jozef of the death camp and he felt angry that in comparison to this, life on the other side of the wall in Catholic Warsaw (known as the Ayrian side to the Jews) was tolerable, certainly desirable, and even relatively normal.

Simon was about twenty-five years old and was in daily liaison with the Home Army in his capacity as an intelligence officer for the left-wing Jewish Combat Organisation (ZOB), which alongside the other main armed group (ZZW) inside the Ghetto, was planning major action to disrupt an imminent 'mass deportation'. After giving Simon a brief history of his own experiences Jozef asked, "I've been told what has been going on here and I've seen the bodies in the streets, but perhaps I could hear it from someone who really knows because there are some in my organisation that are openly anti-Semitic and distort the truth and it pains me greatly to say so."

Simon looked at his new friend with empathy and sorrow in his sunken eyes and replied in a soft monotone, "Coming from the countryside yourself you probably don't know that nearly half a million of us lived in this beautiful city and it was our largest urban community in the world. We had our own civil administration, press, schools, theatre and we enjoyed total religious and political freedom." He went on to explain that the Jews had been well represented throughout the city's professional and commercial occupations and, although there had always been some conflict between the two groups, life was good and they had always managed through their councils to negotiate an understanding with the Christian Poles.

When the Germans came the Jews were pushed into the old quarter and trapped behind their new ten-foot high wall, into what was in effect a prison of only eight hundred acres. Tens of thousands of others from all over the area outside the city were also herded together and forced to move there. Additionally hundreds of Romany gypsies, with no connection whatsoever to the district, had been rounded up in the countryside and driven in, adding to the already seething mix. The gypsies found the situation unbearable right from the start, many were already half dead from abuse and starvation and those inside did little or nothing to help out. "To our shame, our suspicions and hostility towards them quickly led to their being treated as an underclass. Can you believe it? We of all people should have known better but, at last and far too late, a group of us are now trying to help the survivors and despite their bitter experience some of them have even become involved in our operations."

All those inside the Ghetto had been systematically starved, beaten, threatened with death and forcibly robbed of any valuable possessions and those lucky enough to find housing were sharing, at least a dozen to a room. Then typhoid struck, killing thousands each and every month. Those that survived owed their lives to one thing above all else and that was the black-market and Simon illustrated the point, "We've managed to continue to trade and exchange goods with the Poles outside. We go over the wall, under the wall, through holes in the wall, through the sewers, through tunnels, over the roofs and at the same time we bribe guards, police and soldiers to cooperate or just turn a blind eye. In this way we bring in contraband and food in our pockets, in bags on bicycles, in prams, carts, cars and trucks. Tons of it, right under the Germans' noses. The scavengers include hundreds of children who cross every day, sometimes several times a day and many bring back their own weight and more in supplies. Some of them are only four or five years old."

Critics said they were too inventive, even suicidally brazen with the lives of the women and children because there was only one punishment when they were caught – death – and they shot both the guilty and the innocent, adults or children, male or female: even passersby were swept up and machine-gunned during the constant search for smugglers. Nevertheless, the apparent recklessness was born out of necessity because if they failed to keep the massive trade going flat out then they would have starved to death very quickly. The rations for a German was about two thousand five hundred calories a day, for the Poles it was seven hundred, nowhere near sustenance level, but for the Jews it was set at less than two hundred and they often got nothing at all.

Simon continued, "Anyway, no matter what happens in here we can't die quickly enough for the Nazis and so we're constantly being rounded up and five thousand a day were being sent to the death camp at Treblinka on the pretext of being taken to the countryside to recover their health. Well, no one believes that garbage anymore and I know exactly what really goes on at the camp because I've personally debriefed the fighter we sent out to follow the trains. He went as far as he could and discovered that Treblinka was a closed military area. He watched for days as thousands of Jews were trained in but not one single person left and no food or supplies were ever taken in. He feared the worst and when he questioned a Polish Railway worker he discovered that they were all murdered in gas chambers shortly after arriving at the camp. They intend to exterminate the whole Jewish population of Warsaw."

Jozef knew the true nature and extent of the crime being perpetrated, "Jews from all over Europe are being killed in other camps here in Poland and probably in all the occupied countries as well. As I said, I've been at Auschwitz and seen the mass-slaughter," and then he spoke at more length of his own ordeal before Simon continued with his account of life in the Ghetto.

"As we suffered we became more and more desperate and some of our own people tried to buy their survival, even for just a few more weeks or months, by working with the Germans. They acted as Police, guards or informers and sold us out for the price of a meal or two. We hate these traitors with a passion. In fact, I can fairly say that the collaborators inside are despised more than the Germans or the collaborators outside. We have a saying here that if there are three guards blocking your path to safety, one an SS soldier, one a Ukrainian and one a Jewish policeman, then you should first try to pass by the German, then perhaps the Ukrainian but never, ever, the Jew, for there lies certain disaster."

Jozef thought for a moment before responding, "I notice you tactfully didn't include a Pole in your story, but we've also treated you badly and there are many Polish collaborators only too willing to betray Jews, so, at least in the context of your anecdote, you would have good reason to avoid us as well."

"Yes, we must pick our friends with care but in fairness your organisation has, at considerable risk, brought in quantities of food, plans, maps, arms and ammunition and smuggled a few hundred of us out. A similar number have also managed to escape and many have then received help on the outside, so we do have Polish allies who provide practical help and safe refuge. But it's now crystal clear to me that for most of us our fate lies here. Can you believe that there are now only sixty thousand of us left and we are still starving, but no longer will we be marched off to our deaths. We've chosen to fight and live or die here. The next time the Nazis come in we'll not only resist but fight the bastards to the death with all we have and I implore you, in the name of the God we both worship, to get your people to help us in a major way."

"I promise I'll try, but I'm not sure we'll get the response you want."

"If we're to stand any chance at all your people must fight with us. If they don't, then it will surely end in a massacre because once the Nazis sense any weakness then they will throw everything at us. Even with your help it will be hard, maybe even impossible, to hold them off for weeks on end but without your men and weapons our battle will surely turn out to be nothing more than an honourable but ill-fated demonstration of our final resistance."

Simon took Jozef's hands and without saying another word they prayed together: different words, different languages but the same desperate refrain. Before he left Jozef asked, "When my commanders consider what to do I'll be asked how well trained and organised you are."

"Between both organisations, the ZZW (Jewish Fighting Union) and the ZOB, we have some eight hundred volunteers who have a modicum of basic weapons and guerrilla tactics training. Additionally we have hundreds of active supporters aged between four and seventy who act as messengers, lookouts, supply runners, medics, engineers, miners, doctors, nurses, cooks and general dogsbodies. In many ways, but on a smaller, less sophisticated scale we mirror the Home Army but both organisations inside the Ghetto are not at the same stage of readiness."

"Why's that? You've had the same amount of time to prepare."

"Please don't take this the wrong way but the ZZW are right-wing Zionists from Betar and other revisionist groups: they tend to be older and have a number of ex Polish army officers in their ranks. They've naturally used their old contacts within your organisation to obtain much larger quantities of weapons and ammunition and a number of your people have also given them professional training. They're well armed and well prepared. Our group on the other hand, though much larger, is mostly made up of inexperienced youngsters from the Bund, other socialist youth groups, communists, pro-Soviets and even Stalinists, I dare say idealistic optimists just like me and we are nowhere near as well organized, but believe me, we will fight just as hard."

178

"What about weaponry?"

"At the moment we have sufficient for less than a quarter of our fighters and ammunition for about a week. We'll continue to use any time we have to keep training more recruits and obtain extra weapons through the black-market but we'll get most of what we want from the Nazis when we kill them. You know it only takes one bullet to get a submachine gun and then we can kill ten more."

"Thinking about what you've said, are you sure your different groups can work and fight as one?

"Yes, they've got over their initial rivalries and suspicions and are now working well together. We've jointly developed a small factory working flat out making hand grenades and petrol bombs. I know it's hardly enough to fight even a very limited action but we will use the few advantages we have to good effect and all our soldiers, men, women and even a few children, will fight to the very end. There's nowhere else for us to go."

Jozef did not altogether agree, "I'm sure that if we put our minds to it we could organise a mass exodus for your fighters and as many others as possible. We could get you out through the tunnels and supply lines and you could hide out in the forest or join the partisans out there and just wait the war out..."

Simon interrupted, "You're not the first to make such a suggestion but let me stop you there. We both know that only a small proportion of us would get out and many would be turned in by the collaborators, besides, if from now on we openly refuse to comply with every Nazi order that's given and then fight with Jewish pride and ferocity it will send ripples of hope right across Poland and beyond. We've already decided. We'll not run away but we'll wage war with every ounce of our strength and with your help from the outside, we'll ensure that never again will the Jews of Warsaw be herded into cattle trucks and taken to the death camps to be murdered."

Jozef reported back to his superiors and was told that the army would supply as many weapons and as much ammunition as possible and give specific technical assistance and training but would not take part in a general uprising. He was informed that they were now in daily touch with the Allies and the full, horrific detail of what was happening in the concentration camps had also been personally conveyed by special courier to both Winston

Churchill and the President of the United States. According to Jozef's commanding officer the Allies were anxious that the European resistance movements should rise up in a co-ordinated way when, and only when, it fitted in with their overall plans for a land invasion, probably through France and Italy.

Jozef accompanied the next small shipment of weapons into the Ghetto and he let Simon down gently, explaining in as much detail as was authorised, the position of his own organisation but he was himself left with a distinct feeling that not doing more could be a tactical mistake and also seen as moral cowardice. He wondered if Warsaw would ever recover from the shame if the Jewish community were annihilated as the rest of her citizens stood aside. These thoughts troubled him because he understood the broad strategic reasoning of his commanders and he also knew that the suffering of the Jews, which he had witnessed at Auschwitz, inevitably skewed his own judgement in their favour.

He was well aware of the overwhelming desire to resist the Germans that existed throughout the city because they stood for all that was evil and vicious and this common hatred had united the various political factions. On the other hand the influence of the Allies who stood for liberty, justice, truth and tolerance could not be underestimated and the control exercised by the Government in Exile was considerable. Beyond the strategic arguments he also felt that the Government in Exile and most of the Home Army leaders and membership had little sympathy with the Jews in the Ghetto because of their socialist beliefs and their pro-Soviet stance, especially after the treachery of the Nazi Soviet pact and the damage it had done to the Polish nation. He felt this was both a blinkered and shortsighted view, but it reinforced and awakened the latent anti-Semitism amongst the Poles in general and blinded them to the colossal inhumanity inside the Ghetto. He was also certain that the Germans would, at any cost to themselves, ruthlessly crush an uprising no matter how many thousands were involved. He finally concluded that the deciding factor in the decision not to do more was that the general population of Warsaw lacked the necessary element of reckless fatalism because they had not yet reached the darkest depths of despair and abandonment in which the Jews now found themselves floundering.

Jozef met Zenon the next day and said, "I've put it off long enough on the pretext that I had too much to do but it's time I found Father Chepek and faced up to the task of delivering mother's letter and telling him what's happened. It's going to be very difficult and I would appreciate it if you would come along."

Zenon nodded, "I knew you would ask eventually, so I've already traced him: he's now helping out at the Franciscan Church. If you leave it with me I'll make the necessary arrangements, for tomorrow if possible."

It was a very emotional reunion and the priest wept as he read Ewa's letter and then they sat together and talked through all that had happened since they parted. Zenon helped his friend out when things became too difficult for Jozef and some two hours later all three had given their various accounts. The priest then took another letter from his pocket and gave it to Jozef saying, "Well, at least I have some good news for you, it's a letter from your brother Jacek. He was also captured but has managed to conceal his true identity and he is safe. Here, read it for yourself."

Jozef could hardly contain his joy and his hands trembled with excitement and relief as he held the flimsy pages up to the light. He read the words over and over before he fully absorbed the content and then asked, "Have you written back to him?"

"Yes, but I was unable to tell him very much. Nevertheless my prayers have been answered because here you are, safe and well before my very eyes. You must write yourself now and remember, if you two have survived then there's no reason why Jan, Tomek and Maria shouldn't be alive as well," replied the priest who prayed with many parishioners for their missing relatives every single day. "In view of what Jacek said, I have asked around at the churches but as yet I haven't found Maria, but she may still be here and you might have more luck finding her. Would you now both pray with me for the souls of your mother and father and for the safety of all those placed in such mortal danger, and then both of you can join me for supper?"

Following their light meal the priest told Jozef that he was being transferred to the church of the Holy Cross and although he was delighted to be going back home as he saw it, he was also filled with trepidation as the last priest there had recently been arrested by the Gestapo. He asked for their prayers and told them both to visit regularly and not lose touch. After making a few notes for himself he gave Jozef back his mother's letter saying, "This will be the most difficult thing you'll ever have to read but I want you to know that I intend to comply with everything your mother has asked of me. It's so important to me that you're fully aware of what that entails because I need you to hold me to account. I also believe that when peace finally returns you will receive comfort from reading these wonderfully compassionate words from such a holy woman. We'll speak again of your own future when we know that Warsaw is safe and free from the occupiers."

Jozef thanked the priest and said, "Even as a child I always thought that I would be called to serve God in the priesthood and I have tried so hard to keep my faith and live a decent life, but now I find myself going in a totally different direction. I've got to fight our enemies at all costs and inside me nothing else seems to matter anymore. Sometimes I think this is what God wants of me but at other times I'm riddled with doubts and uncertainty. Perhaps I'm not cut out for the church after all. I certainly don't know what the future holds for me or anyone else but I would ask for your prayers and guidance."

"We must all fight in our own way and I have absolutely no doubt you are doing the right thing. Don't worry, when he is ready God will tell you what he wants of you for the future. All you have to do is keep the faith and listen out for his intervention." He then looked at both of his guests in turn and said, "I will pray for you both and may God keep you safe." He then formally blessed them with holy water.

They took their leave with Jozef clutching his two precious letters and then the priest immediately sat down to honour Ewa's wishes by writing to the Bishop of the Polish Government in Exile and through him to the Holy Father. Jozef couldn't wait to send a letter to his brother in France and as soon as he was back in his room, as the tears flowed, he first read and then reread both letters.

Four days later Jozef was called to a meeting with his District Commander and the Chief Intelligence Officer where he was introduced to the third person present: Lieutenant James Ashton, an escaped English prisoner of war. The Intelligence Officer said to Jozef, "I will let the Lieutenant tell you his story and then I'll explain why you are here." He then indicated to the Englishman to proceed.

182

He spoke reasonable German, "I'm sorry but I only know a few words of Polish but I understand we will get by in German. I was part of an ill-fated raid known as 'Operation Jubilee' carried out by a six thousand strong British and Canadian commando force that attacked the French port of Dieppe in August last year. We were accompanied by small detachments of the Free French, and some US Rangers, but we were compromised when the leading landing craft blundered into a small German coastal convoy. The exchange of fire alerted the enemy garrison and they were waiting for us when we landed."

He explained that they were cut to pieces by coastal batteries, machine-gun positions and well-directed mortar fire. They pressed on regardless but were then attacked by wave after wave of enemy aircraft and casualties became unacceptably heavy, particularly amongst the Canadians. "I can't tell you the full purpose of the attack. Suffice it to say that it was for intelligence gathering purposes and was supposed to have been a relatively simple, localised, hit-and-run mission using overwhelming numbers and the element of surprise. As it turned out it was a total, morale sapping disaster for us."

Two thousand of the attack force were captured and almost the same number killed. Only about a third of the men were rescued by the navy and made it safely back to England.

"How did you end up here," asked Jozef.

"I was one of the comparatively lucky ones who survived, but I spent the next five months as the guest of the Nazis at one of their POW camps just outside of Kalisz. I managed to escape three weeks ago and my change of luck held because your people found me before the Germans and hopefully I'll now have the chance to go home. I'm sure you'll be very pleased to hear that one of the destroyers that escorted us across the English Channel was Polish, the Slazak, and if she and the others, despite being under air attack themselves, hadn't hung around for the rescue, and pounded the enemy artillery, I don't think any of us would have survived."

There were nearly fifty Polish warships fighting on every front with the Royal Navy. Except for a British Liaison Officer and a Signal's Operator posted to each ship, all the Captains, officers and men on board each and every one were Polish.

The District Commander spoke for the first time: "I have a

vital mission for you both. Jozef, I have chosen you because of your unique position. You have seen inside the death camps, helped inside the Jewish Ghetto and have a clear intelligence picture of our own situation and needs within the Home Army. Lieutenant Ashton has spent the last week on a guided tour of our organisation and has agreed to report our material requirements for support back to his War Department. It will carry more weight coming from their own man and, from what he has told us, I feel confident that he will take every opportunity to remind our allies that whilst the Polish Free Forces are willingly laying down their lives to defend Britain, it's not too much to expect them to reciprocate by providing us with vital military hardware. Similarly you will report directly to our Government in London with a list of the help that we urgently need and you will also emphasise the desperate position of the Jews. They will probably think that you are exaggerating their plight and so I want you to take a senior member of their resistance with you. Use your contacts and arrange it today. When you return with him I'll brief all three of you with the plan to get you out."

After Jozef had got over the initial shock of the huge responsibility he was taking on he went to see Simon and it took a great deal of persuading and reassurance that the envoys would return as quickly as possible before he would support the plan. He then left to confer with his own hierarchy who took only two hours to agree, and their nominated man was Simon himself.

Within four hours Jozef was back in front of his commander, accompanied by Simon, the English officer and an interpreter because the entire briefing was now in Polish. Once the arrangements had been confirmed they were dismissed, but Jozef was asked to stay behind and the commander spoke to him in a quiet and sombre tone, "You must obey this order above all others. If at any stage it appears likely that the Englishman will fall into the hands of the enemy you must kill him to prevent it. We've shown him a great deal in order that he can achieve the objective, and although we have been as careful as possible to hide the most critically sensitive information from him, some still believe he has seen too much, places, faces, equipment, stores and lines of supply and distribution. I'm confident that Simon is no threat to us and he would probably take his own life if faced with that situation but the Englishman, although a professional soldier, doesn't truly understand that our country is threatened with total destruction. Unless we succeed, here in the capital, our enemies will once again divide the whole country up between them. Can you do as I ask?"

Jozef didn't know how to answer because he seriously doubted that he could obey, but on the other hand he could just about imagine dire circumstances in which the taking of an innocent life to save many others might just be permitted and he had already killed the enemy and now had no compunction about doing so. He just didn't believe he could do it to a friend, "I honestly don't know, but I can assure you that I will do everything in my power to prevent the information we have from being obtained by the enemy."

"Then that will have to do, I would rather rely on a man who fully understands what is being asked of him than one who gives it scant regard and merely acquiesces. Good Luck," added the commander as he stood up and shook Jozef by the hand.

They left the next day and were escorted by a small group of heavily armed fighters. Travelling with guides they avoided the main checkpoints and used side roads and tracks whenever possible. They frequently changed their transport and during the course of their journey many locals, men, women and several children willingly risked their lives and those of their families to deliver them safely to their destination. Three days later they were smuggled on board a freighter at Gdynia on the Baltic, bound for the shipyards at Kalmar in neutral Sweden. They were aware, as they were hidden from the crew amongst the cargo, that the Germans often stopped and searched the ships bound for Sweden and their U-boats had even attacked them on several occasions.

The country itself was crawling with German spies and the Poles had already lost couriers who had been intercepted by the Nazis or arrested following tip-offs to the Swedish Police. However most Swedes were sympathetic to the Polish cause and organised groups existed to provide them with aid and support. They also harboured refugees including a considerable number of Jews who had managed to escape. Jozef's team were passed along one such well-established chain without incident and one week later they were inside the British embassy at Stockholm, awaiting papers to take them on to London and their various meetings with the War

Authorities. Whilst at the embassy Jozef took the opportunity to write to his brother in France and took it on to London with him, hoping it could be smuggled onwards by the Free French and their underground movement.

NINE

A Battle to Fight
9th *June 1942*

At the end of May they had at last finished the new spur line from the camp and connected it to the main Trans-Siberian railway line and so Tomek took little notice of the arriving train. He automatically thought that it was there to take away yet another load of timber to extend the manufacturing centre and armaments plant that had been transferred from central Russia to nearby Kemerovo to be out of range of the German aircraft. It was only when he heard the cheering and prisoners started running past him towards the track that he realised something special was happening.

Stood on the side of the timber truck immediately behind the engine was a soldier wearing a Polish uniform which looked new, at least it wasn't in rags like many of those still worn by the inmates. The soldier was waving papers in the air and calling out, "Gather round, come on lads, hurry up and listen. I've got an important message from General Anders to all soldiers and citizens of Poland." The area alongside the train soon filled up with shouting and cheering prisoners and the guards were rushing across and trying to restore control, a few even fired their weapons in the air. In the end they realised that, short of shooting prisoners, they would have to wait it out and so they simply formed a cordon at the rear of the Poles, preventing any of the Russian prisoners joining them.

Tomek looked around and found his friend and as they met Doc said, "This has to be something important and the guards must already know about it, and are under orders not to intervene, or they would have shot a few of us by now." They moved through the rows of excited Poles trying to get nearer the front and suddenly silence spread throughout the crowd until they could clearly hear the birds singing in the nearby forest. The soldier on the train cleared his throat, spat the offending matter on the ground and then addressed the crowd, "I'm going to read a proclamation from General Anders that has also been agreed by the Soviet High Command. It states as follows.

I have been asked by the Allies to re-form a Polish army from amongst all those servicemen and civilians who are held captive within the territories of the USSR. Shortly you will all be moved to Orenburg, near the Kazakhstan border, where you will be fully cared for and given further orders. We will fight the Nazis wherever and whenever the Allies have need of us so be patient for a little longer and NEVER give up the hope of going home to Poland."

The messenger added, "I give you my own word of honour that your suffering here will shortly come to an end." The shouting and cheers were deafening as prisoners started dancing, hugging each other, kissing and shaking hands and although the visiting soldier tried to give them more details his voice was continuously drowned out.

Tomek, at first not daring to believe what he had just heard, asked Doc, "Is this really true? Can there possibly be an end to this nightmare, after so long?"

Doc looked up to the sky as if seeking divine inspiration, closed his eyes and uttered three words, "Yes - thank God!"

That night they talked for hours, trying to work out what was likely to happen and the next day Genghis shed some unwelcome light on the situation, "It's true that you will be leaving Russia to fight again, but we can't afford to let you all leave here at once. Your work is critical to the war effort and you can only be released in batches of one hundred, as other workers arrive to replace you."

Despite the protests of the prisoners and the verbal abuse they gave Genghis, who seemed to have lost most of his power over them, they were released in groups, sometimes the hundred as predicted and occasionally in larger batches of up to four hundred at a time. Doc and Tomek were released together with about two hundred other prisoners, four long and frustrating weeks after the announcement. Following days of negotiations with Genghis and only after providing him with their complete stash of food and other pilfered articles were they also able to secure the release of Halina and she left on the train with them. She was delighted to be with Tomek, but heartbroken that she had to leave Anna behind because the camp authorities refused point-blank to release any Soviet citizens and Genghis would not take up her case.

When they arrived at Orenburg there were some ten thousand Poles already assembled with more arriving every day. It was not just desperate and diseased soldiers gathering there but old people, women, children and even toddlers. Most were in a terrible state of malnutrition, had no footwear, were dressed in rags and totally exhausted but basic medical supplies and food rations were available and they were able to rest up and, to some extent, recuperate. They later learned that during the short Russian occupation of eastern Poland one and a half million of their fellow citizens had been forcibly moved from their homes and transported en masse to Siberia. Those considered to be professionals or pose an ideological or political threat were either summarily shot or sent to the Gulag. The rest, irrespective of age, sex or fitness were simply dumped in the middle of a barren and hostile landscape. The lucky ones found shelter in barns, outbuildings and makeshift accommodation or were crammed ten to a room in local settlements and worked as slaves for the locals or the Russian war effort, surviving on the most meagre of rations. The vast majority would perish through starvation, abuse or disease.

The lucky few were now resting alongside the Gulag refugees when they were visited by Aides to General Anders and brought up to date on the war, particularly what was happening on the eastern front. They were incensed to learn that on the 22nd June the previous year eastern areas of Poland that had been occupied by Russia had been attacked and taken by the Germans and together with the Ukrainian underground movement they had started slaughtering those Poles who had not yet been deported by the Russians. What they did not know until after the war was that thousands of their fellow countryman, including virtually all of the settlers like the

Dabrowskis, were murdered by the Ukrainian Insurgent Army who, actively encouraged by the Germans, were fighting the Home Army and were determined to clear the area east of the River Bug of all non Ukrainians. This pogrom culminated in the murder of some forty thousand Poles in the infamous Volyn Massacre when the Ukrainian nationalists struck at night butchering all the Poles they could find in the region's villages and towns.

A group of delegates, including members of the Home Army, were sent by the Polish Government in Exile to try to negotiate with the Ukrainians to stop the attacks but despite their diplomatic authority they too were murdered. This ethnic cleansing carried on well into 1945 until most of the Polish citizens were killed, deported east or expelled westwards. Many Ukrainians saw this as revenge for their own suffering, oppression and expulsion when under Polish rule during the previous decade.

They were also told that in April the Germans had discovered the mass graves of thousands of their Polish officers in the Katyn forest near Smolensk and the Germans had claimed that the Russians were responsible. There was considerable argument within the ranks as to whether the Germans or Russians were culpable but Doc and Tomek knew, because of the location and the way the Russians had behaved at the 'transit camp', that they were guilty. The details of what Tomek, Doc and the others had seen with their own eyes at Katyn spread like wildfire throughout the thousands massed together until every single refugee soldier knew the truth.

As many others arrived on foot and at the verge of death, they learnt that thousands of Poles being released from the Gulag were simply being abandoned and left to fend for themselves outside the camps. The Russians often refused to provide any transport and the ex-prisoners were forced to walk hundreds of miles to Orenburg. They left bodies at the roadside along the entire route as the survivors hadn't the strength to bury them and the locals would not help for fear of punishment by the Russian authorities. Stalin's malignant influence was as strong as ever.

They were also told that about twenty five thousand of Anders' men had already left for the Middle East and they would follow shortly. In fact they all left five weeks later, a Polish diaspora that traversed Kazakhstan to ports on the Caspian Sea. A fleet of boats and small ships ferried them across to the port of Bandar-e

Anzali in Iran. The boats had initially filled them with the hope of salvation but they were all vastly overcrowded and there was little drinking water for the journey of over six hundred and fifty miles. There was no sanitation and an outbreak of typhoid quickly took its toll, killing the young and the weakest. The sea became yet another Polish cemetery in the long chain of burial places left in the wake of their tortuous journey. Hundreds of those who had suffered so much perished within sight of help and safety. When they stepped ashore snow and winter once more greeted and taunted them! But this time the local population was warm, friendly and welcomed them with enthusiastic cheering and gifts of food and drink. Refugee camps were set up across Iran and orphanages, hospitals, schools and accommodation blocks constructed.

Tomek and his friends set up home in "Camp Polonia" in Avaz in south-western Iran and were provided with new uniforms and equipment. Even today, that part of the city is known to the locals as Campulu, even though few can now recall how it got its name. Most arrivals were still in a desperate physical condition, suffering from disease and emaciated, but freedom and the promise of action against their enemies were the ideal tonic. They once more began training as a professional fighting force called the 2nd Polish Corps, which by May 1945 would consist of nearly sixty thousand men and women.

In December Tomek and Doc formed part of a work detail from several camps that travelled into the old part of Tehran and there, in a section of the Christian cemetery, they helped to dig yet more graves. Although at last it had reached temporary safety, this bedraggled army and its civilian entourage had suffered so much deprivation that many, despite the local and British aid, still succumbed to the effects of disease and starvation at the rate of about fifty people a day. When they finally left for Iraq, over two thousand of their comrades, men, women and children were left forever in this 'Polish' cemetery, so far from home in the very heart of Iran.

Although the vast majority of this army were ethnic Poles, there were also Ukrainians, Belarusians and Jews from across Eastern Europe. When the Corps moved yet again, this time into Palestine to take part in manoeuvres, most of the Jews, including the future Prime Minister of Israel, Menachem Begin, defected to the Haganah. General Anders, recognising that these people had suffered persecution beyond endurance and had earned the right to go where they wished and to fight for their own religion and nationhood, decided not to take any serious action to recapture or punish them for what others considered to be an unforgivable act of desertion.

Much of their training, which was spread over almost a year, took place in the highland areas in preparation for their expected deployment in Italy. It was also here in Palestine that Tomek and Halina decided that whatever their future held, they would face it together and so they took the opportunity of the relatively normal circumstances to become engaged to be married. Doc was so proud of them both and revelled in his role as acting parent, and the celebration party seemed to be attended by almost every soldier from their 1st Battalion of the 1st Carpathian Rifle Brigade (universally known by the Poles as the Christmas Tree Regiment, after their distinctive shield badge showing a fir tree superimposed on the Polish flag).

They were soon brought back down to earth with the news of the death of General Sikorski, their ex Prime Minister and current Commander in Chief of the armed Services and the Leader of the Government in Exile. It is no exaggeration to say that he had been held in the highest esteem by the Polish military and civilian administrations, both at home and abroad: they considered him to be their very own Winston Churchill. He was also the one man of the old guard still revered by those Poles displaced throughout the world and they all pinned their hopes of revival on his skill as a soldier, statesman and leader. He had been killed in a plane crash at Gibraltar and because of the way he had challenged and ridiculed Stalin (over the disappearance of the Polish officers murdered at Katyn and elsewhere) many Poles believed that the crash was no accident and suspected that the dictator had a major hand in his death. Sikorski, with his charismatic ability to inspire, nurture and fight for Polish nationalism had also become a major obstacle to Stalin's plans to set up a communist government in Poland once it had been 'liberated' by the Red Army. Credibility had also been given to this theory when, on leaving Iran, a Soviet agent had been discovered planted inside Anders' army.

The crash itself was also suspicious because the Liberator aircraft went down within twenty seconds of take off with no apparent mechanical or technical defect and no satisfactory explanation was ever given by the Czech pilot, who was the only survivor. Furthermore, Sikorski's body was found wearing a life-jacket when he was renowned amongst his family and senior staff for always refusing to don one because of a superstitious unease. His daughter Zofia was also on the flight but her body was never found at the crash site and credible witnesses swore to have seen her in the Gulag in 1945. Even prior to this many suspected that the body found was not that of their leader or if it was, then he was murdered prior to the crash.

To pile further conspiracy upon intrigue, at the time of the incident the notorious and active Russian spy Kim Philby was working undetected for MI6 as the head of the *IBERIAN* section. The whole assassination theory had been given further authority by the incredible revelation that, only three weeks before the fatal crash, a Morse code signal had been received at the UK Polish Headquarters from an unidentified source falsely stating that Sikorski's plane had crashed on takeoff and that their leader and everyone on board had been killed.

Over the years the finger of suspicion has also periodically, but with less authority, been pointed at Britain because on the night before the crash the General had been a guest at the Governor's residence on Gibraltar and as Churchill had become progressively more dependent on a volatile and suspicious Stalin, Sikorski could be seen as an unnecessary embarrassment and hindrance to any rapprochement.

The controversy has been so intense and long lasting that Sikorski's body was exhumed at the end of 2008 and comprehensive DNA and other forensic tests undertaken. In January 2009 the results were published, proving his identity and disclosing that he had not been murdered and was alive when the plane crashed. X-rays of the body showed fractures to the left eye socket, forehead, ribs, clavicle, right hand and leg as well as a splinter of wood in his skull. His hyoid bone was, however, not damaged leading experts to exclude strangulation. Tests did not reveal any trace of poison or gunshot wounds and tension on several muscles suggests that he was alive at the time of the accident. Experts concluded that Sikorski died of multiple organ failure of the kind typically sustained in a plane crash or in a fall from a great height.

Whether or not sabotage had caused the plane to crash is a matter still under investigation and yet Katyn continues to claim more victims. On 10th April 2010 the Presidential plane carrying nearly a hundred of Poland's political, military and civic elite, including the President and the First Lady, crashed outside Smolensk. Accompanied by members of the Federation of Katyn Families they were on their way to the 70th anniversary memorial service at Katyn. There were no survivors and once again the flower of Poland had been destroyed: this time by the poignant legacy of the massacre.

On 21st December, 1943, Tomek's battalion was moved to Italy on active service and immediately took up position on the Sangro River Line in preparation for a spring offensive against Rome. It had been hoped when the Italian campaign had been planned that it would tie down huge numbers of German troops and also cause them to dramatically reinforce their defensive garrisons, both in Italy and the Balkans, thereby relieving the immense pressure on Russia. Unfortunately, the progress during the first few weeks after the landings at Salerno on 8th September had been painfully slow and extremely costly, particularly for the Americans. The Allies inched their way east and north over the mountainous and well-defended rocky spine of Italy, constantly facing enemy counterattacks, heavy artillery fire and mine fields. The Italian capitulation did not have the desired effect either, as most troops particularly the garrisons around Rome, simply handed over their weapons to the Germans, tried to forget the war, and returned to their homes. The Allies had not unreasonably hoped that, even if the Italians did not turn their weapons on the Germans, they would at least, by changing sides, tie up German divisions in guarding and controlling them. Disappointingly, things did not improve and by the first week in January the allies had advanced only seventy miles from Salerno.

The Poles were at first restricted to patrol work in an effort to prevent the enemy realising that large numbers of reinforcements were being deployed in readiness for the major offensive. It was on one such patrol that Tomek first saw action just south of the Gustav line on 18th January 1944. He immediately learnt that training and preparation could only take a soldier so far and that fortune and fate were the true arbiters of survival.

Their ten-man patrol entered a hamlet from the south, having been briefed that the Germans had withdrawn overnight from their positions inside the buildings to fresh defensive positions about half a mile beyond the northern boundary of the village. This put the enemy in a strong position, well beyond a stream running in an east to west direction at the foot of steep hills covered in rocky outcrops, any of which offered superb cover for snipers and heavy weapons. As the Poles approached the first building Doc, running low, pulled Tomek towards him and said, "Stay close to me and keep your head down: if we draw fire take cover and listen to me. Don't forget we're only here to assess their strength and identify their units. I don't want any heroics from you today. It's just a patrol."

Tomek acknowledged his friend as they ran behind the cover of the first building, keeping well clear of the doors and windows, wary of booby traps and anti-personnel mines. They slowly made their way forward, building by building, until they arrived at the far side and crawled along the ground to the final boundary wall. From here they had a clear view of the river about a hundred and twenty yards ahead and the rocky hills beyond. Two of their sniper teams had taken up positions on the first floor of the end buildings, overlooking the hills ahead, to provide an observation post and an effective response to the enemy's own sharpshooters. It was a shot from one of these Polish snipers that started the engagement and, as Tomek peered through a hole in the wall, he saw a group of four Germans emerge from a trench on the south bank of the stream. As two provided covering fire, the others started to wade across the river but once in the water they were a perfect target and all the Poles, hardly believing what they saw, opened up.

Tomek lost all conscious sense of his physical surroundings and of time and space as he clenched his teeth and strained every nerve to concentrate solely on firing his weapon. His drills and endless practise automatically took over and with creeping tunnel vision he focussed in on that one small section of river dead ahead, becoming oblivious to the deafening noise of the firefight and the actions of those around him. He leant against the top of the wall, looked through the two fixed sights towards the enemy and, with the Mk11Sten submachine-gun set on automatic fire, he gripped the side mounted magazine tightly, pulled the weapon into his shoulder and squeezed the trigger. At five hundred rounds a minute the thirty-two rounds in the magazine were expended in less than four seconds. Tomek had absolutely no idea whether he had hit a target or not; in fact he knew the distance was beyond the extreme accuracy range of his weapon and he was far more intent on just putting down fire and hoping that it wouldn't jam, as it was prone to do, rather than taking careful aim.

As the weapon dry-fired he realised that during his intense concentration he had stopped breathing and as he gulped in air his ears popped and his head was suddenly full of the noises and smells of battle. He then, for the first time since he had started firing, consciously took in the unfolding scene before him and saw that the Germans had never even made it to the middle of the stream before they had been cut down. The snipers had quickly dealt with the remaining two and then all the Poles stopped shooting. Tomek, realising that he had been foolishly wasting ammunition then inserted another magazine and switched his weapon to single shot. It was only then, with the requirements of self-preservation and rigorous weapons training satisfied, that he once more became aware of his comrades.

He saw that Marius, a relatively new recruit from a Polish community in New Zealand who had joined them in Palestine and had been standing right alongside him, had been hit in the upper right arm, either by a rifle round or possibly by a splinter of stone from the wall. The projectile had punched a hole right through with an inch wide, almost circular entry wound in the biceps just above the elbow and a ragged three inch exit wound through the middle of the triceps, exposing the damaged bone. Small splinters were protruding from it through the gaping wound and there was massive tissue and muscle loss with blood pumping out and rapidly pooling on the ground. The soldier's chest, arms and face were covered in it where he was trying to hold the wounds with his good hand.

Doc quickly laid him flat, cut his clothing away from the arm and ripped open two dressing packs. Although his own hands were quickly slippery and clumsy from all the blood, he managed to stuff one dressing right into the hole of the exit wound and another over the entry wound, applying firm pressure to both. The casualty was already white with shock and moaning, but every time Doc

196

increased the pressure or worked on the arm the moans turned to screams, which became louder and more desperate as Doc attempted to stop the immense blood loss. He then placed a bandage right around both dressings and tied it tight maintaining the pressure on both wounds.

The bleeding still wouldn't stop and so Doc fixed a tourniquet above the injury and showed Tomek just how to keep it tight enough to stop the patient bleeding out and when to ease it off. The patient was still thrashing about and screaming in pain so Doc took a morphine ampoule from its canister and injected the drug directly into the casualty's good arm and then wrote the time and identifying details on the special tag and pinned it to his chest to prevent any possibility of an overdose later on. The patient quickly relaxed and drifted into semi-consciousness and as Doc made him as comfortable as possible he told Tomek, "Just keep him like that. We've got him stable now so your job is to keep a close eye on him and make sure he stays still: we can't do anymore for him until we get out of here or at least make our own position safe."

Tomek seemed to take the added responsibility in his stride but was bewildered by the enemy's actions at the stream and asked, "What on earth were the Germans doing? I don't understand why they would break cover like that in the first place and then why they didn't get some covering fire from the hills?"

"I don't know, just stay where you are and look after Marius, it could be a trap, trying to get us out into the open. Let's wait and see what happens next," replied Doc as he prepared more dressings and tried to make the patient more comfortable on the hard rocky ground.

About five minutes later they saw a group of enemy soldiers appear from behind a particularly large outcrop just below the ridge ahead and withdraw over the hill. The range was too far and so the Poles held their fire and again settled down to wait. Twenty minutes later when the sergeant was considering whether to move forward or send a runner with a report for further instructions and help for the casualty, four more Germans emerged from the trench by the stream, only this time they were waving a white flag.

"Everyone stay where you are, this could still be a trap. Tomek keep your head down but tell them to walk towards us with their hands in the air," instructed the Sergeant.

Tomek called out to the Germans and, when they complied with his orders, they were quickly pulled into the cover of the wall and searched. They were engineers and at first would only give their names, but as soon as they realised that their captors were all Polish they assumed they might be shot and quickly explained to Tomek what had happened. They had been left behind (following a general overnight withdrawal to prepared positions on the next and far higher ridge line) to mine the buildings on the north side of the village, including those now occupied by the snipers. They were just finishing when the patrol arrived and surprised them, but the infantry platoon left to guard them had just withdrawn across the river and could do little as long as the Poles remained hidden. Feeling trapped and isolated, the first group of engineers had eventually tried to run across the shallow water. The four survivors had seen what had happened to their comrades and had spent the last twenty-five minutes debating what to do as the charges were already in place and primed. They didn't know the strength of the Polish unit or their exact positions so they couldn't be sure that the explosions would do enough damage, or cause enough confusion, to provide a safe opportunity to withdraw. The more they thought about it the more obvious it became that making the detonation would only serve to enrage their attackers and would do little or nothing for their chances of escape, survival, or a successful surrender.

The Poles were satisfied with this explanation and felt secure enough to immediately evacuate the injured soldier, report their findings and hold their ground until relieved. Three hours later a whole battalion arrived to take possession of the village and also to secure the hills that had been vacated by the enemy. The captured Germans were then made to assist in making the mines and demolition charges safe before Tomek's unit was stood down. They were then free to return with their prisoners and, as they did, so Tomek said to his friend, "Not bad for our first skirmish, four dead Germans and four prisoners and us with only one casualty."

"We were lucky today because we arrived in the village at exactly the right moment and then the surviving engineers were more interested in saving themselves than blowing us up. On another day it could just as easily have been us as their prisoners or even worse," replied Doc who was already looking forward to a hot meal.

Over the next three months progress on the whole front continued to be very deliberate, slow and costly and the Poles gradually saw more and more action. As their casualties grew and they became more experienced in the ways of the enemy, they moulded into a very determined and effective fighting force that won the respect of their British commanders. Very soon they were to face their greatest and most bloody test at a particularly well-fortified stronghold known as Monte Cassino.

The enemy had, over a six-month period, prepared an almost impregnable line of defences that traversed Italy from sea to sea. Situated at the southern entrance to the vitally strategic Liri valley was a pinch-point dominated by the imposing fortress-like edifice of the Abbey of Monte Cassino. Dozens of allied Divisions, with troops from over thirty different nations, were jammed into this bottleneck and the capture of the fortifications became the major priority. The allied commanders were also anxious to press on to Rome and then relieve as many divisions as possible to take part in the invasion of Normandy, which was increasingly occupying their minds and becoming the main focus of their political masters.

It was against this background that three battles for Monte Cassino were fought, through January to March 1944, with unsustainable losses being inflicted on the Allies. The British, Americans, Canadians, French, New Zealanders and many other nationalities took part in these battles showing tremendous courage and tenacity but the defenders held out against everything that was thrown at them and each time the Allies were forced to withdraw. By May it was clear to all that a different, bolder plan was needed and the decision was made to attack simultaneously on a broad front, along the entire length of the Gustav line, and the Polish 2nd Corps was tasked to capture Monte Cassino.

For Tomek and his comrades just getting to their start lines was a major and extremely dangerous problem. The two supply roads, which merged in a deep valley, were very often under the direct observation and accurate fire of the enemy from their vantage points in the hills and on the high, cliff-like, gorges and it became impossible to run the gauntlet on the main route known as 'inferno road'. The Polish sappers therefore constructed their own road, working only at night. In order to shield it from the enemy they lined the most vulnerable mile long section with a vertical screen.

They also concealed their own artillery in woods but wired the trees that were cut down to provide an arc of fire, so that they would remain upright and not attract attention. When they were ready to fire, the trees were simply lowered to the ground. All ammunition and supplies were also only delivered at night and then carried firstly by mule and then on by hand over the steepest sections.

Doc was amazed when he saw Wojtek (soldier bear), the Corps mascot, also helping to carry ammunition for the big guns across the lower slopes. His jaw dropped as he stared in disbelief and amusement at the ingenuity of the supply troops as he watched the big bear, standing tall on its hind legs, enthusiastically carrying huge boxes of live artillery shells. When he reached a steeper, rockier section the bear put the box down and along with his human comrades, he took a single shell and assumed his place in the crocodile line winding its way up the climb, with the weapon of war clasped firmly between its paws. The well-loved animal, which had developed a love of beer and cigarettes (some of which he actually smoked for a puff or two, or simply ate whilst relaxing alongside his soldier colleagues), had been adopted whilst they were training in Iran and the whole Corps was proud of their mischievous talisman and honorary soldier.

It was against these immense difficulties and the knowledge of previous losses that Doc's unit was being briefed at 8pm on the 11th May. The Captain started with the overall plan, "This is a major push all along the front and such a concerted action will keep the enemy guessing and should therefore help to isolate our own crucial objective - the Abbey. The previous attacks by our allies have faltered, partly due to first getting stuck in thick minefields and impenetrable scrub, and then being caught in the open by strategically placed enemy crossfire and pin-point artillery barrages. Higher up they also found themselves negotiating very steep climbs over fields of loose scree, which slowed them down and exposed them to continuous machine-gun-fire and hundreds of mortar rounds. You will be pleased to hear that we are going to try to avoid most of this by attacking with a long, looping hook from the north-west and taking them by surprise on their weaker, less defensible side. The idea is that we should capture the high points first and when they are safely in our hands it will restrict the enemy's ability to organise any co-ordinated counter-attacks or effectively reinforce the garrison at the Abbey. Our Battalion's job is to capture the key, fortified position of Massa Albaneta and to our left the 2nd battalion's targets are Hills 593 and 569. We will then link up with them and the 3rd battalion for a drive onto the real prize, the Abbey itself. Your own company commanders will now issue communications codes, maps and individual briefings and remember we *MUST* capture this fortress and we haven't got much time because, until we do, the whole Eighth Army is going nowhere."

Some three hours later every artillery piece of the entire invasion force began to pound their designated targets along the whole front and just before midnight the Polish guns switched their attention to their own particular targets: the enemy positions facing them on Monte Cassino. At precisely 1am Tomek's unit, supported by their tanks, moved out into the darkness and headed for the northern slopes of their objective. At first, things went well and only twenty minutes into mission their sister battalion managed to capture Hill 593 on their left, but Tomek and Doc were already in trouble, slowly crawling forwards on their stomachs towards a gorge four hundred yards short of their own target. They were receiving small arms fire from their right flank and mortar rounds from fortified emplacements on the gorge. Doc pulled Tomek close and shouted to make himself heard above the deafening noise of battle, "Make for that small pile of rocks on the left, we can't do much until the artillery and tanks take those mortars out, we're sitting ducks out here in the open."

Tomek and several others to his right all made for the rocks and as they set off they heard the reassuring sound of their own tank engines roaring some four hundred yards to their rear. They were spreading out across the only piece of relatively flat land on the whole approach. They started firing as one and before Tomek and his companions reached their own cover, the rock face of the gorge was peppered with dozens of rounds of high explosive tank shells. Once in the comparative shelter of the rocks they waited while artillery units joined in the vicious bombardment and continued to soften up the enemy positions.

The tank crews, with so little room for manoeuvre, soon came under very accurate fire themselves and two Sherman's were quickly destroyed by a combination of anti-tank bazookas and well-aimed artillery strikes. The whole battle scene was lit up by dozens of flares and exploding ordnance and the ground shook with the continuous detonations. Doc spoke to his friends, "We need to get to the gorge and try to outflank them, we should be able to climb up the side and then hit them from behind and the quicker we do it the better."

There were no better suggestions, but thirty minutes later they were still crawling forward and progress was painfully slow as they were forced to move with extreme caution, seeking whatever cover was available and constantly returning fire into the cliff-top gun emplacements. When they finally made it to the northern edge of the rock face it was almost dawn and, as Tomek looked back into the grey light, he saw that all of the tanks allocated to their sector had been knocked out and there was understandably no sign of any replacements being sent into such a vulnerable position.

The infantry were pinned down in both large and small groups in a semicircle across the whole line of approach. Those on the flanks had made the most progress but those in the centre were still two hundred yards short and he was puzzling over the cause when three mines detonated in quick succession in the middle of the attack line, explaining the distinct lack of progress. He turned to the others and confirmed what they were all thinking, "As if things aren't bad enough, now they're stuck in a bloody minefield and left without any armour support. We've got to knock out those guns on the top and give them a chance of clearing the mines and working their way to safety."

There were eight men and Doc took command, splitting their small unit in two to attack on both sides but first, working in the lee of the rock face, they had to climb. The ascent, though not difficult for a professional climber, was a totally different proposition for fully equipped soldiers, under fire and carrying an anti-tank Piat and a flame-thrower. Twenty minutes later, bruised and lacerated by the jagged rocks, they were on the top and there, spread out before them right across the small plateau were three machine gun emplacements, two mortar positions and several small artillery pieces. Doc issued his instructions, "Give us ten minutes to work our way round to the other side and when you hear my first shot take out the machine gun nearest to you with the Piat. If we catch them by surprise we can both work our way inward and meet in the middle before they know what's hit them."

Tomek, Doc and their two companions made it to the far side without being spotted and immediately attacked the nearest machine gun position whose crew was still concentrating on firing down into the positions occupied by the trapped Poles. Tomek fired relentlessly and in his pumped up condition continued to scream insults in their own language at the already dead Germans even as Doc turned the flame-thrower onto the second position. The Germans caught the full force of the vicious weapon as it spat out its lethal spray of incandescent heat and flame. Two survived the initial burst but ran around blindly screaming like banshees and burning like gigantic roman candles before Tomek mercifully brought them down with a burst from his sub machine gun.

They heard the distinctive sound of the Piat firing several rounds off to their right but by this time the enemy had started to react. A burst of machine-gun fire from alongside one of the artillery sites brought down a member of Tomek's team and Doc flinched, stumbled and almost fell as something stung him hard in the back of his left thigh. The other team saw what was happening and immediately took out the entire artillery site with another round from the anti-tank weapon. With that, the half dozen or so support troops who had been servicing the heavy weapons surrendered just as Doc finished off the remaining machine-gun position and another mortar site.

They did a quick search of the whole area and four more German sappers, who had been hiding since the start of the encounter, surrendered and at this point more Polish troops, having followed on behind Tomek's group, started to arrive. Over the next thirty minutes they established a defensive position on the ridge and the trapped men below, although still receiving fire from neighbouring hills were able to start clearing the mines and slowly join their comrades higher up. As their numbers mounted they became increasingly effective in putting down suppressing fire on the neighbouring enemy positions. The process of extracting themselves from the minefield then became quicker and safer but, nevertheless, a total of eighteen sappers died whilst clearing a way out.

The soldier hit at the same time as Doc had died from his wounds and one man in the Piat group had been seriously injured by a piece of shrapnel from an enemy mortar round that had exploded when the Piat was first fired. Doc's wound was examined by another combat medic and although it had bled heavily, it was found not to be serious, just a very deep graze probably caused by a ricochet off the rocks or a rock splinter. It was cleaned and dressed and, other than being very sore and causing him to walk with a pronounced limp, it had little effect on his operational fitness.

As the afternoon wore on they started to receive more incoming artillery fire and it became clear that the Polish attack was bogged down on all fronts and although their 2nd Battalion on hill 569 had managed to withstand repeated counterattacks, they were gradually being cut off and were now taking heavy and effective fire from all points of the compass.

The 5th Kressowa had also failed to secure their objectives at the Colle San Angelo ridge and also came under intensive artillery and heavy machine-gun-fire. Their difficulties were exacerbated by communication problems and a lack of co-ordination on the ground that left four companies virtually abandoned whilst holding the infamous Phantom Ridge. In the late afternoon, when the overall position became untenable, General Anders gave the order to withdraw under the cover of darkness and return to the start lines. Tomek and Doc left their position at 9pm and, with their prisoners, slowly made their way back down with a great deal of useful information from their captives. They had identified the individual German Parachute Regiment Units defending Hill 575 and the Phantom Ridge and also the San Angelo ridge and hill 608. Other prisoners later confirmed this information and they also discovered that the enemy had already withdrawn most of its elite 1st Parachute Regiment to reinforce their hard-pressed colleagues facing the British on the highway below.

Tomek was downbeat as they sat eating a hot meal the following morning, "I've been talking to the guys from the other battalions and our overall losses have been even heavier than I thought and what exactly have we achieved? Well, I can tell you, the answer is nothing: absolutely bugger all!"

Doc looked up, stretched his stiff and aching leg and said, with some authority, "That's not true. The enemy know they've been in a fight, their losses might not have been as bad as ours but they were heavy enough and it can only get worse for them. They won't be able to rest as the artillery and air-force will continue to pound them, sapping their strength and their will to fight. They're tired, besieged, facing the greatest powers in the world and not likely to get any reinforcements as long as we keep attacking on such a wide front. So young Tomek, you listen to me when I say one more determined push like yesterday and they will fold, perhaps not suddenly like a deck of cards but slowly and inevitably. If, like me, you want to be there when that happens eat your breakfast and stop moaning."

That day the Commanders met and became convinced that the enemy could not continue to soak up so much punishment all along the line. They were also bolstered by a degree of success in the Liri valley which they felt sure was bound to draw more enemy reinforcements away from Monte Cassino and so they drew up plans for another attack. It was to commence at 7am on the 17th May and Doc and Tomek were amongst a small group of volunteers from the 1st Battalion who, because of their previous encounter over the same terrain, were seconded to the Polish 1st Independent Commando Company. They, along with the 6th Battalion of the 2nd Carpathian Rifle Brigade, who were now at full strength, had been given the task of seizing and holding the gorge and then going on to capture the Massa Albaneta. This time Tomek knew what he was up against and felt far more confident of his own ability and that of his colleagues.

Things started to go the Poles' way on the evening before the attack when a company strength reconnaissance patrol, while attempting to take a few prisoners, engaged sentries at two emplacements on the northern edge of the Phantom Ridge. The enemy, caught off guard, were quickly overrun and the Poles pressed home their advantage by moving in a whole battalion and by midnight they had taken possession of the whole northern quarter of the ridgeline. They immediately dug in, making full use of the Germans' own defences. They also brought up specialist engineers and snipers who established a defensive cordon and a major observation post with excellent communications back to their Headquarters.

Tomek and Doc left on time with their adopted unit and within five minutes were in a vicious fire-fight with the machine guns, which the enemy had moved back onto the gorge. This time the Polish tanks were not being tempted into the trap but stood well off and, from cover, joined the artillery batteries and pounded their positions and with the advantage of daylight, British aircraft continuously fired rockets at the emplacements and reoccupied pillboxes. The sappers were also well prepared and in small teams cleared two paths through the edges of the minefield and the infantry poured through. Within fifteen minutes of leaving the start point Tomek was at the gorge and once on the top, his battalion set about clearing the enemy from their positions in vicious hand-to-hand fighting. The German paratroopers who had formed the backbone of the defenders were definitely thinner on the ground this time but nevertheless, all their troops were battle hardened and put up a stubborn and determined struggle. The attackers finally overwhelmed them and the Polish support units, using the cleared lanes, successfully negotiated the minefield and poured through the gorge towards Massa Albaneta.

Tomek and Doc helped set up a concealed fire control point amongst the rocks and whilst his battalion engaged the enemy with heavy machine-guns and bazookas Doc called in air-strikes onto the enemy positions, both ahead on the Massa Albaneta and onto the two hills on their flanks. By mid-day much of the enemy fire appeared to have been suppressed and the battalion started forward in their attempt to seize their next and most vital target. At first progress was good as mortar units gave supporting fire but when the lead elements were within a couple of hundred yards of the Massa Albaneta they came under a concerted attack from heavy machine-guns concealed within concrete bunkers built deep into the rocks and outcrops. Under cover of smoke, which was put down in huge quantities, Tomek, Doc and the commandos crawled forward to engage the gun positions one at a time with grenades and flame-throwers. They managed to destroy two, but things took a serious nosedive as they moved from boulder to boulder towards the next, which had been firing thousands of rounds blindly through the smoke over the approaches towards the gorge in the hope of inflicting serious damage. Two of their platoon were immediately hit in a hail of automatic fire and, as Tomek instinctively started to dive for cover, he was pushed violently in the back by Doc who was also leaping towards the same shell-hole. Tomek landed face down, his helmet flew off, his mouth filled with dirt and the wind was driven from his lungs as Doc's knees caught him squarely in the back. He was still sprawled on his stomach when he heard and felt Doc firing his sub machine gun alongside him and as he turned over others also fell into their refuge.

"Come on Tomek, I need some help here," screamed Doc as bullets whined over their heads and stones and lumps of earth were kicked up and splattered into them. There were now five Poles in the hollow returning fire at a group of six or so Paratroopers who had emerged from a hidden bunker on a ledge about fifty yards away to their left. They had obviously waited until the smoke started to clear in the wind and when Tomek's group had moved past their position they pounced from behind and it had cost three Polish lives and another two men were injured.

"We need to get out of here before they start lobbing grenades at us, so keep their heads down while I try to get around behind them," shouted Doc before he rolled over the top of the shell-hole and started to crawl away from the enemy position. He had only gone a matter of yards when another Polish Commando ran through the shifting smoke about seventy yards away on Tomek's left, firing straight into the group of Germans. Before they reacted, one fell to the ground mortally wounded in the chest and head and another two received serious injuries to the legs and arms. Tomek and his group seized their opportunity and joined the attack, running towards the Germans and pouring fire at the enemy. By the time Doc returned, the enemy group had all been killed or wounded, finally overcome when Tomek had thrown a grenade into the tangled heap of dead and injured.

Miraculously the Pole who had so bravely charged at them was unscathed and he joined Tomek's group who then, rather more cautiously, continued to work their way along the rocks to the next enemy pillbox. Others joined them and, using the flame-throwers, they started to burn the scrub all around the enemy positions and fire grenades into the trenches and pillboxes. After some three hours of fierce fighting the Poles began to get the upper hand and in some positions the enemy surrendered whilst in others they chose to fight on until they ran out of ammunition or they were killed. The number of German defensive positions, even in this small area of the battle, seemed endless to Doc and, weakened by his injured leg, he neared the point of complete exhaustion.

When Tomek and his friends were finally able to take a short rest, in the shelter of a particularly large outcrop of rock containing a concrete buttress supporting a knocked-out gun emplacement, he felt physically sick. The nausea was caused by a combination of the pungent smells from the thick black smoke of the burning scrub, the hot oil from the flame-throwers and the stench of burning flesh and death all around which he had not really noticed until he stopped fighting. By late afternoon the whole line of defences had been destroyed, over two hundred prisoners captured and then their heavy weapons were moved forward to take up new positions and threaten the only remaining quarter of the Massa Albaneta still in the hands of the enemy.

The Polish attacks on the surrounding hills also met ferocious resistance and as they made progress the Germans counterattacked and the battle seesawed all morning. Casualties on both sides were very high as ground was taken and retaken, often involving the use of knives and bayonets, as bunkers and trenches were cleared one at a time in close quarters combat. The Poles were also under constant mortar and heavy machine-gun-fire from the monastery and surrounding hilltops. However, the other big advantage to the Allies during this latest battle for Monte Cassino was that the Poles were drawing in huge amounts of enemy fire, manpower and resources. This eased the potential burden on the British and Canadians below who were able to make substantial progress in the Liri valley and they were also closing in on the southern slopes of Monastery Hill. By evening the enemy on the Massif were in serious danger of being cut off.

The Poles dug in and consolidated their positions on the targets that had been taken and as the reports poured in the picture became clear to General Anders. A huge hole had been punched into the enemy's defensive ring and they had suffered heavy losses, which, as things stood with the Monastery virtually isolated, they would find almost impossible to replace. Many of the hills, ridges outcrops, and fortified positions were in the hands of the Poles and this time they were not going to let that advantage slip. General Anders was well aware that he was now unable to obtain replacements for his casualties because, in retaliation for the official Polish protests over the Katyn murders, the Russians had broken off diplomatic relations with the Government in Exile and refused point-blank to release any more of the tens of thousands of Polish prisoners they still held. The only way he saw to overcome this major difficulty and also increase the overall size of the Polish army and thereby its political influence was for him to push on with the Allies into German occupied territories. He believed that he could then liberate and recruit tens of thousands of Poles that were held in POW and Concentration camps. It was with this and the forthcoming invasion of France in mind that he decided he could afford no further delays at this Italian bottleneck.

He committed himself to take Monte Cassino the next day and as all his proper reserves had been sent to bolster the attacks earlier in the afternoon he now deployed anyone he could find: the cooks, mechanics, drivers, defaulters, clerks, support staff and walking wounded. They were all given new rifles, formed into a makeshift battalion, and then he personally dispatched them to the line. As they left he reminded everyone of how they had suffered and exalted them to take Cassino, write their names in the history of such a bitter conflict and avenge their fallen comrades and their own families. Later he stood alone reflecting on the death and sacrifice of so many men of all nations on this one small spot. He was recapping the list of frustrations and delays heaped upon his allies over the last five months by the defiant and highly disciplined defenders when he received a personal message from Field Marshal Alexander. It congratulated him on the considerable achievements made by his men that day.

Wladyslaw Anders, the knowing and compassionate man inside the General's uniform, felt so proud of these troops who had endured so much, for so long, with endless fortitude and dignity. He was honoured to lead them and was motivated by their spirit, camaraderie and courage. He then prayed that the next day would not be too costly for his men who had so selflessly followed him thousands of miles. Firstly into the darkness of despair in the camps and then finally out into the light of hope, on the promise of an elusive freedom, and yet so many seemed destined to die, still so very far from home and whilst in his personal charge.

At dawn the next day Tomek was awakened by Doc shaking his shoulder, "Come on wake up, we're clear of the mines up here and we can join the Lancers on our left and follow them south." Tomek struggled to get his aching body moving but the company soon formed up and set out towards the remaining enemy positions. They were back in action within twenty minutes, but this time their mortars and artillery had clearer and less well-defended targets and they discovered that a significant proportion of the defenders had slipped away during the night. Nevertheless, the small rearguard fought hard and once again it was necessary for the infantry to mop up and there were still many casualties. By 10am they were in total control of Massa Albaneta and then they pushed on to their final target and en route resistance was light and sporadic. They were greeted by a scene of total destruction. Nothing remained of the Monastery. It had been subjected to repeated carpet-bombing which had reduced this once magnificent, beautiful and treasured monument to a massive pile of rubble.

They quickly gained access into the nearby bunker and command post and discovered that the enemy had retreated during the night to avoid being surrounded and destroyed. Hundreds of German troops had withdrawn to the Hitler Line and the small detachment of wounded Germans left inside offered no resistance and at last the Allies, the Poles to be exact, were in control of the Monastery and the heights of Monte Cassino. It was not long before Tomek and Doc entered the ruin and one of the German prisoners, a Sergeant, asked for a cigarette. Tomek obliged and said, "You're welcome to a cigarette but I'm afraid the war is over for you," and wearily sat down alongside him.

The prisoner, not in the slightest surprised that the Pole spoke such fluent German replied, "I'm glad that I don't have to fight any more and I rejoice that I'm still alive because as I sat here and heard you all speaking Polish as you approached, I expected the worse. Our officers told us that if you Poles took us captive we would be shot out of hand in revenge for what we have done to your country and your families. I didn't want to die here but we are all soldiers and do what we must, although I for one have no more heart for it. Anyway, thanks for the cigarette and, like you, I'm now looking forward to the day when we can all go home and live in peace."

Doc walked outside and immediately called out, "Quick, Tomek come here and look at this."

Tomek ambled out and saw Doc pointing up, and there proudly

blowing in the breeze high above the ruins was the Polish flag and all around them the heights echoed to the sound of thousands of cheering Poles. Many could hardly believe what they were witnessing and the sense of relief and joy was contagious and rippled from battalion to battalion right across those hills that had soaked up so much blood. The Poles alone, in just one week's fighting, had lost over a thousand men, killed, and more than another three thousand wounded or missing. The names of over 25% of their total strength were entered into the casualty list.

Shortly after the Polish flag was raised over the ruins General Anders received the following Telegram at Command Headquarters:

'All soldiers of the 2nd Polish Corps, I can sincerely assure you, that if I were to choose any soldiers to command – I would choose you. I salute you.' Signed – Field Marshal Alexander, Supreme Allied Commander, The Mediterranean Theatre of War.

Winston Churchill later met Anders in Italy to congratulate him on 'the outstanding performance' of the 2nd Corps. The General, not a shy or retiring man, took the opportunity to point out his alarm about what the Nazis were doing in Warsaw and his grave concerns about the Russian military setting up pro-Soviet local authorities and arresting Home Army personnel during its advance into Poland. He yet again reinforced his deep suspicion that Stalin was determined to prevent the re-emergence of a free and democratic Poland. Churchill, in his most resolute and reassuring voice, swore that neither he nor the British people would let Poland down and told Anders to trust him. Anders, determined that Churchill should fully understand the Polish desire for independence and their growing mistrust of the allies and their empty promises, replied rather prophetically, "Our wives and children are in Warsaw but we would rather see them perish and we, as soldiers, would rather die in battle than any of us should survive on our knees."

After Cassino the Corps were switched across to the Adriatic coast and began to work their way northwards. The Allies had over-stretched their own supply lines and needed to capture a major port in the north in order to bring in fresh troops and equipment nearer to the imminent battle areas, and General Anders was given the task of taking Ancona as soon as possible for that very purpose. As the Poles approached, the Germans were again holding prepared defensive positions in the hills overlooking the Musone River south of Ancona. On the 6th July the Poles took Osino just to the south and only eleven days later the battle for Ancona commenced. Two days of intense fighting followed before the town and harbour were securely in Polish hands.

In August 1944 they took a vital role in breaking the Gothic line at Metauro and then held the line awaiting the Spring Offensive. It then fought at Faenza and as news of the Yalta conference agreement filtered through its men felt a deep sense of anger, sadness and embitterment that Poland was to be consigned to the role of Russia's puppet. Whilst thousands of them had felt like throwing down their weapons in protest at the betrayal, they fought on and many more died. Harold Macmillan commenting on this very point after the war said, "They had lost their country but they kept their honour." Similar thoughts were in the minds of Tomek and Doc as they waited for the war to end and wondered what the future held.

Finally the Poles liberated Bologna, entering the city centre on the morning of 21st April 1945, after a ferocious struggle on the Santerno River with the German 26th Panzer Division. The 2nd Polish Corps had fought its last battle but its war for freedom would last almost another forty-five years.

Salisbury, Wiltshire: 20th October 2008

I entered my office to be greeted by a pile of unopened mail and a dozen telephone messages which had built up while I was absent. I had been called away to Manchester on urgent business on the 6th October and it had taken two weeks and endless meetings to sort the problems out. Although I was tired, it felt good to be home and I was eager to get back to the search for the Polish 'man of letters.' I opened the file and took out the last letter, the one I couldn't face last time because it seemed that they were becoming progressively more harrowing and tragically painful to read. It was written in Polish in navy blue ink on coarse paper, which had yellowed with age, and I immediately recognised the writing as Jacek's. There

212

was no envelope and with a mixture of trepidation and curiosity I started to translate:

To Jozef Nowaski
Care of The Rubens Hotel, London.
April, 1943

My dear Jozef,
I cannot describe the feelings of relief and pleasure that flooded through me when I heard back from Father Chepek with his prayers of hope, even though he had no news of our family. Yet those feelings were surpassed a hundred times when I actually received a letter from my big brother! It was made even more precious by the knowledge that several people had risked their lives to get it to me and yet they knew nothing of its contents. My happiness very quickly turned to abject sorrow and anger when I read what had happened to you and the fate that had befallen our wonderful mother. We will be avenged, of that I am sure and the very fact that we two have survived through so much means that there is indeed hope for our brothers and sister and we now owe it to our dearest departed parents to keep faith and pray for both the dead and the living. One day we may be able to talk together of these things in reverential detail and pay our proper respects, but in the meantime I must force myself to speak of other matters.

I was amazed to see that you were in London and I look forward to the day when we will meet again, perhaps in that very city as I fear it will be a long time before we get back home again. I am assured by our brave and loyal contact that this letter will be delivered safely and so I will tell you what has happened to me lately. I have been moved from the mines and my work detail is now employed building massive concrete gun emplacements along the coast where the labour is hard and unrelenting, from dawn till dusk every day, even Sundays. On the positive side we are fed reasonably well and they have now provided us with dark blue uniforms, so please, if you ever get to invade France, don't shoot at anyone wearing this distinctive garb because we only have shovels for weapons and so we can't shoot back!

The underground movement is particularly interested in our work and we smuggle what details we can to them. They are also eager for us to write letters and they undertake to get them out of the country because they read them first and extract any useful intelligence. Over time this enables them to build up a big picture of what the Nazis are up to in this particular area. We are still living in barracks but the guards are mostly old men or young boys and they are not particularly enthusiastic about their responsibilities, so their bored and slipshod attitude means that it's now far safer than it was to write in Polish. One or two of them, however, are far more dangerous and every now and then the SS inspects the works and barracks and then we have to behave ourselves or we are beaten or worse! Nevertheless we have learnt over the years that the Germans always avoid performing heavy physical tasks themselves and overall they tend to keep us healthy to do their dirty work. I can also say, from personal experience, that they genuinely believe they are superior to us and have a God-given right to rule over us. Can you believe that these monsters, many surely spawned by the Devil himself, can invoke the authority of God to their cause?

As I now have a reasonably assured route to you I want you to have the letter that Mama sent to father when we were in Warsaw with Uncle Roman. I found it on the mantelpiece at home just before you were captured and it's been with me ever since. Although it's all I have to remind me of her, I am fearful that it will be found by the guards and destroyed. I can't avoid the spot searches forever and I have already used up more than my fair share of luck in that department. I would also like Maria, Jan and Tomek to see it one day as it illustrates what a wonderful, caring and protective mother she was and how much she loved and cherished us all. I know that if it reaches you I will one day read it again, for what will be the hundredth time.

I will write again and remember, for our parents' sake, we must survive.
    Love Jacek.

I could hardly believe that Jozef had made his escape from Auschwitz, as I thought his chances were virtually nonexistent and I had never heard of anyone achieving such a feat. Presumably he had then managed to make contact with Father Chepek and discovered that Jacek was alive. I wondered what had happened to him since and tried to imagine what conditions might have been like in Warsaw in 1943. I was also relieved to know that Jacek was alive, albeit still in a German labour battalion, some two years after his last letter. How on earth did he then manage to join the Polish army in exile? Presumably, he too must have escaped at some stage, but I found it hard to believe that he could have travelled across occupied France and then crossed the Channel. As I thought more about it I wondered if he had been liberated following the D-Day landings and then joined up, as had happened with a large number of Polish prisoners.

The next thing that struck me was why on earth a letter to Jozef should be sent to the Rubens Hotel in London. It was obviously some sort of staging post for the smuggling of materials to Poland but I made a note to ask the people at the MoD, Polish section, if they could shed any light on it. Reminded of the letter I had sent them, I quickly checked my messages and mail but there was nothing back from them yet. The steward from the Amersham Polish Club had called back to say that his enquiries had come up negative but he would leave the notice up for a little longer. The secretary from The Polish Ex-serviceman's Association had also called back with a list of Polish Internet sites that catered for military reunions and wartime personnel searches. Although she felt it was a long shot she had highlighted two as the most likely to meet the needs of my particular conundrum.

It seemed that there was little more I could do until I heard from the Polish section, as all my other enquiries were peripheral in nature and hinged upon the Polish records. As I made a cup of coffee I wondered if The Rubens Hotel still existed and on impulse reached for the telephone. Directory enquiries were even slower than usual but eventually came up with a number. The hotel is still there, in Buckingham Palace Road and so I rang and spoke to the Deputy Manager who, yet again, was most interested in the précis of my search. He gave me a potted history of the hotel and told me rather proudly that during the war (since 1941) it was the Headquarters of the General Staff of the Free Polish Armed Forces. He told me they still had documents and photographs in the Library illustrating how the hotel had played host to all those within the highest echelons of both the military and governmental arms of the Polish Government in Exile.

When I replaced the telephone I was left contemplating what a young man, a Polish orphan, as far as I could tell not even a regular soldier, let alone a senior officer, would have been doing using the hotel as a personal post office box. I could not believe for a moment that the commanders and administrators, responsible for such a huge military force and the workings of a government would waste resources on, or even countenance such activity. I was awakened from my musings by the telephone ringing and unfortunately the caller was not about to provide me with breakthrough information about my search. No, it was my anxious business partner requiring an update about the Manchester meetings and so I was firmly brought back down to earth and into the present day with my own set of problems. None of them life threatening or even remotely dangerous, but rather mundane and irrelevant in the grand scheme of things: nevertheless they remained time consuming and somewhat frustrating.

TEN

The Ghetto Fire
15th April 1943

As Jozef rushed into the Operations Centre, where a group of senior officers of the Home Army were anxiously waiting for him, his District Commander was the first to speak, "Welcome back Jozef, take a seat and tell us the news from London."

Jozef, still out of breath, gathered his thoughts and then updated his commanders on the progress of the war from the Allies' perspective. He was questioned most closely and persistently about the position in the Caucasus where the Russian advances since Stalingrad had petered out and both armies were currently bogged down. The British and Americans were concerned because their Russian ally seemed to be negotiating directly with the Nazis, actively looking for a settlement, and a way out of the apparent impasse. Jozef and the commanders agreed that any private arrangement between Hitler and Stalin would sound the death knell for the prospect of a future independent Poland. They finally agreed that there was nothing they could do to influence this particular situation one way or another and so the briefing moved on to the requests made and assurances given by The British Ministry of War and their allies. Jozef reported that they were preparing plans for an invasion in northern France and southern Italy and they wanted the resistance groups all across Europe to delay any widespread insurrection until then. This would tie down thousands of German soldiers that could not then be diverted to reinforce either of the invasion sites. They promised to supply the Polish Home Army with more weapons and explosives and in addition special British (Special Operations Executive) and Polish (Cichociemni - the unseen and silent ones) operatives, versed in intelligence gathering, radio communication, sabotage and assassination, were to be parachuted in. Jozef stressed that their own government had also instructed the Home Army to refrain from any general uprising until the Allies, particularly the Free Polish Army, were in a position to provide a whole package of measures.

At this point Jozef became more animated because he wanted to convince his commanders that comprehensive military operations in and around Warsaw were currently being prepared in detail by the Government in Exile. He explained, "General Maczek, the commander of the 1st Corps in Scotland, has trained and equipped an independent parachute brigade under the command of General Sosabowski. They intend to drop these troops here into the very heart of Warsaw to support a general revolt, but only when the Allies are in a position to offer comprehensive air support from captured enemy airfields on mainland Europe. They feel that, without air superiority, re-supply would be almost impossible and our chances of success would be significantly weakened." He paused and looked around the room to allow the significance of his words to sink in and then continued, "The Parachutists will be supplemented by small specialist Commando teams of our own countryman who are also currently being trained in England. They'll be given specific targets to attack and destroy, or capture and hold, inside the city. We've got to select and train suitable members of our own Home Army to provide liaison, reconnaissance and fire-power support to each and every one of these teams."

"We'll be ready but what are we asked to do in the meantime, while we prepare and wait for the opportune moment?" asked the commander.

"Our current guerrilla hit-and-run war must continue or morale and battle readiness will suffer, but we should only attack when and where we have sufficient and recent intelligence to justify the risk. We've also got to consider the inevitable reprisals, often higher than the ratio of ten of us to every single Nazi killed. We need to conserve our men and munitions as much as possible so that we can be at our most effective when we eventually authorise a general uprising."

This observation opened up a wide-ranging discussion regarding future targets and actions and then they finally got on to the one subject that concerned Jozef the most, that of the Jews and particularly those trapped in the Warsaw ghetto. He summarised the outcome of his conversations with the various parties in London following the briefings given in that country by Simon, Lieutenant Ashton and himself.

"I explained to the British that things came to a head in January when the Jewish underground disrupted the last attempted mass-deportation by the Germans. I told them that street fighting inside the Ghetto went on for four days and the handful of Jewish fighters involved killed over fifty Germans and captured a significant quantity of weapons and ammunition. The enemy was undoubtedly taken by surprise and has since stopped the deportations."

The Commander added, "Bolstered by that success, the Jewish underground have now planned a major defence should the Germans try to restart the round-ups. Dozens of extra bunkers, tunnels and defensive positions, similar to our own, have been prepared and more weapons obtained from us and on the black-market."

"Yes, and I emphasised that this time the Jews would be ready and their commanders want to know what we in the Home Army will do when the fighting starts in earnest. Simon addressed our leaders and the British with passion and urgency on this very point but his pleas were not met with any enthusiasm. Our Command Authority seems reluctant to become fully involved in any possible Jewish uprising because of all the reasons we have previously discussed."

"What exactly did they say?" asked the Chief Intelligence Officer.

"They're convinced that we're not yet fully armed or strong enough for such a protracted campaign and they fear we could be totally destroyed before we reach anywhere near our fighting potential, particularly here in the capital. Our government and the Allies also want us to limit any involvement and urge us to keep our powder dry and wait for a more opportune moment, one that better suits their strategic aims. I explained that, on the other hand, witnessing the brutality and atrocities every day and constantly receiving desperate appeals for more help, it has become impossible for us, as close neighbours and fellow Poles, to stand aside.

"How did they respond to that?" asked the Commander, "Did they have any proposals?"

"They didn't say much and so I felt it was my duty to give them my personal view. We should do far more. Some of us, a significant number of volunteers, should be permitted to fight alongside them in the Ghetto. This would show solidarity, boost our own morale and that of the Jews and certainly give the Germans another major headache and hopefully a bloody nose!"

After a great deal of discussion that to Jozef seemed to go round and round in circles without any firm promise of significant help, he became frustrated and angry. He grew even more impatient when ten minutes later the talk focussed in on postponing any decision and he finally snapped, "For Goodness sake, we're all fighters here and at this point in time, in this upside-down world, that's exactly what I believe God wants us to be. When the Jews rise up as one, as they surely will, we must go to their aid because from what I've seen, we've done precious little up to now except treat them badly and we should be thoroughly ashamed of ourselves. They too are Poles but instead of treating them as brothers in arms, as equals worthy of fighting and dying for, they are treated with contempt and disdain. What's even worse, not only do we stand by as spectators while they suffer brutalisation, starvation and transportation to death at the hands of the Nazis, our own sworn enemies, but many of our own countrymen, including members of this army, willingly collaborate in their persecution and annihilation. I've heard the cries of 'Christ killer' shouted at them and seen the contempt, even hate in the eyes of some of my so-called neighbours and friends who all too willingly betray them to the Nazi butchers. Remember, it was Polish boys and young men who accepted the Nazi blood money to intimidate, frighten and even beat them up on the street just because they're Jews. Can't you see that the Germans take full advantage of our anti-Semitism and do everything they can to stir up jealously, hatred and internecine violence at every level of society? It makes me sick and it makes me angry and it makes me want to do something about it. How can we call ourselves Christians and patriots when we add to their humiliation every single day? If we don't act now, with force and determination, history may well judge us as complicit in their mass-murder. Whatever our allies say and ask of us now it will carry no real weight in the future when we, as a nation, stand accused of collaboration. Poland will never be forgiven for such a mortal sin. At best it will be seen as a crime of blatant omission, of cowardliness and bigotry. At worst, by those less sympathetic to our predicament, as one of wilful commission, a massive anti-Semitic conspiracy and a national disgrace."

The District Commander, his face bright red with rage, stood up and looked Jozef square in the face and banged his fist down on the table so hard that it shook, "Now you listen to me boy! You're not the only one who can get angry and feel righteous indignation. Yes, some of us, perhaps even many of us, have treated the Jews badly over the years. They've been looked down on and unjustly blamed for many problems of our own making. They've been bullied and abused and, in some areas, treated as second-class citizens but the past is the past and I can't change it. Of course there are collaborators and anti-Semitic Poles, some who even betray them and give them up to the enemy, in effect signing their death warrants. As terrible and unforgivable as that is, that's what war does to some people. It's not as clear-cut and clean as you suggest but rough, complicated and unpredictable. That's why there are also Poles, lots of them, many in this city, who for one reason or another also betray their catholic neighbours and our resistance fighters and we quite rightly in our current situation ignore their sometimes plausible, even understandable motivations and excuses and shoot them whenever they're caught. The Jews will do the same, but you must keep this in proportion because there are hundreds, perhaps even thousands of others of every age and every background who risk their lives every day to help the Jews. We trade with them, give them food, we smuggle them in and out of the city, we help them escape and we give them weaponry that we can ill afford to lose. Poles, even children, are shot on a regular basis for helping them, feeding them, talking to them, associating with them and showing them the most simple and commonest forms of human kindness. Any man woman or child that dares lift a finger to help a single Jew puts their whole family at risk of summary execution. I'm also under no illusion that Hitler will ensure that what happens to the Jews today will happen to us tomorrow. I draw strength from the fact that right across this once proud nation soldiers of our army and civilians alike risk arrest, deportation and death to help their fellow Poles, both Catholics and Jews."

He paused, drew a deep breath and stabbed his finger out, pointing at Jozef's chest. "You know this as well as I do, so don't you dare sit there all pious, pompous and judgemental and lecture me on what should or shouldn't be done. This is a disciplined army, fighting for its very existence and the survival of our country, not some moralistic debating society, so let me make this perfectly clear: whatever you feel inside you will do exactly as you are told, promptly, without question or hesitation. If we are ordered to give further help to those in the Ghetto then we will. If we are ordered to fight alongside them then we will do that too, otherwise we just do what we can but an order is exactly that, an order, and it's never to be considered by anybody, of any rank, as merely a basis for discussion. There will be no repeat of today's performance. We'll have time enough for recriminations if we manage to survive this occupation."

By the time he finished the commander was beginning to calm down but he was not in the mood for any further business: he was troubled, tired and deflated. He gathered his notes, looked around at the others, stared directly at Jozef again and said in a quiet, disappointed voice, "You are dismissed, now go back to your duties and I don't ever want to hear another word from you on this subject. It's closed!"

Jozef met Simon and Zenon later that evening, told them what had happened and blamed himself for losing his patience and handling the matter so badly. Simon listened without interrupting and then said, "You shouldn't feel responsible, you did much more than we could reasonably expect and your commander is right in the sense that too many of your fighters and the general population have already died on our behalf. After all, it was Waclaw (Codename for Colonel Henryk Wolinski) from your AK who was a prime mover in setting up the Zegota organisation (established to distribute food, medical aid and to provide safe refuge and secure long term accommodation for Jews). You probably don't know it but there are now nearly a hundred secret cells operating in Aryan Warsaw alone, and the Government in Exile, various Jewish groups and the general population all contribute to fund their work. Together with a couple of other groups they also help us escape from the Ghetto and the transports and find homes for our orphaned children (issuing false identity papers so that they could be hidden with

222

Polish families and given the chance to survive). As far as I know, it's also the only underground organisation run jointly by Jews and Polish activists. So there *IS* hope but it's time for us to fight our war on our terms and in our way, the Jewish way."

Jozef summed up his own feelings, "Even so, I'm ashamed of the deplorable way in which your people have been treated by many of us and I wish the resistance would do more to help you now. I understand that our commanders are in a difficult position but our collective weaknesses and prejudices are there for all to see, in the very language we use. Even when we talk to each other we don't refer to ourselves collectively as Poles or citizens of Warsaw but as Jews or Catholics, or Home Army or Jewish Resistance. We never see the many similarities that unite and strengthen us because we are blinded by the few differences that divide and weaken us."

Zenon added, "There's not much we can do to change things now. It's far too late for that."

Simon nodded his agreement and as they shook hands to leave he thanked them both and said, "My people have lived with suspicion and hostility for thousands of years, but we too must bear some responsibility for the discrimination and alienation that now surrounds us. History will be the true judge of events here and if, in making our small contribution, we remain true to our hearts then at least we won't add to the misery. We all know that we can't possibly win this battle. We might not even hold them off for very long but for us, just to fight as soldiers and kill the enemy, here inside the Ghetto, that's a real and telling victory. It will be remembered."

The next day Jozef heard from one of his contacts that the Germans were preparing a 'final action' to clear the Ghetto once and for all. The orders had been given personally by Himmler to SS Brigadier General Stroop to 'celebrate' Hitler's birthday on the 20th April. Jozef immediately informed Simon and his own commander and they made their preparations. Before dawn on the 19th two thousand SS troops supported by tanks, armoured cars, artillery, dogs and surveillance aircraft stormed into the Ghetto and, waiting in ambush, were about nine hundred Jewish fighters. On being tipped off the defenders had taken to the prepared bunkers and ambush points and the whole population of some fifty thousand literally went underground.

The German columns were attacked as soon as they entered and the Jews fought a courageous campaign, making full use of their superior knowledge of the local urban terrain. They picked their positions wisely and once the Germans started to get the upper hand at any one location the defenders melted away through the network of tunnels and sewers only to reappear and fight elsewhere. Although lightly armed they destroyed tanks and vehicles, inflicted heavy losses on the German soldiers and by repeatedly attacking at the bottlenecks they prevented them reinforcing their units already inside. The Germans were surprised by the effectiveness of the Jewish resistance and confounded by their tactics. So concerned were they for their own safety that they withdrew each night and, whilst this may have reduced their losses in the short term, it gave the defenders every opportunity to regroup and set up further traps and diversions for the following day, thereby prolonging the campaign.

A small number of specialist units from the Home Army, including a detachment of military police, were finally authorised to enter the battle and they too fought with distinction, trying to relieve and support their exhausted and besieged countrymen. Additionally small numbers of Home Army volunteers, mostly those from the Bund or with Jewish relatives, friends and military colleagues also fought and died inside the Ghetto, but for the most part the Jews battled alone.

Fighting was particularly heavy and protracted around Muranowski Square in the centre of the Ghetto. Simon's unit occupied well-fortified positions there and they successfully held off continuous German and Ukrainian infantry attacks that were supported by tanks and artillery. On the highest building in the area young men of the ZOB raised both the Polish standard and their own blue and white Zionist flag. Flying side by side they could be seen clearly from outside the walls and they quickly became a proud and defiant symbol of the Ghetto uprising. The Nazis found themselves fighting and dying under those flags for nearly four days and, despite deploying the whole panoply of military resources available to them, they repeatedly failed to take the position. Shortly after this considerable military embarrassment the SS started to burn down the Ghetto, building-by-building and then street-by-street and as they went they used gas, flame-throwers, dogs, explosives, artillery, tanks and even dive-bombers in an attempt to force the population, nearly all of them civilians, from the protection of their bunkers. The whole city was choked under a cloud of thick smoke for days on end and the death toll continued to rise at an alarming rate. It became increasingly obvious to the Germans, the Jews and the residents of the rest of Warsaw that this was such a one-sided battle that the result was not in question, but still the Jews fought on with bravery and pride.

Simon was wounded in the leg and chest on the eighteenth day of the struggle when leading a group of four Jews in a petrol-bomb attack on a tank. The tank was destroyed and he was rescued by his comrades and taken back through the tunnels to the command bunker. This important cellar not only contained the organisers and planners but several hundred terrified women and children, all seeking shelter. Over three weeks after the German incursion the SS reached and surrounded the command bunker and then started pouring in poison gas. The resistance fighters, realising that to fight on would mean a painful and certain death for the innocents trapped alongside them, managed to help many of the women and children to escape into the sewers during the chaos. The gas killed many others and those who survived and managed to surrender were summarily executed. Simon, who had used up all his ammunition, took the single bullet that he had always carried in his pocket for this very purpose, put it in his revolver and after a short prayer, shot himself through the side of the head. These brave Jewish fighters knew in their hearts that their own fate had been sealed the very day that the Germans invaded Poland but before they died they felt so proud of their stand against the might of the murderous SS and Hitler's tyranny.

That was not the end of the uprising however, as pockets of defenders fought on until all their ammunition finally gave out and the Germans continued to lose men until the 16th May. When the SS finally blew up the Great Synagogue the battle had lasted for twenty-eight days and by most estimates the Germans lost some three hundred men. Ten thousand or more inhabitants of the Ghetto were killed in the fighting and another thirty thousand were sent to the extermination camps. General Stroop sent a comprehensive and triumphant report, containing photographs and detailed descriptions of the massacre, direct to Hitler but the title page contained a short, stark and chillingly accurate inscription, 'The Jewish Ghetto in Warsaw no longer exists.'

Some Jews did manage to escape into Warsaw and beyond, into the forests where some joined communist partisans but many were later killed or recaptured, others were informed upon by collaborating Poles, but around a thousand continued to fight on in the ranks of the Home Army.

The horrendous bare facts, as shown by the statistics, are almost impossible to comprehend in themselves, but how much worse is it when one stops to ponder the identities, the lives and the human spirit that existed behind every single number. Of the five hundred thousand Jews that lived in Warsaw and its environs in September 1939, only twelve thousand survived the war. Four hundred and eighty eight thousand perished.

During the battle Jozef and Zenon entered the Ghetto on three occasions before the Germans destroyed their route. On each visit they smuggled in food, ammunition and some of their valuable medical supplies. They also managed to smuggle out a number of children who were then sheltered from the Nazis by Polish families.

Shortly after the Ghetto was destroyed the District Commander again summoned Jozef and this time there were no others present. "A terrible crime has been committed in our city and when this war is over we'll make sure that the Nazis are held to account. I know how you feel but we must never lose sight of the fact that the Germans, and only the Germans, are responsible for this outrage. You and I have not seen eye-to-eye in the past over what the Home Army should have done and so I've called you here to make sure that such a public disagreement doesn't happen in the future. I'm convinced that we were unable to do more and there is no need to go over the reasons, but like you, I'm left with an overwhelming feeling of guilt and shame. I also have a deep sense of fear that Warsaw and its people are now destined to suffer a similar fate unless the likes of you and me turn all our attention to protecting the people. We've got to significantly build up our arsenal of weapons and train thousands of extra recruits. If we're going to stand a chance of taking our city back then we need to become more professional in our thinking right across the ranks and optimise every single small advantage we may have. The Jewish fighters have shown that raw courage and enthusiasm won't be enough because the Germans are better trained, better armed, better disciplined and numerically far superior, so I need your support now more than ever before and we can't afford to dissipate our energies by arguments, infighting and general controversy. Someone's got to survive to bring these bastards to account."

Jozef could see that his senior officer meant every word he said and he admired him for facing up to the issue. He said, "Of course I'll always show proper discipline and I agree that we face a terrible danger. However, I also have an intelligence officer's duty to report any grave concerns or misgivings, especially if they are at odds with the Commander's personal views, but should this occur in the future I undertake to speak to you in private. I also fully agree with your analysis and there's no doubt in my mind either: sooner or later we'll have to rise up and so we need to take advantage of every moment we have left to prepare for battle."

The Commander was satisfied with Jozef's response and, after discussing recent German reprisals and the threat caused by the latest deployment of additional SS troops, they parted company with a mutual respect and a fierce determination to avenge the victims of the Ghetto. As the Home Army made its plans the Nazi grip on the city became even tighter and the daily struggle just to survive became increasingly difficult for the subjugated inhabitants. It was as well that they were unaware that Churchill, Roosevelt and Stalin were about to meet together for the first time, at Tehran, where they dispassionately proposed giving almost half of Poland to Russia after the war and Churchill even marked the new boundaries on a map. The spectre of Katyn hung over this meeting like a poisonous cloud threatening to seriously, perhaps even fatally, damage the alliance. All three leaders, therefore, chose to ignore the truth: Churchill and Roosevelt because they believed that the moral issue was overridden by their need to stop Stalin from seeking any private peace terms with Hitler; and by Stalin because the war crime was carried out on his personal written order. Churchill ignored the evidence provided by his security service proving the Russians were responsible by writing on the report, "I never want this mentioned again…" Roosevelt simply refused to believe his security advisors and took the personal and obstinate view that only the Germans were devious and cruel enough to perform such a terrible deed.

Stalin meanwhile, anxious to mitigate any possible antagonism from his allies, had ordered a massive cover up. Dozens of the Katyn dead were again dug up, this time by a special NKVD squad, and false Polish documents such as letters, personal items, passes and official military papers were planted on the corpses. These items were all dated during the period when Katyn was firmly under German control, following their advance into Russia. They then produced a propaganda film, which was released to the world purporting to scientifically prove, once and for all, that the Germans were responsible. They even bullied and threatened to kill the few locals, who had provided the Germans with witness statements implicating the Russians, until they retracted their original testimony. Even so, few were convinced by the elaborate deception.

It is almost certain that Churchill was prepared to offer Stalin the lands of eastern Poland as a concession, in the belief that the Soviets would then agree to his requirement of a post-war independent Poland. He also proposed that Poland be given German lands in the west in compensation. In other words the nation of Poland would be moved some one hundred and twenty miles westwards. In the end Churchill was outwitted by Stalin who secured Roosevelt's acquiescence to his demands and after only twenty years of independence Poland was once more consigned to occupation and foreign rule.

ELEVEN

Turning Point
18th July 1944

As they sat in the front of the army truck approaching the imposing sunlit fortress of Stirling Castle, Barry reflected on its past history and wondered what William Wallace would have thought about these foreign, east European troops being invited right inside this hallowed sanctuary. He was driving and Jan and Jerzy were sat alongside him but the rear of the lorry was empty as they, along with the rest of their battalion, were there to be equipped for war. The whole of the 1st Armoured Division, some fifteen thousand men, was on the move but first they had to be fully kitted out before their journey south and ironically Stirling Castle had been chosen to host this event. As they climbed down to wait their turn in the already considerable queues Jan said, "I'll be back in a minute, I'm just going to ask around and see what the latest is. We might be able to get a better idea of exactly what we'll be doing."

As he walked off Jerzy said to Barry, "I don't know why he bothers because most of what he hears is false rumour or our own propaganda and, in any event, by the time we get across the channel the position could have changed dramatically. My experience of war is that it's always total chaos and half the time even the Generals don't know what's going on, so what chance do we, the cannon fodder right at the bottom of the heap, have of finding out. Still, I don't want to dampen his youthful enthusiasm even though it won't last long once we get over there."

Barry eased forward in the queue and replied, "I know one thing for sure, I'm very apprehensive and can't really think of anything else except what's waiting for us. I'll be glad when we've arrived so that all this hanging around and worrying about what it's going to be like will finally be over. I'm sure Jan feels the same and rushing around to keep himself occupied is his way of dealing with the tension."

About five minutes later Jan returned, "Well this is the latest. It looks as if we could be landing at Cherbourg or somewhere nearby and at last the big breakout at Caen is about to happen. The adjutant says that's what we're going to take part in and it can't wait any longer because the Americans blame the British for getting bogged down and holding them up. They want us to get a move on!"

Jerzy replied, "If that's right let's be grateful that at least we won't be under fire when we land, whether on the beaches or in the port, and we won't have long to wait, so let's get our equipment together and get the truck loaded up. It's time to earn our pay at last."

They left two days later and travelled by train to the Port of London where they embarked on the allocated troop ships. In the event they landed on the 1st August at the Mulberry Harbour that had been towed across the Channel in sections and then assembled at Arromanches alongside Gold Beach. They were attached to the 1st Canadian Army and on the 8th August Jan and his colleagues went straight into combat. They possessed three hundred and eighty tanks, mostly M4 Shermans, nearly five hundred artillery pieces, the majority self-propelled, and over four thousand assorted vehicles. They did not know it at the time, but not only were they to take a crucial role in a crushing defeat of the German 7th Army, they were also to be pivotal in the chain of events that led directly to the German retreat and the liberation of France, Belgium and Holland.

The Poles operated on the British left flank and their first advance was south-eastwards from St Aignan-De-Cramesnil towards St Sylvain where they were met by an SS Panzer Division equipped with panther and tiger tanks. Both sides attacked and counter-attacked and the Poles called in air-strikes to make full use of the allied control of the skies and although enemy tanks were knocked out, American 'friendly fire' caused over three hundred casualties when a number of their heavy bombers were less than accurate. This in itself caused considerable delay in the advance and it incensed the Poles and Canadians. Shortly after, there was much ironic cheering in the sector when a number of American aircraft were brought down by German flak. For the next week they were locked in a struggle for supremacy with the German tanks and 88mm guns that retreated into prepared positions hidden in woods and copses. Huge clouds of smoke hung over the countryside as Jan and his friends slowly moved forward through areas that had been carpet-bombed and littered with the wreckage of German vehicles, tanks and equipment.

On the 15th August the Poles took a strategically important crossing on the river Dives, putting them on the east bank and simultaneously opening up the road to the major objective of Trun. They were now in a position to seal off the rapidly forming pocket of German forces that were being caught between Falaise and Argentan by the pincers of the American and British advance.

Jan's unit was in the forefront of the attack, supporting the tanks as they pressed on towards Chambois. On the morning of the 18th they moved to the north of Trun and they were ordered to take the high ground above Coudehard. This would give the Poles command of the Dives valley and place them directly in front of the only remaining escape route for the rapidly disintegrating German army.

The enemy had suffered three critical disadvantages. Firstly, Hitler by personal decree had prevented them from withdrawing to more defensible positions while they had the chance, thereby overruling the sensible suggestions made by his commanders on the ground. Secondly, the Allies now had total control of the skies and every time the enemy tanks, heavy weapons or convoys moved in daylight they were targeted and either destroyed or severely damaged. Thirdly, they were running out of fuel, ammunition and food, none of which could be replenished. Their overall position was becoming desperate and the tighter the pressure exerted by the Allies the harder and more resolutely they fought in an effort to squeeze through the shrinking gap and escape.

Shortly after dawn Jan and his comrades together with about twenty Sherman tanks and two Tank destroyer Mark 10s set out to take Hill 262, known locally as Mont Ormel. The tank destroyers consisted of a seventeen-pound anti-tank gun mounted on a Sherman tank body. Unlike the Sherman's own gun it was capable of piercing the armour of a Tiger tank from any angle. Mont Ormel became universally known amongst the Polish soldiers as 'the mace' because its geographical shape resembled the mediaeval weapon.

As the Poles approached they came under heavy fire from German infantry units already on the hill, armed with anti-tank weapons and heavy machine-guns. It was obvious from the start that they were determined to hold on to the position in order to keep the escape route door wedged open and to protect their colleagues as they massed below for the breakout. Two Polish tanks were knocked out almost immediately and it was a couple of hours before the Poles were able to outflank the strongest positions and then storm towards the top under the covering fire of their remaining tanks and supporting artillery. The isolated defenders, although surrounded by superior numbers and low on ammunition, refused an offer of surrender and most were either killed or wounded in the final surge as the Poles used hand grenades, mortars, and finally a bayonet charge to overrun the heavily entrenched and fortified position.

Only when they reached the summit did the attackers fully understand the true value of their prize and see why the enemy had fought so hard to hold on to it. As they looked down from their lofty vantage point they saw that the whole valley was a savage battlefield with thousands of enemy troops, guns, armour and vehicles struggling to escape from the trap. The enemy was being attacked from the air and by allied artillery to the west. Now the Poles realised that they were in the unenviable position of being 'the cork in the bottle' trying to contain the relentless and desperate tide of the German 7th Army, rushing to use the only two roads still open to them, but now they converged, not under the watchful eye of friendly forces, but directly under the Polish guns. The pressure on the cork would build to volcanic proportions and the battle for the mace would become a tipping point on the whole western front.

Jan, Barry and Jerzy dug in deeper on Mont Ormel right next to the Boisjois Manor House which had been considerably fortified by the Germans, who had also prepared a whole network of interconnecting trenches, fox-holes and observation posts of First

232

World War proportions inside the small wood and gardens which surrounded the building. The Poles laboured and sweated to repair the damaged defences and prepared for the inevitable attack with a great sense of urgency and anticipation that was almost palpable. They organised arcs of fire, mortar and machine-gun positions and zeroed in their heavy weapons on the most likely assault routes. Jerzy found himself working alongside their Canadian Artillery Observation Officer, helping to provide the co-ordinates and organise the artillery firing patterns that would target the two roads under the hill. He was also in contact with the communications centre controlling the devastating air strikes of the rocket firing typhoons, mustangs and the night fighter mosquito aircraft that were being used to such good effect to attack the enemy armour, vehicles and columns. Many of these aircraft were flown by Poles, serviced by Poles and armed by Poles, who wrote their own personal messages of vengeance and ridicule, in Polish of course, on the tank busting ordnance.

The Polish pilots were delighted to be there, attacking the pride of the Nazi war machine, a replica of the armoured columns that had decimated their towns and villages five years earlier. They hardly slept as they volunteered for mission after mission: they took off, swooped, fired, destroyed and with a joy in their hearts that only the phoenix can truly appreciate they landed, re-armed and attacked again and again. They always looked for secondary and subsequent targets until, within a matter of days, it became an act of collective pride, a club rule, that they never returned until all their ammunition was gone. The pilots' joy was immeasurable when they saw, for the first time, the markings of the 1st Polish Armoured Division on the tanks as they flashed across allied lines heading for the enemy: flying at extreme low-level, a tactic which proved devastatingly effective against the armour and artillery that was running out of places to hide.

On the ground Jerzy explained the situation as he saw it to his comrades, "If we can hang on here, we can control everything that goes on down there and cause havoc with our tanks and artillery, but before very long they're going to throw everything at us. They know that if we stay, then our other units will form on us and once the gap is firmly closed, they're finished. They're desperate to break out and will see us fresh arrivals as the weakest link. As far

233

as they're concerned their only chance is here and now, so it's our job to keep them well and truly bottled up until either the Yanks or the Brits can close in and deliver the coup de grâce."

Jan was the first to point out the obviously negative aspects of this assessment, "That's all very well but the rest of our division is stretched out so thin towards Chambois and back to La Cour Du Bosq that they can't possibly hold the whole line and that means that our own small battle group is going to be even harder pressed here. So somebody is going to have to get a move on and send us some very serious help straight away or half the German army will get out tonight. There's no way that we can stop all that lot down there, not on our own. It's simply impossible."

Barry agreed and he was far more concerned with their own position than the larger picture, "He's right, we've got to face up to the fact that just like the Germans here before, we're isolated and we've already lost nearly half our strength fighting our way up. I don't think help is on the way and food and water is low and we're not over-blessed with ammunition either."

Jerzy responded with more bad news, "To make matters worse the doctor was one of the ones killed by a mortar-shell on the way up and all our medical supplies went with him. Now we've only got what we carry with us. I can't see help coming any time soon either, so I reckon we're going to have to rely on the artillery and air-strikes to support us."

Jan had heard enough, "Anyway, we can't change anything. Jerzy, you just make sure you keep that radio working and stay close to the Canadian Officer because he certainly knows what he's doing and without him I'm not sure how much artillery support we could rely on from our allies. Most important of all, let's look after each other."

Even as they were talking, a major convoy of Germans approached up the two roads towards the intersection right under the escarpment. There were heavy guns being pulled by horses, trucks loaded with troops and others marching alongside intermingled with tanks, half-tracks, motorcycles, pedal cycles and even a line of large uncamouflaged black staff cars. It looked as if half the German army was approaching their hill. The Canadian called in the artillery and as the head of each convoy reached the bottleneck in the narrow lanes they were caught in a blanket of high explosive and armour-piercing shells put down by sixteen guns. The Polish tanks, hidden in the trees on the crest joined in and the Germans were caught, trapped right in the middle of an infernal killing field as salvo after salvo fell with pinpoint accuracy. Their vehicles caught fire and exploded, several before any of the soldiers could get out. There was total chaos as the dead and injured and the horses were crushed under the tank tracks as the powerful and now irreplaceable machines desperately tried to sprint out of the ambush. Vehicles were driving into one another as they attempted to force their way through, and into this catastrophe the shells continued to fall remorselessly. The Poles on their vantage point deafened by the noise and mesmerised by the bloodbath saw metal, machinery, bodies and body parts flying through the air before the scene was mercifully masked by waves of smoke that drifted up as vehicles, loaded with the last of their ordnance, exploded. The tanks were quickly destroyed as their Polish counterparts treated them as a first priority. As the few survivors ran through the trees lining the lane into the open fields on either side, the Polish machine guns opened up and allied aircraft fired rocket after rocket into the mayhem and within fifteen minutes the entire column had been totally destroyed.

The lane was blocked with burning vehicles, and dead and dying horses were piled high alongside the charred and smoking bodies of the unfortunate soldiers. The smell of smoke, oil, and burning flesh rose up from the valley floor to wash over the Poles until all their senses were inundated by the scale of the German losses. Although the Poles had pulled off an amazing feat of military coordination, timing and pinpoint accuracy, and had received no extra casualties themselves, they did not rejoice in the slaughter, for slaughter it surely was. They had seen too much, in Poland, in France and in their flight across Europe, the promise of vengeance had then been sweet but this harsh reality, close up, was no cause for pleasure.

The enemy was now fully aware of the Poles exact position and their potential to cause disaster, so orders were issued to remove them at any cost. The Poles however, continued to improve their defences, dug deeper and again called for reinforcements but were told that the Canadians, on their way from Trun and the Americans pushing up from the south around Chambois, had both been halted by heavy engagements and had their own hands full. Jerzy, in a serious and uncharacteristically downbeat frame of mind spoke to his two friends, "Listen, we're now completely cut off and nobody's coming to help us, certainly not tonight and probably not tomorrow. The Krauts are trapped and desperate and their only way out is either to sneak past on either side during the night or roll right over us and I think that they'll try both before long. If I'm honest, I don't really know whether we can hold out for very long but like the enemy here before, we can't surrender either. If we want to live much longer we've just got to stop them somehow."

The infantry were given the order to move to slightly lower ground in an effort to limit any infiltration and the tanks were left alone to hold the summit. As Jan and the rest dug in for what seemed like the hundredth time in the last few weeks and occupied fresh trenches they were told that they could withdraw to the higher, and better prepared ground only if they were in danger of being totally overwhelmed.

Once again the Poles relied heavily on the inch perfect accuracy of the artillery and their tanks, as the enemy took to the countryside and advanced in the centre, to the left and to the right. The fighting at the lower levels was intense as the infantry attempted to storm the Polish lines. They successfully breached the defences on many occasions but each time the attacks were eventually repulsed by bitter hand-to-hand fighting and, with their numbers reduced yet further, the Poles were able to reclaim their defensive positions.

Miraculously Jan's team managed to survive the night almost unscathed but come morning they discovered how close they had come when Barry picked up a dud Model 24 Stielhandgranate laying amongst their spent ammunition and other discarded battle debris on the floor of the trench. The fragmentation stick grenade, or the Potato Masher as it was known, would probably have killed them all had it exploded in the confines of the trench. Daylight also revealed the intensity and viciousness of the hand-to-hand fighting. The Germans had been scythed down like wheat by almost continuous automatic fire, reminiscent of First World War massacres. The red-hot curtain of lead had ripped into and clean through them and their shattered bodies had piled up three and four deep to the front and to the sides of Jan's trench. This barrier of corpses had helped to protect them from the subsequent attacks. It had been a close thing as two storm troopers had crawled past the corpses, right onto the lip of their trench before they were bayoneted by Barry and Jerzy and then unceremoniously piled on top of other dead attackers to form another human revetment. All three Poles were near physical collapse and covered in blood, sweat, grime and dust but they marvelled at their narrow escape. Dozens of the occupants of other trenches and positions were not so fortunate and had been killed or badly wounded.

The slopes on three sides were littered with German corpses and in and around the foxholes and trenches dead and dying Poles lay entangled with the bodies of their enemies. Despite their combined best efforts it had proved impossible to prevent pockets of infantry and armour escaping on either side and with the morning light the Poles also discovered that they were now totally surrounded, as the sparse defensive line stretching out either side of the hill had been overwhelmed.

They consolidated their positions at dawn, even as the Germans continued attacking from all sides. The daylight however gave the Poles back their advantage of all round visibility: they could no longer be surprised and they could also call in more aircraft to support their precarious position and prevent further exfiltration by the enemy. Their ammunition was getting dangerously low, food and water had run out and their few personal medical supplies were exhausted, so Jerzy called in priority airdrops and although many canisters fell into enemy hands they were partially replenished by the Royal Air Force. This was in itself testament to the pilots' skills as they ran the gauntlet of enemy ground-fire and Jan wondered if the pilots were also Polish and perhaps they realised what a dire position their own ground troops were in. Gradually, with the use of their last mortars and grenades, the Germans were beaten back from the lower slopes and were then pounded by the Polish tanks and artillery. There was no shortage of reinforcements for the Germans as tens of thousands were trapped in the pocket and from these, hundreds of SS troops, supplemented by armoured vehicles and heavy weapons, were again given the job of driving the Poles off the hill.

Life for the Germans in the trap was unbearable and they could literally not move without being attacked and decimated. It was a case of escape now or die in the effort. Throughout the day, wave after wave of the enemy suicidally attacked in the face of concerted and withering machine-gun-fire. Hundreds died in the attempt but by sheer force of numbers the Poles were gradually driven back up the hill: but still they clung on, fought on and died rather than give up. Their Major, who had been badly wounded, staggered from position to position encouraging his men to hang on a little longer, although he knew that relief was not imminent.

It was as he spoke to Jan and his team that the tanks were first heard and as they watched they thought the end had definitely arrived, because a line of Tiger tanks was advancing on their rear. Elements of the 2nd SS Panzer Corps were attacking from outside the pocket in another desperate attempt to open the road for their trapped colleagues. The leading tanks broke through the perimeter and started to shell the Polish tanks whose crews had been caught by surprise. Several were destroyed almost immediately but the remainder were ordered to do the very thing that the Germans did not expect – attack!

As the German shells burst all around, Jerzy lay in the bottom of his trench with the Canadian officer who was calling in the prepared co-ordinates for the artillery, the only thing that could possibly save them. Even as he spoke he thought the call might be too late: if the enemy were too close then in a few seconds their own shells would also rain down on the Polish tanks and probably themselves as well and that would be it. The Major took the risk of looking out and saw that several more Polish tanks had been knocked out, but only one approaching Tiger was burning. Then the ground shook and the air was sucked from their lungs by the force of the sudden explosions only a hundred yards from their position. The roar caused temporary deafness and the ground continued to shake as more and more shells crashed into the enemy tanks and supporting infantry.

One Polish tank was also knocked out by the 'friendly fire' but the rest survived and pressed home their own attack. As soon as the shelling stopped the surviving Polish troops poured from their holes in the ground and charged forwards, following their remaining operational tanks as they raced towards the Tigers to attack from close quarters. The shelling had destroyed half a dozen Tigers and now those left unscathed could not make the best use of their armament without risking hitting each other as the nimble Shermans manoeuvred amongst them, attacking them from the

238

rear, their weakest point. The German attack stalled and then, as another Tiger was destroyed, they finally broke into full retreat.

Jan, Barry and Jerzy, amazed at the accuracy and rate of fire of their artillery crews, ran screaming down the hill: all fatigue a thing of the past as the adrenaline coursed through their veins. As the enemy tanks sprinted for safety they dived to the ground and, working as a disciplined and well-practised team, started to machine-gun the retreating infantry who were now caught unprotected in the open ground. Hundreds fell before they could make it back down the hill and then, in the ensuing lull, the Poles returned to their more concealed positions in the woods. The tanks did not attack again but the infantry did and the Poles continued to take heavy losses throughout the afternoon and into the evening, and when some ran out of ammunition they charged the enemy with bayonets and then used captured weapons. Many German prisoners had been taken on the slopes, some of them no more than children, fifteen and sixteen years of age and a dozen turned out to be men of Polish birth. When given the choice they decided to change sides. Within minutes they had enthusiastically joined the diminishing ranks of the defenders, replacing their grey tunics with khaki jackets taken from the dead and turned their weapons on the Germans.

The two country lanes and the slopes of the hill on every side were like a charnel house with thousands of bodies and the critically injured lying on top of each other. Some of the survivors had crawled under the bodies of their dead comrades to avoid further injury from the Poles who, although conserving their ammunition, fired at any target that they considered to be a direct threat.

There were less than two hundred fully fit Polish fighters left on the hill and that night they withdrew inside a small defensive enclave on the summit. The wounded were moved inside the perimeter of these trenches that were now to be held come what may. This was to be their last stand and the Major chose his words carefully as he addressed them all, "Even now when all is probably lost, we will fight on. We will not surrender and if the SS take this hill it will be because we are all dead. Whatever happens to us, your stand here will be written in our history and our country could not have asked any more from any of you. As your commanding officer I have been astounded by your unswerving courage, emboldened by your ferocity and inspired by your patriotism. It has been an honour to fight alongside you and if I am to die, then it will be in the finest company on God's earth. Our ammunition is all but gone and it's now going to be every man for himself, but I know that if you have to you'll throw rocks and anything else you can find at the enemy: the same bloodthirsty hoard that have raped and murdered their way across our country. I am proud of you all and I know you won't give up, so good luck and God bless every one of you."

They prepared for the next attack and Barry who had received a severe cut to his upper left arm without even realising it, pulled the makeshift shirt tail dressing tighter and said to his friends, "I don't know about you two but I'd like to think we'll all live to see this through or all die together. Since I was a boy I've never really been any good on my own, so I don't fancy being the last one left and I certainly don't want to end up facing life as a cripple, so if things come to the worst I hope I've got the nerve to finish myself off."

Jerzy shook his head, rubbed at the gritty tiredness in his eyes and threw his helmet into the bottom of the trench in exasperation, "For goodness sake, don't be so bloody morbid. Despite my initial fears we've fought well, been lucky and made it through the worst, so we certainly don't need anybody else preaching doom and gloom on our hill. Now is not the time to be pessimistic. I know the Major meant what he said but I still want to grow old and anyway if we were meant to die, then I think that grenade in the trench would have done for us already. No, I'm convinced that God is keeping us going because he's got a purpose for us, so we'll definitely live to see tomorrow and perhaps, if we're really lucky, even the next day."

Jerzy was right, for at dawn the next morning the tanks of the Canadians, the 4th Armoured Division to be exact, arrived to relieve them and yet even then the Poles did not sit tight in relative safety and wait for them. There were Germans still dug in between the oncoming Canadians and the hilltop and they possessed anti-tank weapons, so the Poles formed up, shared out the little ammunition they had salvaged from the dead and injured along with the captured German weapons and told the Canadians what they were going to do. As the whistle sounded they fixed bayonets, gritted their teeth, and in a skirmish line rapidly charged down the hill. The enemy were watching the oncoming tanks and still deciding what to do in response when the Poles, now screaming and shouting abuse, caught them by surprise.

Once the attackers were in amongst them the enemy broke and, although a few ran off towards the flanks, hundreds of others lowered their weapons and surrendered there and then. Caught between the tanks and the fired up, fatalistically reckless charging infantry they had no fight left. The Poles jumped up and down and ran around cheering and congratulating each other in delight but as the euphoria quickly subsided many sank to their knees and prayed and others cried, with tears of relief or a deep sadness for their lost comrades.

Totally exhausted by lack of sleep and the accumulated physical and mental strain they slowly drifted back up the hill for the last time. For three days and nights they had been fighting continuously for their very survival, and against all the odds, the 'cork' was still in place. They had paid a terrible price. On this one hill over four hundred and fifty were dead, over one thousand wounded and they had also lost a dozen tanks. For the Germans it was total carnage, some two thousand dead or missing, five thousand taken prisoner and over fifty tanks lost. This was not the true cost, however, because once the pocket was firmly secured fifty thousand German prisoners were taken.

Amongst the prisoners, across the whole front, there were hundreds of Poles who had been forced into penal battalions and labour battalions. They were rounded up, interviewed and then given the opportunity to join the Division or continue as prisoners of war until their true status could be established. Almost to a man they joined their countrymen and the 1st Polish Armoured Division found itself in the strange, unique and enviable position of immediately being able to replace most of its numerous casualties. Within a week it was back to full strength. This was an amazing achievement when one considers the fact that the Division had lost a total of two thousand three hundred and twenty seven killed or wounded: a quarter of its front-line force.

The Allies won an astounding victory with the destruction of the German Seventh Army and most of the Fifth Panzer Army. A total of fifteen thousand German soldiers were killed and virtually all their tanks, heavy guns and vehicles were destroyed. It was said that after the battle it was possible to walk for miles along those narrow country lanes stepping on nothing but dead, maggot-ridden bodies and decaying flesh. The fields were covered with burnt-out tanks, trucks and tons of abandoned equipment and supplies. The rivers and streams were full of the bloated bodies and body parts of men and horses and Jan was surprised to have discovered that the modern, mechanised, well-equipped SS army, the pride of Hitler and his Generals, still relied on hundreds of horses to transport its heavy guns, just like the Polish equivalent that he had seen as a boy back home.

Of the twenty thousand who escaped the pocket, most were quickly caught as the Allies rushed forward from Falaise. The success also saved many lives as it prevented the enemy from withdrawing in good order and then fighting a series of attritional delaying actions, from defended positions that would have slowly ground down the Allies resolve.

The Division was given six days in which to rest and replace their damaged vehicles and equipment before returning to the front and driving towards Holland and Germany. The Rifle Battalions were reorganised to absorb the hundreds of new recruits and Jan and his friends found themselves transferred to the 9th. They pursued the enemy along the coast and liberated Abbeville, St Omer, Ypres, Passchendale and Roulers and then relieved the 7th Armoured Division at Ghent. It carried on northwards and on several occasions the Germans turned and fought, particularly fiercely along the Scheldt River and canal system, but the Poles pushed on relentlessly.

They were anxious to reach the Rhine and cross into Germany to release more Poles from the POW and concentration camps. Of all the allied troops they were the most impatient and yet their commander, General Maczek, who was in the habit of leading his men into battle by riding in the forward tank, did everything he could to limit his own casualties and prevent civilian deaths. He had seen in Poland what unrestricted warfare by the Nazis could do to the general population and he was determined to be humane and protective to both his men and the people he had come to liberate. He was admired and deeply respected by his soldiers and it is no exaggeration to say that they would have followed him anywhere.

They called him 'Baca' which means 'Head shepherd' because he constantly watched over them and, as much as possible, kept them out of trouble.

They then linked up with the 1st British Corps and captured Baarle, Nassau and Alphen and by the middle of October they were closing in on the city of Breda, which the Germans had turned into an armed camp. At 0600 hrs on the 27th October Jerzy and his two friends were amongst a platoon of soldiers being briefed by Wittold Vranek, their relatively new Sergeant. "This is a combat patrol to test the strength of the enemy in Ginneken, the village about a mile ahead. Locals have told us that the inhabitants were expelled last week as the enemy moved in en masse and set up observation posts and heavy machine-gun positions. The small reconnaissance patrol we sent out last night didn't return and we've had no contact from them. So we leave at dawn in full company strength."

They approached the village making full use of the woods and hedges but almost immediately came under fire from a couple of self-propelled guns hidden in the woods on the far side of the village. Sgt. Vranek shouted his orders, "Run for the village itself, they won't fire if we can get near their own positions. Jerzy, call in some help to get stuck into their artillery and get some suppressing fire put down into those nearest buildings so we don't get cut to pieces before we get there."

Jerzy relayed the commands and then sprinted forward in an effort to catch his colleagues, who were now within a couple of hundred yards of the nearest buildings. As he closed the gap he heard his own mortars start to land just beyond the first houses and the company ahead hit the ground and started to fire their light machine-guns just as the enemy opened up with their own automatic weapons. The mortars started slowly creeping back towards their own positions as their crews zeroed in on the enemy and in no time they were exploding on and around the houses. The Poles took their chance and charged towards the buildings, even as the mortar rounds were still landing, trusting to the timing and accuracy of their comrades who had learnt their skills and precision over three months of continuous combat. Three of the Poles were brought down by rifle-fire before they reached the buildings, but they were soon cleared of the enemy as Jan and others threw in grenades and then burst in through the doors and windows firing short bursts to mop up any survivors. Within five minutes the first row of houses had been taken over and six Germans had been taken prisoner.

Jerzy and Jan quickly interrogated the prisoners who told them that the Germans were dug in on the other side of the village in Battalion strength and snipers with small assault teams had been scattered amongst the houses. Jerzy gave a full report over the radio as enemy shells continued to fall into the fields they had just crossed. The Polish artillery was also firing in an attempt to knock out or drive off the enemy guns. Unknown to Sgt. Vranek or the Company Commander, another Polish unit had been ordered to bypass the village and attack the enemy gun positions.

After a few minutes the German guns suddenly went silent and the Poles moved forward into the next line of houses with the Polish mortars firing over the village into the area in which they suspected the enemy had dug in. Once in the built-up area the enemy resistance seemed to melt away and Jan quickly found himself unopposed, right in the middle of the village. As he looked around from his vantage point at a second floor window he instinctively sensed that the enemy had suddenly and uncharacteristically withdrawn from what was clearly a perfectly defensible position and he suspected a trap was being set. He heard over the radio that the rest of their battalion was now coming forward to take possession of the village and his company was ordered to try to outflank the enemy position and report back on their numbers and deployment.

Jan became even more uneasy and voiced his concern, "Sarge, I think something is seriously wrong here. The resistance is too light compared to what the intelligence and the prisoners have told us. I think it's a trap and once the battalion moves up towards the village the Germans will open up with everything they've got and we'll all be sitting ducks, especially if they manage to get around behind us."

The Sergeant thought about it and again looked at the prisoners: he didn't think they were lying but he also suspected things were not what they seemed, the whole set-up seemed wrong. It wasn't a properly prepared defensive position, the approaches hadn't been mined and the enemy was too thin on the ground. He made up his mind, "Tell them what we think and get the battalion recalled until we get to the other side of the village and can see what we're really up against."

244

Jerzy called up on the radio but before the battalion could fully withdraw back to their starting point the enemy artillery opened up again, but this time there were ten times as many guns and they were far more accurate and the lead elements of the battalion were caught in the open. Dozens were killed and wounded in the first few salvos but fortunately most were not committed too far forward and withdrew to safety as the barrage continued. Sgt. Vranek was livid and blamed himself for not reporting their suspicions earlier. He ranted and raved at the prisoners and threatened to shoot them but Jerzy intervened, "They probably didn't even know what was going on, they were the bait in the trap and we walked right into it. Let's find out what they've got waiting for us up ahead."

As they moved forward slowly, clearing a few buildings at a time they came under sporadic rifle-fire, but it was nothing they couldn't deal with. When they reached the far end of the village they had about twenty prisoners and there were a similar number of enemy dead, mostly by the initial mortar fire. Two more Poles had been killed and several wounded. There was a brief but heavy fire-fight with a group of about fifty Germans who were withdrawing across the open ground towards their own lines and this caused about ten more casualties on both sides. At this point the enemy artillery turned its attention to the village. Several houses took direct hits and the Poles decided it was time to leave. Jan was just walking out of a backdoor when, in between the explosions, he heard a child crying. He thought he must have imagined it but as he stood there in a sudden and almost unnatural silence, cocking his ears, he heard it again and it was definitely the distressed wailing of a young child. He called to the others, "I can hear a baby crying in here, come on back and help me look."

They scrabbled around the broken and abandoned furniture and as Barry pulled a rug from the floor they all saw the dust-covered trapdoor. Barry opened it up and light flooded down the wooden steps but there was no immediate sign of life: just as he started down they all heard the muffled cry of a child. Jan signalled Barry to wait and called out in German, "We're Polish soldiers, here to free you. The Germans have left but we're all in danger from the shelling. We've got to get out now. We'll take you with us, so please come on up."

The first to emerge was a man of about thirty-five years of age:

he was covered in dust and looked overcome with relief when he saw their British uniforms and Polish insignia. He spoke in broken German but it was soon clear that he had been hiding from the Germans with his wife and child. They had no time for further conversation and they ran to the cover of the next building as the shells whistled down once again. As they withdrew they dived for cover on several more occasions. Each time the soldiers shielded the civilians with their own bodies and the woman clung on to her two-year-old daughter who was terrified and screaming. When they were about two hundred yards from the couple's house it took a direct hit, was virtually demolished by the explosion and then engulfed in flames and smoke. They heard another shell on its way and again dived to the ground, Barry sprawled across the woman's upper body and Jan fell against him over her legs.

The detonation was very close and Jan was immediately spattered with blood and he knew that one or more of them had been hit. Nobody moved as they momentarily lost their senses from the noise and shock of the explosion. They were all covered in a thick carpet of dust and rubble and were choking from inhaling the dust-laden air. Jan was the first to move and he immediately saw that Barry was dead having been struck in the side by a six inch piece of shrapnel that was embedded against his spine having ripped a huge hole through his rib cage. He carefully removed his body and as Jerzy staggered to his feet alongside he checked the woman and her child. The woman was in deep shock and couldn't take her eyes off Barry's mutilated body but she and her child appeared to be physically unharmed. Her husband and Jerzy were also uninjured and as they staggered from the village they saw the battalion streaming across the open ground towards them. They were to learn later that the enemy gun-battery had finally been outflanked and attacked. Although they attempted to withdraw, leaving their artillery pieces behind, they were finished off by the combined efforts of British aircraft and the Poles own heavy guns.

The shell that killed Barry was one of the last fired before the guns were abandoned and then destroyed. They recovered the bodies of all the dead and Jan reflected on the randomness of war and was deeply troubled that his friend had died right next to him and yet, apart from a few scratches and bruises, he was unscathed. He felt guilty that he had survived and the consoling words and practical advice from his other close friend did little to assuage his self-recrimination.

Jerzy was also deeply affected by the death of their close friend but was comforted by the fact that his death had saved the life of the woman and her child. They learnt that Eduard and Ingrid Crutzen had been hiding in the cellar because he was a member of the Dutch underground and although wanted by the Germans, he had been secretly visiting his wife. For this reason he could not allow himself to be evacuated from the village with everyone else for fear of being recognised or informed upon. His wife, fearful for the life of her husband and child, would not leave without him and so they elected to stay and wait for the allies to arrive. They, like Jan and his friends, had not anticipated that the whole exercise was a trap to pull the unsuspecting Poles into a lethal, concentrated artillery barrage.

Mrs. Crutzen personally saw Sergeant Vranek and expressed her eternal gratitude, explaining that the family owed their lives to the Poles and she was distraught that, as she put it, their unselfish Christian compassion had cost Barry his life and put the others in such jeopardy. She wrote down the Sergeant's details together with those of his unit and promised she would contact him after the war to tell him of their situation and express her gratitude in a more fitting manner. The soldiers moved on the next day towards Breda and although thoughts of Barry were constantly with them and they continued to mimic his accent as a tribute to him, they quickly forgot the details of that one Dutch family that owed the soldiers their lives and their freedom.

The battle for Breda started with a classic pincer attack: from the north into the Germans' weakest front, and simultaneously from the south. Although the confrontation was hard-fought the Germans were caught off-guard and by the time they moved reinforcements across the city the Poles were already in the outskirts. The enemy never recovered its ground and was constantly being outmanoeuvred and several elements of the defending units surrendered almost immediately while others retreated with the hope of regrouping. The German commanders soon realised that their position was weakening rapidly and they failed to create a really cohesive plan in response to the Poles' sudden and unexpected appearance to their rear. The whole City was liberated by the end of the following day and the civil celebration lasted considerably longer than the German resistance.

General Maczek had managed to take the City without causing any major damage to its infrastructure and, as many of its inhabitants rushed back from the surrounding countryside, they were amazed to find their homes and businesses remarkably intact. The Officers and men of the 1st Polish Armoured Division, known to the locals as The Black Devils, were all given the freedom of the city in recognition of their feat. Today an original Polish command tank still sits proudly on display as a monument to the foreign soldiers who, in the course of seeking their own freedom, succeeded in securing the freedom of so many Dutch citizens. The depth of their gratitude can be measured and witnessed at the appropriately named General Maczek Museum. On the fiftieth anniversary the Dutch authorities struck a special medal for their liberators, simply but respectfully inscribed, "We thank you Poles." The medal lists all the battle honours of the Division's campaign across Europe.

Jan's abiding memory of Breda was the sight of the massive spire on the church, towering over the other buildings as, surrounded by the detritus of war left by the retreating Germans, his company marched along the country lane towards the battle. It seemed to guide the Poles like a sacred beacon. Later, in the city centre, his spirits were lifted once again when he saw the Dutch and Polish flags flying side-by-side from the upper windows of the Vroom and Dreesmann (V&D) department store. As he marched past he felt so uplifted by the warmth of the reception given by the Dutch population and he prayed that the Polish people would one day feel the delirious happiness and release as shown by those who danced around and kissed the marching soldiers. He also reflected on the last few years of his young life and hoped that the war would soon be over: perhaps before his nineteenth birthday.

After securing the town of Moerdijk the Division had taken all of their allotted objectives and they spent the rest of the winter holding the front along the Maas River and unit-by-unit they managed to get some well-earned leave. As the weeks went by they became increasingly frustrated, wanting to push on into Germany but being held back. Their allies were involved in political intrigue, arguing over who would hold sway over Europe post-war, but all were giving ground to the Russians.

The Poles started to fear that Stalin would tighten his grip on Poland and when news spread of the brutal crushing of the Warsaw uprising by the Nazis and of the Soviet complicity, inaction, and political duplicity, their worst fears were realised. They wondered what the five years of heartache, suffering and the sacrifice of so many men and women had been for, because by now many suspected that they would never return home, never see their families and perhaps even be destined to live as refugees themselves. However they honoured their commitments and when allowed to advance they finally entered Germany on 9th April. Three days later they liberated the Oberlangen POW camp and released one thousand seven hundred women who had been captured while fighting for the Home Army during the Warsaw uprising. Many told their personal stories of the unbelievable brutality, degradation and evil perpetrated by the Nazis' on the Jews and Poles alike. Less than a month later they captured the naval base at Wilhelmshaven where, along with the port and the East Friesian fleet, ten infantry divisions surrendered to the Poles. As the war ended they settled down to occupation duties in the Emsland region of northwest Germany, near the Dutch border and were soon given an extra but welcome responsibility. There were seven million people in Germany at the end of the war who had been deported from their homes all over Europe as slave labour and over nine hundred thousand were Poles.

The Allies started to create a Polish enclave in the area controlled by the 1st Armoured Division because most of the homeless Poles refused to be repatriated fearing Russian persecution. Poles from all over Germany, including many Jews released from concentration camps and Polish prisoners of war, were drawn to this area by the prospect of aid from the Free Polish Army. German villagers were evacuated to make room for them and they were amongst the first of the fifteen million of their countrymen that were forced to give up their homes to make room for eastern European refugees at the end of the war. Most were forced out of the area of eastern Germany that was handed over to Poland following the Potsdam Conference and the redrawing of borders. They later became known collectively as 'the expelled' and the Bund der Vertriebenen (BdV) was formed within Germany to represent them. Ironically, most of their former homes were quickly occupied by Poles that had also been forcibly removed from their towns and villages and sent west: this time by the Soviet Government as they took possession of the eastern third of Poland and repopulated it along ethnic lines.

Before August was out some forty thousand Polish refugees had arrived in Emsland. Within months this was a self-sufficient community with its own schools, police, fire service, Mayor, churches, newspapers, health service and even theatres and a university. The liberated women from Oberlangen worked throughout the various villages in every role imaginable and it was one such woman, a nurse at the hospital, that stole Jan's heart. They met at the theatre where Jan was enjoying a traditional Polish comedy, to such an extent that he couldn't stop laughing. It was a long time since he had experienced such fun, enhanced as it was by the security and familiarity provided by the close community: almost a normal Polish town within Germany. As he left he was still thinking of the play and chuckling to himself when, in the darkness, he accidentally bumped into Nurse Magda Macuta and then stepped on her toes. Despite his clumsiness and her initial embarrassment their attraction was instant and mutual and within days the romance blossomed into a passionate and carefree affair. They spent all of their free time together and Magda quickly won the respect and friendship of Jan's friends, especially Jerzy, who was delighted that his charge had at last found happiness and a sense of normality in his young and all too violent life.

TWELVE

Both Sides in a Day
6th June 1944

Jacek looked out across the huge swell in the English Channel towards England, as he did several times every day, but the low cloud and sea mist limited visibility and so he returned to his task of mixing the concrete. Six months ago, along with many of his friends in the mine, he had been reallocated to the army of prisoners that were now building massive gun emplacements and other coastal defences to protect northern France from an Allied invasion. As he worked away mechanically he considered how ironic and repetitive history could be and wondered if the long-talked-about invasion, the thrust to finally remove the tyranny of the Nazi occupation, would ever come.

The locals had told him that at this very spot in 1803 Napoleon had assembled a massive fleet so that his 'Grande Armee' could invade England. Could it be that the British and Americans would now make the same decision as Napoleon and very late in the day call off their planned invasion? If it went ahead, would it land at the very location where another military dictator had stood staring across the narrow strait towards his enemies? On the exact same spot where Jacek and his colleagues were now being forced to build impenetrable bunkers for the massive 'Atlantic Wall', a project undertaken by the paramilitary Todt Organisation, named after its founder Fritz Todt who had won acclaim for building the Autobahns. Following his death in 1942 the organisation was taken over by Albert Speer who ran the Ministry of Armaments and War Production and now also made vast profits from the toil, blood and all too often the death of many of the one and a half million slave labourers, euphemistically called Fremdarbeiter (foreign workers) who had been placed at his disposal.

At school Jacek had been an avid student of European history and now he remembered how he had listened intently as his teacher told the stories of Napoleon waging war on Prussia, Austria and Russia, the very countries that by partition had eradicated Poland as a nation. He knew that tens of thousands of Polish patriots had rushed to the banner of their enemies' enemy and so he fully understood why many Poles still saw Napoleon as a friend and liberator, not as the self-serving despot and tyrant seen by many others who believed he had always intended to betray such naive Polish loyalty. The famous Polish Legions formed from this flight to the flag had fought with distinction in Italy against the Austrians and in Iberia against the British and, in response, Napoleon created the Duchy of Warsaw, which Poles across Europe hoped would be the foundation of a free Poland. In Italy the Legion formed under General Jan Dabrowski adopted a battle song (Dabrowski's Mazurka) that was later to become the Polish National Anthem, and as Jacek remembered his school lesson, which had been delivered with such passion and inspiration, he realised that the famous words were still just as poignant and relevant as they were some hundred and fifty years earlier. Without further thought he found himself singing:

> *Poland has not died yet*
> *so long as we still live…*
> *That which alien force has seized*
> *we at sabre point shall retrieve…*
> *March, march, Dabrowski*
> *to Poland from Italy…*
> *Let us now rejoin the nation*
> *under thy command.*

The Emperor had been impressed by the military competence of the Polish Officers and their men, their strident determination in adverse battle conditions and their personal bravery. He was quoted as saying 'eight hundred Poles would be a match for eight thousand enemy soldiers.' In 1812 he additionally offered them the promise of independent statehood if they would again rise up and give him the excuse to invade Russia. Not only did they comply but Prince Jozef Poniatowski's Vistula Legion were the first to cross into Russia, the first to enter Moscow and, showing themselves to be amongst his most battle-hardened, resolute and ferocious fighters they then also formed the rearguard to cover Napoleon's disastrous retreat.

The Polish Lancers were the crème de la crème, not only of the Polish Legions but also of Napoleon's Imperial Guard, and they became so famed and feared throughout Europe that many nations imitated their training, equipment, deployment and tactics. Of the five hundred thousand soldiers of the Grande Armee, Polish troops of the 5th Corps had made up almost one hundred thousand, but at the end of the Russian campaign only 25% had survived. Jozef Poniatowski proved himself a warrior of epic proportions, a hero of heroes who, following his gallant and well-documented death on the battlefield became a swashbuckling cult hero. His achievements were exaggerated by repetition and, over time, he grew into a legendary figure of derring-do and an inspiration for Polish freedom-fighters ever since. He was also held in the highest regard by Napoleon who said, "He was a man of noble character, brimming-over with honour and bravery. I intended to make him King of Poland had I succeeded in Russia"

In recognition for his unswerving loyal service and his military prowess he was awarded the rare and distinguished military honour and title of Marshal of France and the inscription on the baton presented to him was most appropriate: *Terror belli, decus pacis*, Terror in war, adornment in peace. The remnants of the Polish Legions remained fiercely loyal to Napoleon and later at the battle of Waterloo they fought with distinction and once again, held their ground to the very end.

Jacek was snapped out of his reverie by the noise of whistles blowing right across the site and he saw that the guards were running around, in uncharacteristic panic, shouting demands at each other and screaming at the labour gangs to stop working and to fall in. Several of the workers, bemused by the unseemly and unprecedented chaos, nervously stood their ground, unsure of the consequences of what was happening, and one pointedly asked what on earth was going on. No answer was forthcoming, but Jacek instinctively knew that such a strange reaction from all the guards could only mean that they didn't have a clear picture of their own situation, whatever it was. Matters appeared to be slipping out of their control and that wasn't necessarily going to be a good thing for the prisoners.

Jacek, unable to kerb his glee at the Germans' discomfort, looked up at the nearest guard, a member of the Hitler Youth and no more than fifteen years old but with the rank of Obermeister. In a quiet but mocking voice the Pole asked, "What's all the fuss about? It's only mid-afternoon and nowhere near time to knock off for the day, so it must be serious. I know: either Hitler's decided to let us all go because we've done such a good job for him building these bunkers or he's had a good long think about things and he's now sorry he started the war in the first place. It was all a big mistake and he's on his way here right now to apologise in person."

The guard unslung his rifle, pointed it at Jacek's chest and spat at him, "You Polish pig, I should shoot you where you stand. How dare you insult the Fuhrer? Just because you speak our language it doesn't mean you can drag yourself up from the shit where you live with the rest of your Slavic degenerates. You're still an ignorant bastard and it's about time you learnt some respect for your betters. You're not fit to live on the same planet as decent people, now fall in before I blow your insolent head right off your unworthy shoulders."

Jacek was somewhat surprised by the guard's violent reaction. Such threats would have been typical a year or so ago but over recent months they had been far less hostile and the beatings and abuse had become rarer. He knew that he was asking for trouble by ridiculing Hitler but the guards' uncharacteristic behaviour and their obvious alarm had encouraged his defiance.

All two hundred workers were loaded onto the trucks to be driven back to their barracks just outside the fortified old town section of Boulogne on the English Channel, twenty-five miles south of Calais. Jacek's neighbour asked, "What do you think's going on? They're definitely worried about something and I get the feeling we aren't going to like it very much."

Jacek suddenly realised that only one thing could send them into such a spin, "It's the invasion! The Allies have landed, that's why they're all in such a state."

"But surely if the invasion had happened we would have seen it, or at least heard the guns firing from all the emplacements and bunkers that we've built over the months. No, it can't be that, the sea's too rough anyway," chipped in one of his friends and many others added their agreement.

"Let's just think about this. If you were going to invade would you do it where your enemy has prepared massive defences and would you do it on a day when the sea is like a millpond and the entire world expects you? No, you'd do it while the sea is rough so no one is watchful and you'd do it elsewhere so that you can take him by surprise. I tell you it's happened and probably earlier on today," reasoned Jacek. There were many nods and statements of approval but most were reluctant to allow themselves to believe it for fear of disappointment.

Once the transport arrived back the prisoners were not allowed to return to their barracks but were paraded on the square where twenty additional SS troopers were lined up under the command of a Captain. The prisoners had learned to hate the SS, and with good reason, but Jacek and his comrades immediately recognised that there was something different with this particular squad. The officer looked the typical arrogant, self-possessed, Hitler worshipping, Arian bully but his men were decidedly uncomfortable, were unusually slovenly and were definitely Slavic in appearance.

The Captain addressed them, "The foolish British and the pampered Americans have attempted to land their inferior army on the coast of Normandy and, even as we speak, our brave and victorious forces are slaughtering them on the beaches and pushing them back into the sea. As a reward for your hard work and diligent service to the Reich you will now be given the chance to win your freedom and at the same time perform a service for the Fuhrer. You will be split into groups of ten and each group will be allocated one of my men who will command you. You will be armed and when we reach the line each man will be given ten rounds. You will then stand your ground and fight the enemy. When they are all driven back you will be freed and given the honour of German citizenship or you will be dead. Heil Hitler."

The prisoners remained totally silent as the Captain marched forward and stood directly in front of the first line of Poles. He looked at the first person in the line and asked in a perfectly normal voice, "Do you undertake to do your duty and fight to the death for the glory of the Fuhrer?"

The unfortunate prisoner didn't know what to say. His previous knowledge of the SS and his drive for self-preservation strongly urged him to reply in the affirmative. However his innate patriotism, his hatred of the Germans and the fact that he had been singled out first in front of his peers caused him to hesitate whilst he tried to think of a non-committal answer that would satisfy both pressures. As he deliberated the Captain pulled out his Luger pistol and without a second's pause shot the prisoner in the heart. He fell as if pole-axed and the only noise to be heard immediately following the loud report of the weapon was the sickening thud as the body hit the hard ground. He then calmly holstered the weapon, took out his handkerchief and began to wipe the blood spatters off his uniform tunic. As he did so the sun appeared from behind a bank of cloud and the rays reflected and bounced off the Captain's wrist-watch as his hand moved, dancing across the labourers' faces as if searching for his next victim.

They remained rooted to the spot as the other SS soldiers cocked their machine pistols and took a threatening pace forward towards the Polish labourers. There was not a single Pole present who did not believe that the Captain would order their execution there and then if they gave him the slightest provocation. He then coolly and menacingly moved on to the next man and asked the identical question and the words had hardly left his mouth before the prisoner answered, "Yes, Sir."

The SS officer went along the whole front row and all the Poles answered in the affirmative. Apparently satisfied, he addressed them once more, "Let me make your position absolutely clear. Whether you live or die is entirely up to you and yes, you may fight and be killed by the enemy, but I assure you that if you disobey just one order or if you hesitate for just one second like your dead friend, you will be shot. Now return to your quarters, training starts at dawn."

Once in their huts the Poles were divided up into groups of ten and as their SS 'minders' started shouting orders it became clear that, although they spoke German, they were Ukrainian collaborators attached to the Waffen SS and they did not like the Poles. Every order was accompanied by a rifle jab or a punch or

256

kick and they only ever spoke to give orders or utter a stream of verbal abuse. Like the Captain they expected immediate and complete compliance and Jacek was prepared to acquiesce and bide his time but he had already decided that now that the allies were close, he would escape. There was no doubt in his mind and despite his current circumstances he felt a rush of real optimism and excitement.

For the next eight weeks they remained in the barracks and underwent training every day, each session being supervised by the SS Captain who only spoke to threaten and cajole. They had been given standard infantry rifles and learnt how to strip and clean them, but at no time were they given any live rounds. They constantly practised weapons drill and undertook physical exercise and unarmed combat training with instructors who visited daily. Jacek and many others entered into this regimen with enthusiasm and vigour, learning as quickly as possible and soaking up information like a sponge.

At one session a dog ran onto the training ground and started barking and playfully jumping up at the prisoners. Jacek whistled and when the dog approached he knelt down and spoke soothingly to the animal. As he petted it the SS officer approached and stood over them. He watched impassively as the dog rolled contentedly onto its back. He pulled out his Luger, cocked a round, ejected the magazine and then handed the weapon down to Jacek. "Shoot it," he commanded without emotion or further explanation.

Jacek slowly stood up with the weapon in his hand. Such was the power and coercion flaunted by the SS man that he had no doubt that if he refused, then he would be killed. For a fleeting second he considered shooting the officer but he knew that the reprisals would be swift and numerous.

"Shoot it," and this time the order was screamed at him.

To his everlasting shame Jacek pulled the trigger. He was to be haunted by nightmares of his betrayal of the trusting animal because the incident would inexplicably and permanently scar him far worse than many of the human horrors he had and would endure.

On the 6th August they were driven to a staging area near Rouen where they were always kept under armed guard and separated from all the other units that were being mustered. The Poles took every limited opportunity to plan and discuss escape and most resolved that if they were ever given ammunition for their rifles when on the battlefield they would turn them on their guards and attempt to surrender to the Allies. That afternoon they were loaded into the trucks and driven off towards the west having been told that they were going to the front. They had heard the sound of distant guns all day and had sighted British aircraft to the west on several occasions whilst waiting at the staging post. Several times during the journey the transports pulled in under trees to avoid the British spotter planes and everyone was ordered out of the vehicles to take cover.

They spent the night in their trucks and the following afternoon they arrived safely at their destination, Potigny, six miles north of Falaise. They marched forward and took up positions in an orchard alongside a small farm to the east of the village. They were ordered to dig in but were still not issued with any ammunition, even though the sounds of battle appeared very close to the north and west. Returning reconnaissance patrols told them that a Canadian armoured regiment was only a few miles north.

They spent a sleepless night as the fighting got ever closer and in the morning hundreds of German troops and tanks passed by their orchard, moving forward to engage the Canadians. The Poles were kept on alert all day and listened with increasing concern to the sounds of a very heavy engagement taking place just forward of their position. That evening German troops started pulling back through their position and the Poles were finally issued with the promised ten rounds of ammunition. Just as darkness approached they came under attack as the Canadians and their tanks appeared out of the woods about three hundred yards ahead. The Ukrainian guards started firing at the advancing infantry and Jacek calmly turned to his right and shot the one in the trench alongside him. Other Poles had the same idea and one shouted at the top of his voice, "Come on, let's get the bastards," and they attacked the guards all along the trench lines.

Three or four Poles were killed in the initial exchanges with the Ukrainians, but most jumped clear and started running south. Before they had covered ten yards the Canadians also opened up and several Poles who were caught in the open were immediately cut down. Most then sought cover behind the fruit trees and in the hollows in the ground but Jacek and about a dozen of those leading the escape were then fired on from in front. Someone shouted, "It's the SS Captain – over there to the right!"

Jacek saw him standing behind a tree deliberately firing at the Poles, picking them off one by one. He knelt down, aimed carefully at the German and fired two shots in quick succession and was surprised to see his target go down. Bullets were ripping into the trees and tearing up the ground all through the orchard and the leading Poles were already sprinting into the lane that ran south from the farm. It was lower than the surrounding fields and its banks and hedges offered significant cover. Jacek reached the SS officer and saw that he had a bad stomach-wound but he was still conscious. He looked up at the Pole and with pain and hatred in his eyes he spoke accusingly in a weak and rasping voice. "You treacherous, cowardly Polack, I knew you would break and run. You'll be hunted down and killed for this and I hope you rot in hell with all the other worthless bastards."

Jacek dropped to his knees, looked the German straight in the eye and then picked up the German's machine pistol and placed the leather strap around his own neck. Next he took the Luger from its holster at the German's side and whilst still holding his stare he forced the barrel into the German's mouth and pulled the trigger. As he stood up he noticed the expensive looking watch on the Captain's right wrist and on impulse he took it. As bullets stitched the ground around him he took one final look at his victim and felt exhilarated that he was finally fighting back. Revenge was sweet but there was no time to savour the moment and he ran for his life towards the lane with bullets ricocheting through the tree branches above his head.

Several dozen Poles were running ahead of him and Jacek instinctively made a decision that probably saved his life. He realised that if a group of them approached either the Germans or the Canadians, no matter how carefully, they were inevitably going to be fired upon because the soldiers would all play it safe and shoot first. Furthermore they were bound to run into more Germans within a matter of yards. He decided that it was time to take his chances, rely on his own ability and strike out on his own. He scrambled up the bank on his left, pushed his way through the hedge and started to crawl back towards the farm to hide in an outbuilding and wait for the opportunity to surrender to the Canadians. He had only crawled a few yards when machine guns opened up about another hundred yards south along the lane. He imagined his colleagues being cut to ribbons in their escape route, the sunken lane that had now become a death trap as it approached the next line of German defenders.

It took him over an hour to crawl to the farm and on the way he heard the Canadians pass by and several tanks roared through within fifty yards of him. He was terrified that he would be squashed by a tank and several times he had an overwhelming urge to stand up and surrender. The increasing darkness was both a blessing and a curse because whilst it helped him hide it also meant that if he made any noise at all he would draw fire. He was wise to resist the temptation to show himself and to wait for daylight. Very soon the attention of the Canadians was taken up as they engaged the next German line that had already fired on the escaping Poles, further down the lane.

He used the cover provided by the noise of the engagement to burrow his way into a massive pile of logs and dead tree branches leaning against a wooden chicken-house at the side of the farm buildings. He wasn't too sure of how well he would be hidden from view come the morning, but he was relieved to hear the battle moving south. He started thinking about the practicalities of surrendering and shuddered at the thought of being shot by the Canadians after he had endured so much at the hands of the Russians and then the Germans. He remembered something from school and thought that the Canadians spoke both English and French and that might help because he had learnt a fair bit of French at school and practised it down the mine in Mazingarbe. He decided that however he made contact, he must not startle them and he tried to stay awake so that no one could get too close without him hearing.

Despite his best efforts fatigue caught up with him and he eventually drifted off into a shallow sleep and when he woke it was already daylight. He kept perfectly still and listened intently but, other than the birds and the distant sound of heavy guns, he could hear no sign of life. He decided to stay where he was, as he could see to the north through a gap in the logs and he felt that he was reasonably well hidden, although he suspected that he would be easily discovered by a close or careful visual inspection. He remembered the watch he had stolen and took the opportunity to examine it. It was certainly a fine piece of Swiss engineering; a water resistant TAG Heuer chronograph with a replica of an Olympic Games medal engraved on the back with the words 'Berlin 1936' underneath. Jacek wondered if the Captain had been a successful athlete at Hitler's showpiece Games or whether it was just a commemorative issue: either way he was sure it was valuable and worth holding on to.

He began to get cramp in his legs and was just about to shift position, in an effort to stretch the seized muscles, when he heard voices. He held his breath and kept perfectly still and then he caught sight of movement off to his left. As he watched a patrol of about ten soldiers appeared round the side of another barn. They were being very careful, moving slowly and staying low to the ground. They were not bunched up and from their khaki uniforms he knew they were definitely not Germans. As he watched they moved across his line of vision towards his right and as he strained to hear he felt sure that they were not speaking French and he became unsure what to do. If he called out, even in French they might just shoot and if he called in German or Polish that response was even more likely. He agonised for a second or two, fearful that if he let the opportunity go he might not get another one all day or worse still, the Germans might counter-attack and retake the position. Just before the Canadians left his field of vision, he made up his mind.

He pushed his way out through the logs and to his tired, stiff and cramped body it seemed to take forever and when he managed to stand up reasonably straight he shouted in his best French, "Don't shoot, Don't shoot, I surrender. I'm a Polish prisoner of the Germans."

At the first sound of the logs falling several of the soldiers turned in his direction and trained their weapons on him. By the time he had finished speaking every single soldier was concentrating on him and they had all dived to the ground. Just as he was about to breathe a sigh of relief, convinced that the worst was over, several shots rang out and the bullets slammed into the wood pile a yard to Jacek's right. He instinctively fell to the ground uncertain whether he had been hit, expecting another hail of bullets at any second. Instead he heard orders being shouted but he couldn't understand the English.

"Hold your fire, he says he's Polish and a Kraut prisoner, just keep him covered while I speak to him." The same voice then spoke in French, "Stand up slowly and put your hands on your head."

Jacek did exactly as he was told and the Canadian ordered him forwards but almost immediately shouted again, "Put your weapon down immediately or we will fire."

Jacek suddenly realised that although he had left the machine pistol in the woodpile the Luger was still in his belt. He slowly took it out and holding it by the barrel dropped it on the grass. "I'm sorry, I forgot I had it, my name is Jacek Nowaski and I was in a forced labour battalion and escaped last night."

The French-speaking soldier approached him and picked up the Luger, spotted the SS insignia inscribed on the handle, examined the Pole closely and then inspected his dark blue, almost black uniform. "I think you're lying and you're SS. How else would you possess this gun? They don't give them out to prisoners."

One of the other soldiers then examined the Luger and said, "It's a lovely weapon Sarge, a really accurate semi automatic P08, a recoil operated 9mm. One of the best they've ever made and judging by its shine and immaculate condition it's been well looked after. There's no mistaking these symbols, he's SS alright; the same lot as those assholes who run the concentration camps that the Intelligence Officer in England was telling us about."

A colleague added, "His sort has given up any right to fair treatment. I say stuff the Geneva Convention and we should do ourselves a favour and shoot the murdering bastard here and now." He then noticed Jacek's wrist watch and roughly snatched it off, took a quick look and triumphantly declared, "There you are, this proves it, look - Berlin Olympics - he's a Nazi alright."

Jacek didn't need to understand what was being said, the meaning was clear from the soldiers' tone and demeanour and so he thought he should explain all before it was too late. He quickly and desperately told the French speaker what had happened over the last couple of days and finished with how he had shot the SS Captain and stolen his weapons and watch. He told them that the body was probably still in the orchard, only a few hundred yards away. His account was still treated with great suspicion but after further exchanges in English they tied his wrists and went in search of the evidence. They soon came upon the bodies of the Ukrainians and about thirty of Jacek's former comrades and he was deeply saddened by the pitiful sight. He pointed out the position of the SS officer and as the Canadians searched his body for identification and any useful documents the French speaker stood staring down at his brains which had been blown all over the roots of a nearby tree and were now providing about fifty slugs and snails with an unusual breakfast. They collected the abandoned weapons from the orchard and the machine pistol from the woodpile and as they did so Jacek told his story as best he could to the French speaker, who then gave Jacek back the Luger and the watch. He said, "They're yours and you can keep them, after all you've earned the right to some spoils and you've certainly done it the hard way. We'll take you back to our Headquarters where they'll interview you and after that I suspect they'll hand you over to the Poles who are fighting alongside us. Welcome to our war, I'm sure you'll have plenty of opportunities to get your own back."

At the Canadian Battalion Headquarters Jacek was interviewed by a sceptical, German speaking intelligence officer who immediately confiscated the Luger despite Jacek's vehement protestations, but he was allowed to keep the watch. After taking his details he insisted that the Pole write down everything that had happened to him since he left his home in September, 1939. Whilst he did this he was kept under guard but separated from the other German and Polish prisoners. He was now beginning to feel safe again and as he relaxed, hunger pangs started and he realised that he hadn't eaten for nearly three days. He wondered when they were going to feed him and started to look around outside the wire compound for some indication of the cook-house. As he paced about one of the guards kept staring intently at him and at first Jacek thought it was because he looked so forlorn and dishevelled. He knew he must be quite a sorry sight: filthy, unshaven and dressed in a strange, tattered and disgustingly smelly uniform. He realised that the guard was not interested in his appearance but had been looking at his watch all along, when he suddenly and repeatedly motioned for Jacek to take it off. The Pole shook his head in refusal and the guard walked off only to return a few minutes later carrying a tin can. He pointed at the tin and then at Jacek and made eating motions with his hands rapidly moving to his mouth, before he again pointed at the watch.

Jacek was at first undecided but inevitably hunger won out and he sacrificed the watch for the tin. Having no knife he soon discovered that he couldn't open it, despite banging it on the ground, then against a brick wall and finally attacking it with a stone. The guard, who was now roaring with laughter, wandered over and showed him how to use the small metal key, a device that Jacek had never come across before. Despite the now misshapen tin, the corned beef soon became accessible and the wonderful smell made him salivate and lick his lips with anticipation. Lacking a spoon or other utensil he impatiently scooped out huge chunks with his fingers and ravenously gulped it down.

It was the best thing he had ever tasted and he enthusiastically pushed his fingers right into the corners to remove every last trace of meat and fat from the tin and then licked his fingers clean. Such was his hunger that he then scraped the hard packed remnants from under his dirty fingernails and unashamedly ate the gritty mixture. He had no doubt at the time that the exchange was well worth it and on reflection he realised that he had in fact obtained the best of the deal. The watch wasn't really his anyway and ever since, whenever he saw a tin of corned beef, he immediately recalled the incident and simultaneously he could taste the delicious contents once again, even though it was still sealed within its tin.

The following day he was taken to a forward reception centre at Caen for captured non-German nationals and it was there that he met his first soldier from the Free Polish Army. A smart, physically impressive and battle hardened, well-educated Lieutenant originally from Warsaw who, although initially more supportive, again talked him through his life history in minute detail. He probed and tested Jacek's responses and his knowledge of Poland and its culture until it felt more like an interrogation than an interview. Once he appeared satisfied Jacek was given the option of joining up with the 1st Polish Armoured Division or being taken into custody and taking his chances as a prisoner of war and probably having to sit out the war in a British POW camp. He was told that his chances of surviving in such a place, alongside his German enemies and depending on them for everything, would not be good. His decision was one of the easiest of his life and he elected to join up, as they knew he would.

He learnt later that many other Poles, who had either surrendered or were captured by the Allies or deserted from the German lines, were offered the option of joining up or being shot on the spot. He thought it astonishing that men who were mostly in forced labour battalions or had been ordered to fight by the Germans or face instant death were then given exactly the same chilling option by their own countrymen. He had heard of numerous examples of Poles forced to fight on opposite sides in past wars but he wondered if he and his colleagues were to be the first to fight on both sides in this one - probably in the same battle!

Another illustration of the crazy world in which they struggled was that, once they signed up with the Free Polish Army, they did indeed go straight back into the line. The few that had benefited from any military training at all had received it courtesy of their real enemy, the Germans.

The very next day Jacek was examining his new uniform, the basic British infantry style with Polish insignia, and introduced to his unit of the 1st Anti-Tank Regiment. He, along with several hundred other infantry soldiers, was to provide emergency perimeter protection and a rapid mobile reconnaissance capability for a specialised artillery battery. It was also their job to protect the spotters and radio operators who, by the very nature of the job, were often right in the front line and risked being overrun or isolated. They were basically a self-contained tank-busting unit and the men in Jacek's group were also issued with, and underwent a crash-training course on the use of, an assortment of hand held anti-tank weapons such as the Bazooka, Piat, flame thrower and grenade launcher.

On the afternoon of the 11th August Jacek's battery was redeployed towards Sassy as a part of the preparations for Operation Tractable and they set up position on a wooded hilltop north west of the village. Their targets were the tigers and panthers of the 12th SS Panzer Division that were holding the high ground in front of Falaise. At first all seemed to go well as their position was well camouflaged, their communication system was working and enemy tanks had been sighted. They had only managed to get off a few rounds when what appeared to be a whole German Brigade was spotted in the valley behind them, travelling east to west along the river Laison. This massive column, although its course also threatened to cut the artillery off, was an imminent and serious threat to the left flank of the advancing Canadian 2nd Armoured Brigade and therefore became the priority target.

"Turn the guns and set up on that column immediately," shouted the Captain who then tried unsuccessfully to report the incursion over the radio. Almost immediately there was another shout from a spotter, "Enemy infantry approaching from the south-west, looks like full company strength."

The Captain spoke to the Sergeant in charge of Jacek's unit of ten men, "Prepare to intercept the infantry. I'm afraid that you'll have to take care of it on your own as I'll need all the guns to concentrate on that column. I'll keep trying on the radio and see if I can get you some support, but don't bet on it, because once I can get through my priority must be to call in air-strikes on the column."

Jacek watched the approaching German infantry as they reached the foot of the hill some four hundred yards away and thought that there were probably about seventy, armed with rifles, machine-pistols and three or four light machine-guns. They were moving slowly and purposefully but suddenly they dived to the ground as the battery started firing again. Jacek was a lot calmer than he thought he would be and even though they were outnumbered seven to one, he did not feel that their position was hopeless. Like the others he quickly scooped out the soft soil and made a nine inch deep bowl in the ground next to a tree to give himself some extra protection. He made ready his weapons, placed four hand grenades on the ground within easy reach and waited.

The Sergeant crept along the rear of their makeshift line and between the deafening reports of the big guns said, "Pick your targets carefully and firstly concentrate on the officers and the ones with the machine guns. We'll hit them when they're half way up the hill but remember to wait for my order. Don't shoot before I say so or we'll lose the only advantage we have."

The Germans, having got used to the noise of the nearby guns, were back on their feet and edging their way up the hill in three separate skirmish lines. When the leading line was about two hundred yards away the order was given and the Poles opened fire. The front line of the enemy was a second or two too slow to react and about half were killed or wounded in the first bursts. Although the rest had managed to go to ground they were still in a very exposed position and the Poles continued to inflict considerable damage. Whilst the centre portion of the enemy engaged the Poles, the troops on the extreme left and right started to work their way to the side in an effort to get around behind the position that controlled the approach. The Polish Sergeant spotted what was happening and sent two of his own men, armed with their sub machine guns and extra grenades, out to each flank to intercept them. Jacek was one of them.

As he ran through the trees, surrounded by the noise of battle, Jacek suddenly wondered what on earth he was doing there. Why him and why now? He thought of his family, his home and the injustice and randomness of war and for the first time in a long while he muttered a prayer. Not for himself but for his mother, his sister and his brothers. It dawned on him that in all probability he would be dead in a few seconds and he felt a twinge of guilt that he no longer feared it. Having witnessed so much suffering and death, he was now ready.

He stopped and slowly edged to the tree line and there to his left, approximately a hundred yards away downhill, were about a dozen Germans. The other Pole crept up alongside and they made ready. At fifty yards they started firing and again caught the enemy in the open and several fell in the first burst. Both the Poles then threw two grenades at the area where they were all trying to hide in the grass. Surprisingly, however, bullets continued to pluck at the foliage and slabs of bark were ripped off the trees all around the Poles. Jacek's colleague let out a scream and fell to the ground with a bullet in the right shoulder. As Jacek looked down to see how bad his comrade had been hit, two Germans, who must have been crawling through the grass behind the other group, appeared fifty yards away sprinting straight towards him. They all fired together as Jacek jumped behind a tree but a bullet from the second Pole's gun brought down the leading German. Neither of the enemy had spotted him on the ground, as they were so intent on targeting Jacek who then dived to the floor and as he fell he fired a burst across the other Germans legs. Simultaneously a stream of rounds from the German's weapon smashed into the tree behind which he had been sheltering only a second earlier.

Before Jacek could fully appreciate his own lucky escape the German started screaming as blood poured from numerous gaping wounds just above both knees. His left leg had been virtually cut in two and he was in desperate need of urgent medical treatment, but Jacek picked up the German's weapon and left him floundering so that he could attend to his own colleague. He knew there was really nothing he could do for the German and it was certain that he wasn't going to get any help from his hard-pressed colleagues back at the guns. For a second he considered finishing off the German but as he had now stopped screaming and was unconscious he didn't think he would be saving him from suffering. He did however wonder if he could do such a thing and as he took another look at his injured colleague, he concluded that he could. His friend asked, "Did we get them all?"

"It looks like it. Their firing has stopped, although some may have escaped back down the hill. I can't hear any more firing back at the centre position either and as the anti-tank guns are still happily blasting away I should think we've driven them off. Now let me finish patching you up before we move."

He had applied field dressings from their packs and tied them on with bandages in an effort to stop the bleeding and, supporting his barely conscious friend, he slowly made his way back. The Poles had lost two men and, including Jacek's companion and the Sergeant, four others had been injured, but the Germans had been beaten off after having lost half of their strength and the Polish guns had kept firing throughout. British aircraft had also relentlessly attacked the enemy column and between them they had succeeded in fragmenting it to such an extent that it was no longer a major threat and it was finally overrun by the Canadians three days later.

Jacek's battery was reinforced that night and, once the injured had been removed by the Poles' own field Ambulances to the British field hospital, the guns were repositioned to assist in the Canadian 4th Armoured Brigade's attack on Sassy. It was another three days of tank and vehicle spotting on the plain before they were redeployed to support the Poles' own tanks on their drive to link up with the Americans at Chambois.

The Polish column was just short of La-Cour-Du-Bosq at dusk on the evening of the 18th August en route to reinforce other hard-pressed units that had become isolated from their Division, when disaster struck. They were heading for the heights above Coudehard when they inadvertently drove into a convoy of German tanks and infantry attempting to smash their way out of the Falaise pocket.

The leading Polish trucks took the full force of the impact as half a dozen enemy Tiger tanks burst across the road from the fields on the right. Neither side was aware of the others presence until they were suddenly colliding in the road.

The front of the Polish column took the brunt of the assault and having been completely taken by surprise they came to a sudden halt. Further back vehicles ran into each other and soldiers, alerted by the gunfire and the noise of screaming tank engines, scrambled out of lorries before they had fully stopped. There was an immediate and fierce fire-fight between the opposing infantry units as they literally stumbled into each other and all along the road troops were engaged in hand-to-hand combat. It was a situation of total chaos but fortunately for the Poles the enemy, armour and infantry, was more intent on escaping than fighting. The German tanks didn't even fire a shot as they smashed through the trucks and burst through the other hedge and carried on eastwards.

The last thing Jacek heard was the screeching sound of a tank's engine that was literally on top of them and, as it fell from the top of the bank down onto the road, its right track caught the back of the lorry and spun it round. As the front of the lorry hit the offside bank it toppled over, slid along the road surface for about thirty yards and only came to rest when it hit the lorry in front. By this time the first tank was already in the opposite field and then a second tank followed in the wake of the first, but fortunately its path was clear.

Jacek was only semi-conscious, having hit his head when the vehicle turned over and he was lying in the middle of a pile of soldiers most of whom were scrambling around, trying to orientate themselves and work out exactly what had happened. One or two were reaching for their weapons and a few others were climbing out the back when three German soldiers ran across the road and fired several bursts into the back of the lorry as they passed by. All the Germans were then brought down, as they tried to scale the far bank, by troops from the following lorry who had managed to find cover under their own vehicle.

Twenty minutes later when the fighting was over Medics entered Jacek's truck and discovered eight dead men and three seriously injured. When they finally reached Jacek he was unconscious and covered in blood, but a close examination revealed only one wound apart from the scalp injury and concussion sustained when he fell. A bullet was lodged up against the femur in his left thigh and although he had lost a fair amount of blood it was not life threatening. The doctor who later removed the bullet told him that by the time it struck him it had spent some of its force, almost certainly having passed through someone else or having hit the bed of the lorry first. Nevertheless, he had sustained some quite serious tissue and muscle damage and his femur had been chipped but he was told that if it remained infection-free he should make a full recovery.

The Polish column had lost nearly fifty men in the incident but had the German tank commanders' decided to stay and fight, then the death-toll could have been ten times that number and they would have lost their precious anti-tank guns.

Jacek spent three weeks in the field hospital and another three recuperating before being reallocated to a battalion support role where, as a messenger, he was attached to a brigade dispatch group. As part of his new duties, despite his leg injury, he was quickly taught how to ride a motorcycle and within another two weeks he was an operational dispatch rider with the Highland Rifle Battalion waiting for the next offensive outside Breda in Holland. Over the next three weeks, as one of a team of five dispatch riders who had been temporarily drafted in for the purpose, his job was to escort prisoners from the front to the forward prisoner reception area for initial documentation and interrogation. This normally entailed a round trip on foot of a couple of miles and they took two or three prisoners at a time.

He had been doing this for nearly a week when it registered that one of the team was always over eager to do the prisoner run and would even swap duties to facilitate it, but he invariably returned far more quickly than the rest: too quickly to have completed the full journey. Intrigued rather than suspicious Jacek asked, in a light-hearted way, what he was up to and to his utter amazement he received a quite open and spontaneous reply, "I just take them down the road and shoot them. The only good Nazi is a dead Nazi. They murdered my mother, my father and my sisters and if they think they're going to stay nice and safe in a cosy British prisoner of war camp and then go home to Berlin or wherever, and take up life just where they left off, then they are seriously mistaken."

At first Jacek thought he must be playing a sick joke on him but as he looked into his face he could see he was very serious and completely unrepentant. Jacek said, "You can't do that, if you get caught theÿ'll put you up for court martial and lock you up, they might even shoot you for all I know. In any case we can't sink to their level. We're fighting to stop that sort of thing from happening. I know you've every right to hate them but you've got to stop shooting them in cold blood. They're prisoners and we're supposed to protect them. It's plain murder!"

The other Pole replied, "Don't worry, I'm working to a plan and I'm not a crazed killer like those SS bastards. The Dutch told me that when the Germans take reprisals they kill ten innocent citizens for every German. Well I'm not going to be anywhere near so severe but I'm going to kill three Germans for every member of my murdered family. So that's a total of twelve. Just remember that the Germans murder ordinary civilians and terrorise whole populations whereas my victims are soldiers who live alongside the threat of death every day. Anyway you needn't fret because I'll finish tomorrow and that'll be an end to it. Justice will have been served," he then turned and left.

Jacek sat there and considered what he had been told and after just a few moments he knew it was the complete truth. Until the prisoners arrived at the forward reception centre there was no paperwork for them and to the authorities the prisoners didn't yet exist. The despatch rider, by accident or design, had picked the one point in the chain where it was not only possible to murder the prisoners but almost impossible to prevent. It was also unlikely to be discovered unless it was on a large scale or the bodies were left in full view. It would not even be unusual for fellow prisoners to quickly lose touch with comrades with whom they had been captured and even if one suspected the truth he would probably be too frightened to complain. As Jacek thought about the consequences of what he had been told he became angry that yet another heavy burden had been placed on top of his already unbearable load of personal heartache and grief.

As he calmed down he agonised over what to do. His instincts told him to report the matter but he knew he too had thought about doing the very same thing to the Germans himself on more than one occasion. No matter how he looked at it he found his inner sympathies were with the man who had lost his family. He was also

271

concerned that if it was discovered and investigated, it would reflect badly on both the whole Division and the entire Polish contribution to the war. He then tried to rationalise doing nothing. He considered that, in the large sphere of things, where people were dying in their thousands, it was of no real consequence. On the other hand, if he kept quiet, he was in effect condoning it and could perhaps even be implicated and so his unease grew by the hour, as did his own feelings of guilt.

When he awoke in the morning he still could not make up his mind because he found the decision just too difficult. In the end he did nothing, not because he rejected the clear course prescribed by his religion and his military and moral duty, but because in his heart he felt he was no better than the killer. He tried to shut the whole issue from his conscious thoughts but a sense of dishonour and failure hung over him and drained his energy. It didn't ease when, just three weeks later, the dispatch rider concerned was killed when he rode over a mine near Moerdijk.

As the months passed by and the Division pushed further eastwards into Germany, Jacek gradually recovered his spirit and when the end of the war came he too was enveloped in a total sense of euphoria and relief. He learnt to drive whilst on occupation duties in Meppen and shortly after his course he was assigned as the official driver to the army chaplain of the Highland Rifle Battalion. This meant he often escorted the priest when he conducted business and interviews at the Command Centre and the Regimental Office. It was here that he met Marta Dudek, a Polish Red Cross worker who had been liberated from Sandbostel camp by the British Grenadier Guards on the 29th April 1945, a date that was etched into her memory. Originally known as Stalag XB, the camp had been used at the beginning of the war as a POW camp for British Royal Navy prisoners. It was later converted into a death camp to take 'overspill' from the nearby Belsen concentration camp. The English doctor who attended her on her release stated that she would have been dead from malnutrition and general abuse within a week.

She had then taken six months to recover and was now working in the repatriation and resettlement office, offering whatever help was possible to those Polish civilians who had been deported to Germany for forced labour and were now homeless and stateless.

She quickly fell in love with the serious-minded handsome Polish soldier who was so intelligent, attentive and persuasive. She travelled to England with him when he returned with his unit and they became inseparable. All her friends and the priest, who also set up home in their adopted country, were convinced that Jacek was the right man for her. They were married in late summer sunshine to the sound of bells, organ and choir in a picturesque, quintessentially English country church in September 1946. There could have been no bigger contrast compared to the trials and tribulations previously endured by the wedding party and their guests.

THIRTEEN

Uprising!
1st *August 1944*

The hospital was already short of essential medicines and equipment but, as rumours of an uprising had spread, the staff had been told to preserve as much as possible because matters were certain to deteriorate and further supplies were unlikely. Maria, now a nursing Sister, had been working around the clock because of staff shortages and had not left her ward in the building's basement for over a week. She managed to grab a few minutes rest whenever the opportunity arose, but because of the chronic overcrowding she was forced to sleep on the floor, alongside her patients.

The doctors and nurses were dedicated professionals but were finding it increasingly dangerous to travel between their homes and work. The occupying forces, fearing major civil unrest as the Red Army approached the Vistula, had progressively tightened their grip on the entire civilian population. Citizens were harassed every day and being a hospital employee was no protection against arbitrary arrest, detention and interrogation, as the Germans made random sweeps across the city in a desperate attempt to capture middle ranking and senior members of the Home Army. The German senior command were even offering rewards to their troops and the civil population for the arrest of suspects who could then be tortured to force them to reveal their organisation's future plans. As a result of this crackdown the staff without family responsibilities found it easier and safer to live in the hospital, but even so, the facility functioned every day with half of its employees absent from the wards.

On their arrival in the capital some four years earlier Doctor Puzak, fearful of the circumstances surrounding their disappearance from Pelplin and anxious to ensure their continued safety, used his Jewish contacts to provide new identities for his wife, himself and Maria. This was a mutually beneficial arrangement as Maria would, if necessary, be able to vouch for their 'Polishness' and in return he had used his professional contacts to arrange for Maria to take up a post at one of the hospitals in the City Centre.

After settling in Maria immediately went to see her uncle Roman in the hope that he would have heard from, or received news of, her mother or brothers but she soon discovered that his flat was unoccupied. She sought advice from the doctor and his wife as to whether she should make a direct approach to the landlord and the neighbours in an effort to trace him but, after considering all the options, they concluded that the risks involved were too great. Their new identities and false papers were of sufficient quality to satisfy both the occupying army and the civil authorities and so they were reluctant to take any action that could possibly lead to the discovery of their true history. Having resolved to make a totally fresh start they quickly settled into life in their new surroundings with its challenging and chaotic demands.

As time went by life became increasingly difficult as food shortages, oppression, disease and direct violence against the general population took their toll. Following the Jewish uprising the German hostility had grown dramatically, as they doggedly strove to prevent organised resistance by direct force and brutality. In consequence the hospitals became desperately overcrowded and the German military authority provided little or no medical assistance, blaming the predicament on the Poles' own reckless actions.

As the bitter and violent realities of Nazi occupation were biting even deeper during the summer of 1944, the Russian offensive had managed to push the German lines back from Minsk right up to the banks of the Vistula. In a little over four weeks the Germans had yielded about six hundred miles of territory on a two hundred and fifty mile wide front and with their backs to the Polish capital Hitler personally ordered them to hold at all costs. They sent urgent reinforcements and at the end of July the Soviets, already exhausted by their unprecedented advance, were finally halted in the very outskirts of Warsaw.

When Maria started her morning ward rounds, spotters for the Home Army who were hidden on a nearby rooftop saw Soviet tanks operating to the east of the river near the suburb of Praga. Although this was wonderful news, the sudden jubilation which quickly spread throughout the hospital was soon tempered by the realisation of the patients' obvious vulnerability to an escalation of hostilities and their innate suspicion of Russia's future intentions.

As the Red Army travelled through eastern Poland they had rounded up Home Army troops, set up pro-Communist committees and established local 'puppet' administrations. They were intent on turning the population's sympathy and support away from the Polish Government in Exile and towards a pro-Communist, pro-Soviet Administration run by their own 'appointees'. This was anathema to the Home Army whose declared intention was to establish a non-communist democratic post-war government. The underground leadership had therefore become desperate to control Warsaw before the Russians arrived to 'liberate' them. Indeed the Russians were also encouraging them to rise up and therefore cause the Germans to divert troops away from their over-stretched front. The Polish resistance was also concerned about the latest intelligence reports of German plans to deport the entire male population from the city and the escalating number of deaths from reprisals against the civilian population.

It was the Poles' belief that once they were in control, the Russians and the allies would be far more amenable to negotiation and unlikely to override their wishes for an independent Polish state. The Commander of the Home Army contacted London, informed them that the Russians had arrived and were now in a position to provide assistance and asked permission to start the long planned general, city-wide uprising. Permission was granted immediately as both London and Washington also wished to see Warsaw in the hands of the Poles in order to strengthen their own hand in subsequent dealings with Stalin, who they were finding increasingly untrustworthy, rigid and stubborn.

The Home Army had spent the last six months preparing for an all out offensive war and had stockpiled quantities of weapons and ammunition. They had developed manufacturing units, which

276

fabricated handguns, Sten sub machine pistols and rifles to their own specifications and designs. Hand grenades and petrol bombs were also manufactured in large numbers and they converted and armoured normal vehicles to create mobile attack units equipped with machine-guns supplied by the allies. Captured weapons that had been obtained all across the country by attacking small German units and patrols were also smuggled into the capital. Weapons caches that had been buried outside the city at the start of the war were unearthed and although much of the weaponry and ammunition was no longer serviceable, they took the view that every little helped. In total they could muster about one thousand rifles, three hundred machine-pistols, sixty sub machine guns, seven medium and light machine-guns, thirty five anti-tank grenade launchers, Bazookas and Piats and twenty five thousand hand grenades. Ammunition was scarce with less than two hundred rounds per rifle and between two hundred and five hundred per machine-gun. With demand still far outstripping supply they also stepped up the manufacture of their own weapons such as the 'lightning' sub-machine-gun and several additional types of hand grenade.

The proximity of the Russian forces emboldened the Home Army Commanders because, despite their suspicions, they believed the Soviets would re-supply them and, if things went badly, would definitely come to their aid: after all they were now allies. However, the single major influence on the Poles' decision to start the insurrection had nothing to do with the many outside influences: it was their own national pride and thirst for freedom. They had suffered for over four years under a brutal and ruthless regime, the likes of which had not been seen in the modern world and they could take no more.

General 'Bor' Komorowski, Commander of the Home Army, gave the order and set the hour for 5pm on 1st August when forty thousand fighters (about 10% were women) of the Warsaw resistance movement (less than 10% were armed) put on their distinctive armbands and rose up to topple the German occupation. Their intention was to drive the Germans out of the City and then to hold their ground until the Russians arrived to relieve the pressure. The Varsovians expected to fight their own war of liberation for a matter of a few days only, perhaps a week at most, but there could be no turning back. The enemy garrison that faced them, although considerably reduced to bolster the defence against the Russians, still stood at over twenty thousand, mainly well trained and battle hardened troops.

Zenon was ordered to take part in the attack on the Okecie airport and his job was to assess the feasibility of Polish paratroopers and allied planes landing there once the position had been secured. He was to then act as liaison officer to any Polish, British or Russian reinforcements, including Special Forces that could be brought in. One of Jozef's colleagues from the intelligence cell was to undertake the same function at Bielany airport. As hostilities commenced Jozef was with the District commander waiting for the reports to come in. It was a beautiful clear summer's day when the offensive started but before the day was out huge columns of smoke spread right across the city and the sun, unlike the light and spirit of Polish euphoria, was obscured for days on end.

A major problem for the Home Army throughout the German occupation had been the number of 'volksdeutsch' (Polish citizens of German origin) who collaborated with the enemy and constantly attempted to infiltrate the resistance movement. The result was that their operations were not always as secure as they should have been and the more widespread the information became, the more likely the Germans were to discover the truth. This time, probably because of the level of public anticipation, the Germans had been tipped off and in many places large detachments were lying in wait behind fortified positions when they were attacked by men, women and boys, only a minority of which had ever seen combat.

What the Poles lacked in experience and weaponry they made up for by raw courage and a determination to wreak revenge for years of suffering. This drive for freedom and justice was at times reckless in the extreme, as illustrated by one unit of almost a hundred volunteers who, armed only with revolvers, attacked a well-defended German position. Although they eventually achieved their objective only seven survived the suicidal attack. The initial casualties were heavy on both sides as the Poles managed to secure possession of most of the city and gained the upper hand. They could not however maintain this momentum as their enemy quickly regrouped and counter-attacked in force.

Despite the Poles desperate efforts and numerous acts of collective and personal gallantry, key areas were firmly retained in the hands of the Germans who immediately called for urgent and substantive reinforcements to be dispatched to the city.

The attacks on the airports and the radio station were driven back by particularly resolute and aggressive German defence and Zenon was lucky to escape with his life. Just as critically, they were also unable to hold any of the bridges across the Vistula, which left the Home Army in the Praga district totally isolated and facing certain defeat. Even in the huge areas controlled by the Poles on the first few days there were many significant and well-fortified enclaves of German troops that proved almost impossible to dislodge and some would later act as rallying points and observation posts to harry, disrupt and attack the Poles from all directions.

From the outset the Home Army fought with ferocity and belief in their ability to take the whole city, and the Germans used all of the mighty resources at their disposal. Stuka dive-bombers attacked relentlessly, supported by heavy artillery and huge mortars: Tiger and Panther tanks counter-attacked and pounded the barricades and fortified bunkers in an effort to drive the Poles out from their defensive positions. The streets filled with a cacophony of exploding bombs and shells. The constant rattle of machine gun fire, the roar of tank and aeroplane engines and the whine of bullets and flying shrapnel, all competed with the dreadful background rumble of falling buildings to insistently drown out the shouts of command and the screams of the wounded. Amongst the chaos at street level dashed the fighters, looking for targets, jumping onto tanks as they slowed or lost a track and then throwing in a grenade: trying to capture another precious yard of Polish soil before diving back into cover, carefully picking their targets and hoping to preserve their precious ammunition. Messengers, mostly children, and unarmed civilians who tended the wounded, were covered from head to toe in the smog of street warfare, a grey amalgam of soot, oil, blood and dust. They darted like wraiths through the carnage from casualty to casualty or from unit to unit with orders to hold, advance or regroup. Within a few hours some of the most defensive positions had lost seventy percent of their strength to the initial battle and German counter-attacks, but they fought on, bolstered by their comrades courage and ferociousness and their exhilaration at the staggering sight of burning tanks and retreating German infantry.

Positioned in and on the buildings, most of which were from three to six floors high was another motley army of both sexes aged from fourteen to sixty: a deadly militia of snipers, spotters, machine gunners, petrol bombers and anti-tank units all pouring fire down at the enemy. Dozens of tanks and vehicles were destroyed; streets were taken, lost and then retaken by both sides leaving them strewn with the debris of war. Burnt-out wrecks of every description, piles of fallen masonry, smashed barricades and abandoned equipment were scattered across a stained and threadbare carpet of charred bodies, discarded field dressings and spent ammunition cases. The casualty rate was exceedingly high on both sides and, as in all urban warfare, the civilians suffered disproportionate and unsustainable losses. The fighting was so intense, desperate and concentrated that Himmler was reported as saying to his Generals at the time, "This is the fiercest of our battles since the war started. It's as bad as the street battles in Stalingrad, maybe even worse!"

On the first day the civil population had eagerly offered their support, local knowledge and significant military help in the form of hoarded supplies, extra weapons, information on informers and medical assistance. When the Polish flags started to wave over the Prudential Tower in Napoleon Square and other tall buildings across the city many more civilians, some reminded of the icons of the Ghetto uprising and others just filled with national pride, rallied to the cause. The public mood was triumphant and a social life of sorts briefly returned within the liberated areas with recitals, concerts and poetry readings. One cannot overstate the euphoria of freedom that existed here after so many months of deprivation, oppression, murder and suffering.

As the fighting progressed rumour and counter rumour spread like wildfire and a separate propaganda war was waged by both sides. Millions of flyers circulated throughout the city, alternately calling on each side to give up their lost cause and surrender. Poles also produced false German leaflets and vice-versa in an effort to undermine the morale of their enemy. At first the Poles seemed to be winning this particular exchange, optimism was high and the 'vox populi' predicted an early Home Army victory. It was, however, a huge blow to Polish hopes when the enemy garrison, which had been severely mauled and ejected in disarray in many areas, was immediately reinforced. Significant numbers of troops from their 19th Armoured Division and the Herman Goering Armoured Airborne Division, who arrived at the City that very day, en route to face the Russians at the front, were diverted into the urban areas. They were deployed to push the Poles back from the river and split the insurgents into more manageable and vulnerable units. The German priority was to stop the Poles linking up the various areas under their control and to prevent any possible assistance from the Russians.

More huge barricades, using trams, vehicles, furniture and machinery, in fact anything the Poles could lay their hands on, were erected in the streets to prevent any rapid intervention by the fresh German forces. They were also used to try and provide some protection to the Home Army from enemy snipers at points where the insurgents had to cross streets above ground. The sewers and tunnels were the preferred highways for the Poles and, in some streets in their possession, holes had been made in all the connecting basement walls so that there was underground access throughout the entire length of the road. The basements would then be connected to the sewers to provide underground street-to-street access. Where this was not possible, protective barricades were again built at street level and reinforced by the provision of a prepared defensive position for the Home Army volunteers. It was not unusual for the Poles to occupy one side of the street and the Germans the other and some buildings changed hands several times in a few short hours.

By 4th August three large areas of the city were firmly in the hands of the Poles and although they had received reinforcements from the Home Army units outside the city who had been ordered in, they were already running short of ammunition and support supplies. Their senior commanders were also repeatedly demanding the immediate dispatch of the Polish Parachute Brigade, which had been assembled in England for this very purpose. There was also considerable consternation that the Russians had not crossed the river to take advantage of the sudden German vulnerability and had provided no arms, ammunition or any other form of help. When the Home Army commander again implored the Red Army to help, he was informed of their strict conditions. Before any support whatsoever would be given Poland must recognise the Soviet claim to the eastern third of Polish territory and agree to cede those lands; endorse the Polish puppet government established in Lublin by Moscow; and also publicly proclaim that the Katyn Massacre was committed by the Germans, not the Russians. Such demands were unconscionable to the Poles and the response was predictable in its absolute rejection, which included the words, "Our years of struggle against the Nazis have shown that we love freedom more than life itself." As events later showed this was not mere rhetoric but a truthful and tragic statement of the Polish spirit.

Although frightened herself, Maria tried to comfort her patients as once more the sounds of fighting to the south of the hospital intensified, "Try not to worry, I'm sure we are safe enough, both sides will do their best to avoid the hospitals. They all need us and we don't pose any threat to them." She went from bed to bed checking dressings and offering reassurance and when she came to the last man and helped him to sit up she asked in German, "It sounds as if the fighting is getting much closer. Do you think we are in any real danger here from your people?"

The young enemy conscript had been in the hospital for two days recovering from his injuries after being captured by the Home Army. His small unit had been guarding a nearby police station when it had been overrun and the prisoners released. His left hand had been mutilated by a hand grenade and had subsequently been amputated by the Polish surgeon. He thanked the nurse for her help and although in obvious pain replied in a confident and sympathetic manner, "I'm sure you have nothing to fear from us as long as the insurgents don't operate from inside the hospital."

Maria was about to take his temperature when the room shook from the impact of a nearby explosion and a cloud of dust and smoke blew along the corridor towards them. Before she could fully react, a contingent of heavily armed German soldiers that had just stormed the hospital, burst into the ward. Maria, terrified and desperate to protect her patients, screamed at the leading soldier, "What on earth are you doing? This is an absolute disgrace, now get out at once. Can't you see these patients are very sick and badly wounded?"

He stopped, grinned at her, and then slapped her hard across the face with the back of his right hand, knocking her to the floor. With tears of pain and indignation in her eyes she shouted up, "Some of these patients are your own men and we look after them and care for them exactly the same as we do for our own people, so please leave us alone and let us do our work. For pity's sake, why don't you fight your battles and do your killing somewhere else? We try to save lives here."

The soldier decided he had heard enough and as his men looked on he leant down, grabbed Maria by the front of her uniform and dragged her to her feet. She smelt the alcohol on his breath, saw the anger in his eyes and then felt his fingers tighten around her throat and she feared for her own life and the safety of all her patients. When he spoke she knew he was a Ukrainian and his words petrified her. "We go where we like and we do as we like. If you don't shut your mouth and do exactly as you're told, I'll shoot you and all your so-called patients and think nothing of it. So, not another word from you. You stinking Polish whore."

The German patient rose slowly from his bed and walked unsteadily towards Maria addressing her attacker, "Look, let's calm down here. There's no need to let things get out of hand. We don't need to shoot anyone, so please let her go. I can assure you there are no insurgents here, other than a few of their wounded." He then reached out with his good hand towards the nurse and as he touched her hand the Ukrainian released his grip and grabbed the German's bandaged stump and spun him round. As he screamed out in pain the Ukrainian shot him in the chest and then kicked his body as he slumped to the floor. He shouted at the dying man, "You treacherous bastard. How dare you fraternise with the enemy? You're nothing more than a deserter and a coward and now you've paid the price, you worthless piece of shit!"

The German patient had told the truth, as the only insurgents present in or around the hospital were the badly injured and, like most of the hospitals in the city, it also contained a significant number of wounded Germans who the Poles treated as prisoners of war. The Ukrainian then said to his men, "It's time to sort this place out properly and give them something to remember us by so let's get on with it." He pushed Maria violently in the back forcing her to collide with one of his subordinates saying, "You can have this one first and make sure you beat some sense into her. Quieten her down, so that I don't hear a single word of complaint when it's my turn to have her. I'm sick to death of their whining and whinging. They like to dish it out but they can't take it and that sums up the trouble with these bastards. They go on moaning forever and ever about how hard-done-by they all are. They're never satisfied with their lot. Well we'll make sure they're all bloody well satisfied today."

On his order the injured were immediately tipped from their beds and savagely beaten with rifle butts and boots and throughout the hospital, as the nurses and doctors tried to protect their patients, they too were set upon. Most of the German troops were drunk and even before they had properly secured the building they started sexually assaulting the nurses. They were chased from room to room, their uniforms were ripped and cut off and they were all repeatedly raped on the floor and on the tables surrounded by the blood and moans of the injured and dying patients. Like the young conscript many of the German patients pleaded with their countrymen to stop, but their lives were then threatened and they were roughly removed, some even dragged, to trucks and taken to their own field hospital. Others were less fortunate and those few not fit enough to be moved were shot out-of-hand by their own men or left to die in the carnage on the wards.

All the surviving patients, nurses, doctors, visitors and other staff were then driven out into the garden, penned up against a wall and shot with machine pistols. The deafening noise of a dozen deadly weapons and the cries and screams of the terrified, injured and dying finally gave way to an absolute and unnatural silence. The scene of crime mirrored that of a stinking, bloody charnel house as the drunken German orgy had moved off to strike again or sleep off their crapulence before embarking on their next atrocity.

Maria was lying towards the middle of the huge pile of bodies and she tasted blood and felt it running into her eyes. She could hardly breathe from the weight pressing down on her but was too frightened to move in case the Germans were still nearby. It seemed to her that she waited many hours whereas in reality it was only about forty minutes before she forced herself to move. She pushed upwards with her hands and, although nothing moved, there was a horrible gurgling sound followed by a soft sigh and another stream of blood, urine and faecal matter ran onto her face, up her nose and into her mouth. This caused her to spit, cough, gag and panic and she started to frantically push up with her knees and hands and kick out with her feet. At first there was very little movement and she thought she would choke to death or drown in her own vomit but she eventually created enough space to use her feet and hips more effectively and managed to force her head sideways. She was then able to clear her throat, mouth and nose and after vomiting again she started to control her breathing.

After another fifteen-minute struggle she emerged exhausted and, almost naked, she half-fell and half-crawled from the gruesome heap that had once been a whole hospital community. She lay on the ground floundering in the blood, vomit and excrement of the slaughterhouse and cried out in despair to God. She realised it was not a nightmare and that she was somehow still alive and forced herself to her feet: she stood there trembling with both shock and relief and slowly examined herself. She was covered in gore and as she wiped it away with what was left of her uniform she discovered that she had also escaped serious injury. Her lips were split, she had cuts, scratches and bruising all over her lower body and she felt very tender and sore inside but she didn't think there was any permanent damage. She could distinctly remember being raped three times and it may have been more but she was too shocked and distressed to be sure. Both her eyes were badly swollen and several teeth were missing where she had been punched in the face and a bullet had made a large gouge mark across her forehead. She was also bleeding from the tips of the toes on her left foot and she concluded that a bullet fragment must have struck her. She had no recollection of when or where she had lost her shoes and other clothing.

She stood there briefly in disbelief and denial before forcing herself to turn around and look at the bodies and, although she was a nurse, she had never seen such carnage or so much blood. She fell to her knees and vomited repeatedly until she collapsed from the pain and shock. She finally found the strength to stand again and it made her weep to see her friends and patients, the centre of her life an hour ago, now robbed of their dignity, butchered and left to rot like discarded rubbish. She ran back into the deserted hospital, dressed in a spare uniform and as a broken woman, crept out a side-door forcing herself to make for home for the first time in weeks. She cried all night and as she wept the images of the massacre haunted and enraged her and so the very next morning she volunteered to fight for the Home Army.

At first she was told that she was far more valuable to the organisation as a nurse, as they were in very short supply, whereas there were still far more volunteer fighters than weapons available. Nevertheless, once she told her story she was immediately issued with a rifle and shown how to use it. Over the next month she lived in the tunnels but fought from the rooftops taking every opportunity to shoot at those, who for the time being at least, had robbed her of her faith in humanity and filled her with hate. The face of the Ukrainian was burned into her memory and every night she unashamedly prayed for the opportunity to find him squarely in her sights. Although she willingly risked her life every day she developed a growing fear of dying without knowing what had happened to her family and so, having decided that she now had nothing to lose, she actively searched for her uncle Roman.

FOURTEEN

Final Destruction
10th August 1944

In the early days of the uprising the Poles had managed to capture large numbers of prisoners, many of whom were wounded in the intense house-to-house and close-quarter fighting. Jozef was given the task of heading up a small team of Intelligence personnel, all fluent German speakers, to interrogate the prisoners in their area and try to establish the Germans' future tactics, local plans, likely levels of reinforcement and particular areas of vulnerability.

On the 10th August, he visited a temporary hospital in the basement of a building in the Zoliborz District in the north west of the city on the left bank of the Vistula. Here he interviewed another prisoner, a thirty five year old Sergeant Engineer in the Wehrmacht, who had been captured the previous day. Although there were a total of eight German soldiers in the hospital only the one was well enough to be interviewed. Despite their terrible treatment at the hands of the Germans the Polish doctors and nurses, in accordance with the Home Army policy, treated all the wounded, friend or foe, with equal professional care, even though their drugs and resources were scarce and very basic. The Poles also adhered strictly to the Geneva Convention regarding prisoners, whereas until the end of September most of the captured resistance fighters were immediately shot.

The German had a severe knife-wound in his thigh and two of his fingers were broken, but he was fully conscious. When interviewed, unlike so many others, he did not just give his name and rank and then refuse to answer any further questions. In addition to his personal details he told Jozef that he was an engineering teacher from Munster who had been conscripted into the army and he was currently a Panzer Combat Engineer in command of a Rapid Entry Squad. He explained that his small team were trained to gain quick access into fortified buildings of any description and were in high demand during the occupation and had proved particularly useful during the uprising. At one end of the scale this would simply mean using a crow bar or battering ram but, depending on the structure of the doors and degree of reinforcing, he could use hand grenades, prepared and shaped charges, measured and timed explosives and even the use of a remote-controlled miniature tank known as 'Goliath'. Jozef had seen these machines in operation and they were basically a disposable tracked vehicle jam-packed with up to one hundred and thirty pounds of High Explosive that acted as a mobile bomb and, when fully laden, it was capable of bringing down a whole building. Several resistance fighters had met their death from enemy snipers when running from cover to sever the command wire that trailed behind before it could reach its target.

Jozef sensed that the soldier was willing to continue to talk and so he asked, "How were you captured then Erich?"

"We had just forced the street doors into a building where insurgent snipers were operating on the third floor and as we entered we were attacked by several Poles who were lying in wait behind piles of furniture and mattresses on either side of the door. Before we could call in the SS who were in charge of the operation and waiting round the corner, my friend was knifed to death and I was stabbed and held on the ground. I was told that I was a prisoner and two of them carried me down into the basement and took me through the tunnels."

Jozef, knowing that Polish prisoners were invariably shot but trying to hold out some hope of repatriation for the soldier said, "I'm sorry about your friend. We've also lost many of our fighters already but at least you're still alive and being a prisoner is not so bad. Nobody is shooting at you now and when you've recovered from your injuries we might even be able to arrange a prisoner exchange."

The German suddenly looked very worried, "I don't want to go back out there. I'm a soldier and I accept the facts of war but I'm an educated, God fearing man and not a gangster or murderer. This occupation of ours has become genocide, there's no other word for it and I've seen things that would make my students cry with sadness and my friends back home would be ashamed of us. I'm glad it's finished for me, and now my friend is dead I don't think I could go through it again anyway. What we've been doing here lately isn't right. We shouldn't be driving hundreds of women and children from their homes and murdering them in cold blood. It's all the fault of 'the butcher' and his thugs."

"Who do you mean, 'the butcher'?"

Erich looked up at Jozef with tears in his eyes as he recalled what he had witnessed and quietly said, "I'll start at the beginning and tell you all I've seen myself and learnt on the military grapevine since I arrived here six months ago. After von Stauffenberg's attempt on the Fuhrer's life he has understandably become suspicious and angry with all his Generals and he's lost patience with what was going on here. He's now ordered the destruction of Warsaw and when he heard what you rebels were doing here he told Himmler to sort it out personally, once and for all. So Himmler has sent in the butcher. His name is Oskar Dirlewanger of the SS Sturmbrigade."

Erich explained that Dirlewanger's men were violent criminals, some already sentenced to death. They had been released from prisons all over Europe specifically to join his command. He also took on all the poachers from the German gaols not just because they were cunning hunters, good shots and used to setting well-disguised traps and snares, but because they were a law unto themselves: determined, resolute killers who shunned the normal rules of war. They possessed all the skills to make them ideal for fighting a dirty war and just to make sure they would be prepared to do anything, he also recruited scores of the most violent, criminally insane inmates from the lunatic asylums. He continued, "The butcher himself is a convicted child molester, an alcoholic and a psychopath. He's also recruited the worst of the military prisoners, those who've been expelled from their own regiments for serious crimes including rape and murder. He is utterly ruthless. He's been known to shoot his own men when they upset him and they are always drunk. They drink vodka all day, every day, even for breakfast. A few days ago he told us he was going to destroy the Wala district and all the units there came under his command so that he could have total control."

Jozef, who had also seen so much cruelty and evil, recognised the same anguish and shame in the Germans eyes and so took a minute or two to reflect on the consequences of what he was being told. He then asked, "What have you seen that has made you tell me about this man?"

"Before I tell you what I've seen with my own eyes you need to understand that you're now up against people who seek your total destruction, even our own command officers are powerless to stop the slaughter. To make matters worse for both of us the butcher is now directly supported by the Kaminski Brigade, the 29 Waffen Grenadier Division SS. They're made up from Russians, Ukrainians and Cossacks and they hate you Poles with a vengeance, even worse than the normal SS do, and they relish the opportunity to work alongside Dirlewanger."

Jozef encouraged him to continue, "Where are these units based?"

The soldier thought before replying, "Look, I've had to pluck up the courage to tell you about the butcher and what is happening because I can see that to do so will be considered treasonous and I'll surely be shot or hanged if they find out. Having accepted that, I'm also certain that what they're doing is even more treacherous and an insult to both the Fatherland and the people of Germany. I can honestly say that I now consider it my duty to tell you about the terrible crimes that I've witnessed, but no way will I reveal any information that will help you attack military targets."

Jozef let the debatable distinction pass without comment and asked, "What have you seen?"

"It started with using the civilians as human shields. I watched them marched in front of, and even loaded onto the front of tanks so that your side wouldn't fire and risk hitting them. I saw a group of men, women and children forced at gunpoint onto the front of a tank. A young child slipped and fell off and a woman, her mother presumably, jumped down to help her. The butcher shot them both in the head and threw them and several others who protested under the tracks. He then told another group who had been forced from their homes that he would do the same to them unless they climbed up onto another tank." Suddenly Erich stopped and seemed to drift off into his own thoughts.

Jozef was reluctant to interrupt but he felt compelled to

comment, "I've seen similar things, it's become common practice amongst the SS."

The German refocused and continued, "He drove groups of civilians along the road at bayonet-point towards your positions and when the first shot was fired against us they were all shot down at his order. I saw several hundred people rounded up from one block as they fled when we set light to the basements with petrol and grenades. They were herded into the park and forced to dig a massive pit. Then they were marched, ten at a time, up to the pit and the butcher and his men shot every single one of them in the back of the head. There were children, babies and old men and women. No one was spared and then the heap of bodies in the pit was machine-gunned just in case someone had survived."

Jozef asked, "Do you know the names of any of the other officers involved?"

"You must understand that all his officers and his troops are involved and they enjoy what they do. Other soldiers are sickened by it but if they object or interfere they themselves are shot or hanged. I've seen him shoot his own men in the back and hang them just because they've spoken out of turn. I was with one of his units on the first day he arrived and since then I have seen them murder thousands of innocents and I'm not exaggerating, I mean literally thousands. It's as if we've gone back in time to the Dark Ages."

"Have you murdered any civilians yourself Erich?" asked Jozef, not really expecting to hear the truth.

"I've fought in the cellars and I've shot at anything that moves including the rats, so I've probably hit and killed people who live in those houses. You Poles must also take some responsibility for that because you always fight from buildings containing civilians, but I have not deliberately killed or injured any person who was not a threat to me or my comrades."

Jozef could see from Erich's face that there was more to come and so he prompted, "Go on, what else is there?"

"We captured a church which was being used as a refuge and first-aid station and we found several dozen wounded saboteurs in the crypt. They were dragged outside where the Ukrainians and some of the butcher's men beat them to death with their rifle butts. They were laughing and placing bets on who could kill the most.

They found it particularly funny that one poor soul only had one arm. He must have lost it fighting or it had been recently amputated by a doctor, so one of the Butcher's men hacked his other arm off, doused him with petrol and then set light to him. They roared with laughter, jeered and cracked jokes as armless, burning alive and blinded from the shock and the pain from his injuries, he ran down the road screaming for help. When a priest protested they hung him from a lamppost and then used his body for target practice. Two nuns from the same church who were acting as nurses were repeatedly raped in front of me and the whole time that they were being brutalised they continued to pray. When they were finished the nuns were shot and then all the bodies were piled up, petrol was poured over them and they were set alight. I can't remove these images from my brain and I'm ashamed of my uniform, my country and my fellow soldiers."

Jozef had heard stories and rumours of such atrocities but he had never imagined that an enemy soldier would so graphically and remorsefully corroborate them as everyday occurrences. He asked, "Would you like to take a break now, we can speak again later?"

The German, having come this far, was anxious to unburden himself and so replied, "No thanks, there's not much more I can tell you accept that Dirlewanger isn't really interested in fighting your army openly, street by street. I've heard that he was once a brave man having been wounded many times and decorated for gallantly leading from the front, but now he's the total opposite, a coward who hides behind others, either his own men or civilians, thinking he can beat you by simply murdering most of the population. He's become a man without conscience or pity, a loose cannon who murders and rapes because he enjoys it."

"Thank you Erich. I know it hasn't been easy for you to tell me this."

"There's one more thing. To my eternal shame I helped blow open the doors of a very large house that turned out to be a school. There were children and teachers all over the building and the butcher's men and the Ukrainians ran from room to room rounding them up. There must have been three hundred children and nine or ten teachers. The ones they found hiding were shot there and then. The rest were ordered out into the street with their hands behind their heads and they were machine-gunned. The screams of those still standing, waiting to die, mingled with the moans and cries from those who were wounded. The officers then walked over the piles of bodies shooting any who showed any signs of life. Some of the children were only five years old. We were ordered to stand and watch it happen."

Jozef stood up and, although he was not totally sure that Erich had finished what he wanted to say, he knew that he could listen to no more that day. He thanked the German for his honesty and told him he would speak to him again and then left to write up his report and analyse how the information could best be used. However, before he could do either he was sent to assess and report on the latest enemy action that seemed to be building into a major attack on the Old Town District which was already virtually surrounded and cut off at ground level. Across this major and vital sector Jozef's comrades were running desperately short of ammunition and medical supplies and their commander was doubtful that they could withstand a major offensive without urgent and substantial replenishment.

Throughout the first few weeks of the uprising the British had attempted to honour their promises by flying in supplies from their captured bases in Italy. The two thousand mile flight across Yugoslavia, Hungary and the Carpathians and back, with only a short period of summer darkness proved dangerous in the extreme. To make matters worse the supplies had to be dropped from under four hundred feet at an air speed of only one hundred and fifty miles per hour in order to stand any chance of accuracy. Such manoeuvres made the aircraft very vulnerable to ground attack and losses of fifty percent were not unusual and, on one particularly calamitous night, only one of the seven planes returned.

The Allies appealed to the Russians for the use of their facilities. Stalin refused point blank, despite personal requests from Churchill and Roosevelt. The British later concluded that the air-drops were not cost effective and threatened to call them off and so Polish pilots volunteered and took over the role, but they faced exactly the same problems and there was no significant improvement in the success rate. Churchill even proposed to Roosevelt that they should send planes directly into the Russian controlled areas to refuel and thereby force Stalin's hand. Roosevelt who by this time was sick and weak would not sign up to such a risky strategy. After suffering continued heavy losses the airdrops were reluctantly cancelled and although further desperate requests were made to the Russians on an almost daily basis, they refused to change their stance.

Some two hundred aircrew lost their lives on these missions in just a few weeks and most of the parachutes with their precious cargo of weapons, ammunition, food and medical supplies fell into the hands of the Germans. The few canisters that were recovered by the Poles were worth their weight in gold. Some even contained desperately needed blood donated by the Polish army in Scotland, frantic to help their beleaguered countrymen. It may even be that, in makeshift Home Army hospitals across Warsaw, young German soldiers' lives were saved by those unknown Polish patriots in Scotland: such are the contradictions and absurdities of war. The Poles were left to fight on without aid or resupply. At Stalin's insistence the Polish paratroopers were never sent to do the one job most of them had specifically volunteered and trained so hard for: instead just one month later, they were dropped at Arnhem during operation 'Market-Garden.'

After a week of taking very heavy casualties in the street fighting the Germans changed tactics and decided to drive a limited number of wedges into the Polish positions, instead of attacking on a broad front. Then they systematically destroyed the buildings on the perimeter of the Polish held areas using tanks, artillery, heavy bombers and rockets, driving the insurgents into ever decreasing and more manageable pockets or islands. A particularly frightening weapon was the 'Nebelwerfer' rocket launcher, which could fire four or six rockets at a time with devastating effect. The Poles dreaded these weapons because they could carry both high explosives and incendiary charges, and the injuries caused to anyone sprayed by the burning fuel were horrendous. They became known as 'cows' because as they closed on their targets they made a distinctive mooing sound. Once a group of buildings had been demolished their engineers set further explosive charges destroying the cellars and sewers to prevent the Poles from infiltrating back into the area.

Jozef met up with Zenon at their group's new base where the Kapo had just been briefed on their mission. He was seething with anger, "I've just been told what the Russians are up to and you won't believe the tricks they're pulling to make sure that we'll be absorbed into a Greater Soviet Union. They want our army crushed so they can govern us, control us and then neutralise us. If we're not careful we're going to lose everything."

Jozef was used to the constant stream of alarmist rumours and speculation that fed the Home Army's desperate need for outside information but he had never seen his friend so agitated. "What on earth has happened now?"

"They've created their own Polish army ready to move in. Not Russian sympathisers from our country but actual Russians. They've trained hundreds of officers to speak and write Polish, given them cover stories and false documents to prove their Polishness, and even created a convincing paper trail for their previous education and employment. They've been issued with Polish uniforms and equipment and then put in charge of whole sections of the Red Army. Thousands of Russian troops, whole regiments, have been turned into Polish units overnight. They're being kitted out with everything Polish even as we speak. Weapons, kit, vehicles, radios, the whole works. To all intents and purposes they've become the new Polish national army. They intend to deploy them into the most strategically important and sensitive areas across Poland to take control of all Government functions and deny us a voice while they install their own 'chosen men'."

"How do you know? It all sounds a bit farfetched to me."

"Oh this is genuine all right. It's come direct from one of our agents who infiltrated Berling's army as it moved deeper into Poland. The imposters are all Russians and Ukrainians and nothing at all to do with Berling's Poles and we've been given documentary proof, supplied by someone from the agent's Headquarters Staff whose family have been arrested and threatened by the NKVD, so that he would cooperate with his Russian masters. He's now personally responsible for overseeing their whole training and familiarisation programme but he's still man enough to risk everything to get this information out. It's an outrageous and audacious plan and has Stalin's fingerprints all over it. Even if we can expose what he's doing it has the potential to cause chaos and considerably weaken our control once the Germans are driven out."

Shocking as this news appeared to be, they had an urgent assignment to complete and so in a sober mood they set off together to assess the German attack, meeting up with their guides for the hazardous trip. Irena, a fourteen year old schoolgirl and Jacob, an apprentice baker who was just seventeen were known as sewer-rats because they spent most of their time underground acting as messengers, couriers and guides. They were short in stature and very slim, ideal for travelling quickly through the underground networks of tunnels, basements and sewers. They entered the main drainage system via a tunnel concealed in the basement of an apartment building, well within the area controlled by the Home Army and hidden from aerial observation and sniper activity. It was permanently guarded by a detachment of Home Army Police and led straight down to the underground canal system some forty feet below.

The tunnels were the shape of an upturned egg: the largest measured five feet wide by eight feet high and the smallest two feet wide by three feet high, but the majority were five feet wide by six feet high. They had been designed by the English engineer William Lindley and were installed between 1881 and 1889. There is still a street in Warsaw named after him and he also constructed similar systems across dozens of cities throughout Europe.

Irena led the way and Jacob brought up the rear. Because of the narrow, concave floors they had to walk with their legs bowed and braced against the two sides. It was pitch dark but their guides were forbidden by their standing orders from talking underground or using torches except in a dire emergency and so they walked with one hand on the shoulder of the person in front and the other on the side wall for support. Their guides appeared to be able to see their way clearly but it took Zenon and Jozef several minutes before their night vision kicked in and they could detect enough shadow and movement to make careful progress.

Between their legs flowed a mixture of water, sewage and toxic chemicals from the gases that the Germans frequently pumped into the system. At first the going was relatively easy but within minutes the tunnel shrank dramatically in size where a side wall had collapsed. They were forced into an ever narrowing funnel of debris and had to crawl through the filth as it gushed across a small weir which had been formed between the surviving wall and the pile of rubble, which almost reached the roof and arched over their heads across a huge block of fallen masonry. The guides had no trouble squeezing past but Zenon and Jozef had to be pushed and pulled, slowly twisted through, inch by painful inch, lying on their backs to keep their mouths clear of the flow so that they could periodically stop and draw breath. Then with their arms once more outstretched and their lungs emptied they wriggled, squeezed and wrestled forward. It was only the lubrication provided by the slime and ooze that ultimately permitted their passage through this ragged edged 'maggot's crawl'. When, sweating and exhausted, they eventually scrambled down beyond the dam-like obstruction, they were confronted by a chest-high lake of the foulest smelling waste that literally took their breath away.

The putrid stench was all-pervasive, a cloying, suffocating fog that was so bad that Jozef, even though he was used to the noxious smells in the death camp, felt weak and nauseous. As his legs buckled he suddenly felt himself being supported from behind by Jacob who had quietly moved up and grabbed him, holding him upright by his clothing and whispering, "It's the gas. The residue has formed a pocket here, so hold your breath again and keep moving. We'll be through it in a minute or two."

They reformed into their crocodile formation and stumbled on for another five minutes and by this time Jozef, although recovered from the debilitating effects of the over exertion and the gas, was disorientated and he had uncharacteristically completely lost his sense of direction in relation to the world above ground. They pressed on as Irena, seemingly unperturbed and constantly pausing, listening and checking her charges, loped through another hundred yard stretch and then turned right, climbing up into a feeder pipe that was less than half the size of the main sewer.

They moved forward crawling along on their hands and knees when just a few moments later there was the sound of a huge explosion in the main sewer behind them. It was immediately followed by a mighty crash and roaring echo of a major collapse and, as they froze in surprise, a rush of compressed air, gas and spray passed over them like an express train, coating them all with a glutinous mixture of debris and effluent and sucking the air from their lungs. Before they could speak or move, another, even larger explosion followed and the main sewer behind was brilliantly lit up by a flash of heat and flame that then surged on past the end of their pipe, leaving them in sudden and total blackness as they were temporarily blinded by the loss of their night vision and also deafened by the proximity of the massive detonation. The ground shook violently and the sound of collapsing brickwork reverberated along the tunnel walls as masonry and mortar debris started to fall all around them.

Jozef collapsed onto his stomach and remained stock-still, petrified, as the pipe seemed to come alive and close right in on him, threatening to crush both his fragile body and his will to fight. Then he started trembling: at first it was his face that twitched and quivered but it rapidly spread through his arms, body and legs until he was shivering uncontrollably from head to toe. The noise and pulsating vibrations which seemed to him to have been of earthquake proportions had combined with the smell, the darkness and his growing fear of being trapped forever to form a claustrophobic terror that rendered him totally helpless. He was rescued by Jacob who, although closest to the source of the explosions was the first to recover his faculties and he crawled onto Jozef's legs and shouted, "Come on Jozef, get moving, we're right underneath the Germans and they must have found us with one of their listening devices, They're trying to finish us off, or flush us out into a trap, so they'll be putting more gas down soon. We've got to put some distance behind us and then get out as quick as we can. Now move!"

Jozef, still frozen to the spot, only heard muffled, indistinguishable words amongst the ringing and static in his ears, but as he became aware of the trembling throughout his body he also felt shame and humiliation for the fear and weakness seeping into his soul. He was used to the tunnels and yet this time, whilst children were dutifully and fearlessly risking their lives for his sake, he had vividly and terrifyingly imagined, perhaps even experienced, being buried alive. He felt as if he had been abandoned to suffocate: sealed forever in a watery tomb. He had snapped like a twig, given up and cowered, twitching and unthinking, but even then a residue of reason survived and instinctively he knew he needed to break the spell somehow, yet he still could not move forward.

He bit down hard on his lip, trying to gain some control with pain, until his mouth filled with the sharp metallic and bitter taste of blood and as he coughed, almost choked and then violently spat it out, it was as if the sudden action had turned a switch in his

298

brain and he was shocked right back to the existent, but no less dangerous, world of reality. He remembered that he had overcome his first such attack when hiding underground in the barn and so he knew he could do it again. His hearing returned and he realised that Jacob was shouting a stream of obscenities at him and alternately beating down on his legs and pushing him hard from behind, desperately urging him forward. He finally, but agonizingly, slowly started to function again and as his vision cleared he could just about make out Zenon's feet a few feet ahead in the gloom. At first he concentrated everything on moving one leg forward at a time until he gradually built up a familiar rhythm and before long he was once again crawling quickly through the cesspool of a passage. Despite the horrors of his past he had never experienced such incapacitating and agonising terror and, although he drew some consolation from the fact that he had come through the panic and conquered his worst moment of crisis, he now decided that come what may, once this mission was over, he would never, ever enter the sewers again.

They dropped down into another main line and as they turned towards their destination they were able to see slightly more clearly because most of the manhole covers above the section ahead had been removed by the enemy, allowing light to filter down every ninety yards or so. Fearing an ambush and booby traps they slowed right down to cautiously pass beneath these hazardous inspection hatches. As they approached the last one they could clearly hear a group of Germans talking in the street above their heads, but they silently crept along undetected and once they were safely moving back into the shadows they felt much less vulnerable.

They had only travelled another twenty yards when they came across more obstructions underfoot in the waste. Zenon stumbled and fell forwards and as he put out his hands to break his fall they both connected with the torso of a decomposing body, breaking through the bloated chest cavity with a sickening crack and squelch. Hardened and prepared as he was to shock and war Zenon could do nothing to stifle an involuntary scream before he recoiled in horror, jerking himself up and away from the remains, vigorously shaking the putrid flesh and gore from his hands.

There was a burst of machine-gun-fire from behind and they could hear rounds bouncing off the walls all around them as they started to run, pushing out against the side walls for support, as they tripped and stumbled over a dozen or more corpses before they cleared the once human obstacle. There was no pursuit: fortunately, most German units were extremely reluctant to enter the confinement of the sewers where they became just as defenceless as their quarry. As a result of their short but bitter experience during the 'rattenkreig' (war of the rats) in the sewers of Stalingrad they had developed an almost paranoid aversion to the prospect of such a battle. Their SS commanders, try as they might, could not persuade them to take the battle to the Poles underground. They preferred to use gas, hand grenades and explosives or, as in this case, stay close to an inspection hatch and fire wildly down through the tunnel.

Miraculously the Poles had suffered nothing worse than bruised fingers and lacerated knuckles as they had struggled to stay on their feet and escape the bullets. Five minutes later, although not yet at their destination, they reached a Polish held sector where they rapidly made for the surface to avoid the inevitable follow up gas attack.

Jozef and Zenon now had their bearings and after receiving an update and briefing from the locals they decided to push on. They embraced and thanked their young guides leaving them in the protection of Home Army fighters to await their next orders. As they walked away Jozef, still smarting from his experience underground commented, "If we all had only half of the courage and mental strength of those kids then victory would be assured."

Zenon put his arm around his friends shoulder and replied, "That was you not so long ago and you've proved yourself time and time again since, so you've got nothing to reproach yourself for, but we're all going to pay a very high price indeed for using children to fight our war. I bet those two thought it was all a great adventure at first but reality soon sank in once they'd seen their friends shot, had walked past the bodies hanging on the gallows and rotting away down the sewers and then found the very people they've been living with today, dead and gone tomorrow. Who knows how it will affect them in the future."

"I doubt if they've even got a future. The problem is that there's no longer a time or place to grow up and enjoy the journey, only time to die or grow old overnight. But there's nothing you or I can do about it, so let's get on with the job in hand. By the way, you stink something dreadful! I should think the Germans can smell us a mile off."

Ten minutes later they found themselves at a particularly hazardous intersection and neither of them liked what they saw. The barricades that had originally given some protection to those crossing the street had been blown apart by shelling and the whole street was littered with dozens of bodies. Even more worrying was the fact that a number of weapons were lying alongside the dead, indicating that the crossing was regularly covered by enemy snipers. Weapons and ammunition were in such short supply that only the risk of certain death would prevent their recovery. Zenon looked at his old friend and said, "I don't know of another way around, we either cross here or go back. I suggest that I go first and draw their fire. If we both zigzag our way across and keep as low as we can, at least one of us might make it."

Jozef didn't like the odds and could see another problem, "Even if we make it this time, we've still got to get back across and then they'll definitely be expecting us and our chances will be even worse."

His friend was not as pessimistic, "Once we make contact on the other side they might know a safer route back. From the state of some of those bodies this has been a problem for a long time so perhaps they've figured a way around it. One thing's for sure: we won't find out until we get over there." Without further comment Zenon started sprinting across the road. He had only gone a few paces when a shot rang out and the bullet hit the ground a foot behind Zenon's legs but he kept sprinting. Jozef stayed where he was, as he knew the sniper would expect someone else to follow and he wanted to wait long enough to place a seed of doubt in his mind. The delay just might cause him to return to his original target and thereby give both of them a chance to take advantage of his hesitation.

When Zenon was in the middle of the road Josef took a deep breath and prepared to run but at that very second he heard the incoming 'cow' and instinctively dived to the ground and covered his ears. Zenon heard it too but kept sprinting from side to side with his head down hoping to take advantage of what must be a major distraction to the sniper. The first rocket burst right in the middle of the junction and Zenon was thrown through the air by the force of the explosion. The rest of the salvo fell on the buildings opposite, which collapsed almost immediately and burst into flame. Jozef could see that his friend was in a very bad way from the rag doll way in which he had landed and the unnatural position of his body, but then he heard him call out weakly, "Go back Jozef, I'm finished."

Jozef reacted without thinking but in blind rage. He ran straight to his friend, lifted him from the ground, threw him over his shoulder as if he was weightless and turned to sprint back to where he knew he could get him to a hospital. He was only two paces from safety when he was knocked to the ground. He couldn't breathe, felt a crippling and intense pain in his stomach and as he looked down he could see blood oozing through the front of his smock jacket. He slowly crawled forward, grabbed Zenon by the feet to drag him towards safety but, try as he might, he couldn't move his friend. He remembered everything that the Kapo had done to save him in the death camp, with no thought for himself and so, duty bound, he knew he couldn't give up on his guardian angel and mentor and again he pulled with every ounce of his failing strength. Despite his immense power of will and determination his friend never moved, not even an inch and as he tried again two more rounds from the sniper's weapon slammed into Zenon's already lifeless body. Jozef crawled to the safety of the building, leaving a trail of blood behind on the cobbles and before he lost consciousness he felt a huge weight of guilt. He had known in his heart that the crossing was just too dangerous and if he had overruled him his friend's death would have been avoided. His last thought was that he owed Zenon everything, loved him like a brother and yet he had let him down badly and now they were both dead because of it.

Jozef was found five minutes later by a patrol of the Home Army who had come to investigate the results of the rocket attack. He regained consciousness in a casualty station where they did their best to stabilise him and an hour after that he found himself in another makeshift hospital.

Jozef thought he had arrived in hell. The scene matched the frightening Old Testament paintings of his childhood scripture books. Burns and blast victims, the living dead were everywhere. The conscious were screaming and howling with the pain and many could not lie down or sit or even stand still because of the severity of their injuries, but stumbled around in desolation as the orderlies and nurses tried to soothe both their shattered minds and their roasted bodies. The unconscious, many barely recognisable as humans and beyond any hope of recovery or treatment, were just waiting to die and were seen as the lucky ones. Some of the survivors had lost limbs and their sight as the burning liquids from the rockets had turned them into human torches and whilst several prayed out loud others, past the point of palliative care, were heard cursing, crying out for their husbands, wives and mothers and begging for someone to do the merciful thing and put them out of their misery. The noise and horror were beyond endurance.

Amongst this bedlam Jozef noticed that one of the orderlies, trying desperately to bring some compassionate order to this chaos of misery, was dressed in a strange blue uniform. He later found out that he was a British Royal Air Force pilot who had been shot down in the countryside outside Warsaw in the first week of the uprising whilst trying to drop weapons and ammunition. He had been brought into the city by the reinforcements and, as his leg and chest injuries were not too serious, he had been helping in the hospital ever since. Like most of the population he was now trapped as Warsaw was being destroyed district by district.

Josef had been shot through the gut and he could tell, from the searing pain, his continuous fight for breath and the knowing way in which the nurses treated him, that he was dying. At first, as he lay there surrounded by abject suffering, he longed for death to take him. He was convinced that with Zenon gone he did not deserve to live anyway. On the one and only occasion that his friend had ever truly needed him he had failed to deliver: this, he told himself, made him even guiltier than the sniper or the unknown Nebelwerfer gunner.

The following day, while staring blankly at the British airman, he realised that he did not want to die without his brothers and sister having the small comfort of knowing what had happened to him. When he noticed the airman talking in English to a doctor the germ of an idea began to grow in his mind. He mustered the energy to fight against the unspeakable pain and struggle on a little longer so that he could talk to the doctor, brief him on his intentions and then he was ready to call over the pilot. Jozef gave him a potted history of his wartime experiences and asked if the Englishman would do him a massive favour after he died. The Pilot answered that he would do all he could and then, as both men tried to delay the morbid finality of making any detailed arrangements, their conversation turned to what was happening in the streets outside and then to the wider war in Europe. After a while they discovered that using the Englishman's smattering of Polish and schoolboy German they could communicate without the doctor and from then on spoke together often and only referred to the doctor when they became stuck. On the third day Jozef felt even weaker and deciding that he could wait no longer, called the Doctor and the pilot across. "I would like to dictate a note to you and give you a small package for delivery in England when you finally get home."

The pilot, who also knew that Jozef's time was close, nodded his agreement, took out a pen and paper and wrote down the Pole's words as best he could:

> *To the manager, The Rubens Hotel, London.*
>
> *My name is Jozef Nowaski and the bearer of this letter will vouch for me. It is my dying wish that these letters are delivered to my brother Jacek. Please do this in memory of my parents and all the friends I have lost. The Polish authorities in exile know who I am and they have seen that I am a true patriot and have loyally served our country, even until my death. I authorise them to use the information contained within these letters to trace my brother and deliver them to him. Please do not fail me. He must be told of what has happened to me and of how we fought for what we believed in.*
>
> *Long live Poland.*

Jozef was now too weak to even attempt to sign the note but he was relieved that he had managed to complete this final task. He then indicated to his jacket pocket and the pilot removed the small tin box, looked inside and found the package wrapped in an oilskin. He said to Jozef, "You have my word that I'll do my best. If I manage to get home I'll deliver it safely and also make sure that the authorities comply with your wishes. Many Poles have gladly risked their lives to save me and so perhaps in this small way I can start to repay their kindness. It's been a privilege to know you and your people and it grieves me to see so much unnecessary pain. I honestly consider it to be both an honour and a duty to do as you ask."

"Thank you my friend but there's one more thing I must ask. Can you please arrange for a priest to see me? I think my time is close and I would like to be ready to meet my maker," asked Jozef in a failing voice.

Two hours later the chaplain arrived and an even weaker and fevered Jozef asked in a barely audible voice, "When you get the chance could you let Father Chepek know what has happened to me and apologise to him because I didn't get to visit him again as I'd promised?"

The priest held Jozef's hand and said, "I'm afraid he was murdered by the Germans as he tried to protect the nuns at the church of the Holy Cross. He died a very brave man and is surely in heaven now. There is no reason to apologise, essentially this war is to blame for almost everything."

As Jozef heard these words, even wracked with burning pain and on the very edge of consciousness, he still made the connection with the account of a priest's death given by the German prisoner Erich. He could not understand why he had overlooked the obvious possibility at the time and not made proper efforts to question the prisoner further and clarify the full facts. After all, so he told himself, Father Chepek had helped him immeasurably and was a true friend: they had risked their lives together and Jozef had once, it seemed so long ago now, aspired to the priesthood himself.

His imagined guilt regarding an oversight that had no practical consequences whatsoever took on a totally unrealistic importance to him and was further exaggerated by his pain-induced confusion. He fervidly accused himself of gross incompetence and military failure and he seethed within. This mental turmoil and self-recrimination built exponentially with his fever until it vented in a violent explosion of anger and bitterness. Having lost his ability to reason he ranted, thrashed about and cursed the world, abandoning all hope of Poland's salvation.

The priest heard this chaotic, nonsensical and unremorseful confession, told him he had nothing to fear from death and assured him that he had done all that God had ever asked of him. He then tenderly administrated the last rites and quietly prayed for him.

Minutes later, with the certain knowledge that Warsaw was now doomed and Poland would follow, Jozef no longer possessed the will to resist and collapsed, exhausted and defeated. Together with the English pilot the priest then sat with Jozef as he drifted in and out of consciousness until he finally died some two hours later. He was just twenty-two years old.

The pilot carefully put the box in his battle dress pocket, looked around the hospital and wondered if all the wounded and dying Poles could tell such equally heart rending and remarkable stories. From what he had seen during his limited time in the country he suspected that many could and he was inspired by the notion.

The fighting dragged on for another month but the Germans now had the upper hand and, with no significant supplies getting in, the Poles ammunition finally expired. The Russians still refused to provide any real military help and although, after continued and desperate allied pressure, they provided some airdrops, from mid-September onwards it was too little and far too late. Russian forces continued to wait on the east bank of the Vistula whilst the Polish Home Army was slowly but relentlessly destroyed within the city.

After weeks of ever more desperate but fruitless appeals to their high command, whilst watching their capital and its population being annihilated, the Poles fighting with the Red Army under General Berling finally won permission to act but only on a limited scale and without any support from other Red Army units. They made several valiant but costly attempts (over five thousand casualties) to establish a foothold on the western bank of the Vistula, but strategically the size of the force was insufficient and the optimum time for action had long past. Unfortunately the Home Army were now too decimated to supply much in the way of military support and the bridge-head could not be held. It has since been suggested that in fact General Berling had finally lost patience with his leaders and acted on his own initiative before he had received any orders from above. In either case it was no coincidence, but more a sign of Stalin's displeasure, that he lost his command shortly afterwards and was posted back to Russia.

On the 2nd October, with the Soviets still holding their positions, what was left of the Home Army surrendered and Warsaw, a once splendid city was again under German control. In the sixty-three day battle over one hundred and eighty thousand civilians died, together with some fifteen thousand Home Army and other underground fighters. To put this in perspective, in those two months Warsaw alone lost the same number of people that the Americans lost in their three and a half years of ground war. The Germans lost some sixteen thousand dead and missing. The Poles also destroyed over three hundred tanks, armoured cars and self-propelled artillery pieces and three hundred and fifty trucks and other vehicles.

Not satisfied with the Polish surrender, the Germans continued to inflict cruelty upon cruelty. They started burning Warsaw to the ground, block by block, street by street and district by district. The SS poured petrol into the basements, added combustible material such as flock or furniture, threw in hand grenades or flares or even used flame throwers and then methodically moved on to the next property. As the neighbourhoods burned they ordered the population to leave Warsaw en masse and air dropped leaflets across the whole city. They fell like snow, drifted and piled up, covering the ground in swathes and then, as the nearby fire storms created their own winds they blew along like tumbleweed, their lies adding to the desolate humiliation of defeat:

ULTIMATUM

To the people of Warsaw:

The German High Command wants to avoid unnecessary bloodshed, which will mainly affect innocent women and children and therefore has issued the following order:

1.	*The whole population must leave Warsaw in a western direction, carrying white handkerchiefs in their hands.*
2.	*The German High Command guarantees that no one who leaves Warsaw of their own free will, will come to harm.*
3.	*All men and women who are able to work will receive work and bread.*
4.	*People unable to work will be accommodated in the western district of Warsaw's province. Food will be supplied.*

307

5.   *All who are ill, as well as old people, women and children needing care, will receive accommodation and medical care.*

The Polish people know that the German Army is fighting Bolshevism only. Anyone who continues to be used by them as a Bolshevik's instrument, irrespective of which ideology he might follow, will be held responsible and prosecuted without scruples.

This ultimatum is for a limited time only.

SIGNED:
THE SUPREME COMMANDER-IN-CHIEF.

The city was emptied of its inhabitants, thousands sent to prisons and labour or concentration camps and, when Soviet forces finally marched in during January, some eighty five percent of the city had been razed to the ground. They inherited an empty wasteland. Stalin then took full advantage of the situation and deployed his 'Polish army' as intended, rounded up many Home Army leaders and political activists and shipped them off to prison or the Gulag. Invitations were sent out to groups, organisations and individuals across Poland inviting them for talks, negotiations or social functions and those that turned up were arrested, interrogated and often imprisoned or executed after 'confessing' their crimes.

The iron curtain came down swiftly and resolutely across Poland and in its massive shadow Soviet totalitarianism and vindictiveness thrived. The full dictatorial weight of the state apparatus was employed to cover up Stalin's most hideous and barbaric crimes against humanity. It is said that he was responsible for more murders than Hitler, Mao Tse-tung and Pol Pot put together and yet, in comparison, he has managed to escape total condemnation and vilification and even retains a host of ardent admirers.

Historians today argue over Stalin's motivation for refusing to help but there is no ambivalence in the minds of the Poles. Stalin had never forgiven the allies for their conduct in the spring of 1942 when the Red Army was suffering unsustainable losses as the Germans relentlessly advanced on Moscow. Following Stalin's appeal for the opening of a second front in the west to relieve the pressure Roosevelt and Molotov, fearful of a Russian defeat, had signed and published a communiqué of understanding stating that the invasion of France would take place in 1942. When this did not happen Stalin was incensed and felt a deep sense of betrayal.

This disbelief was reinforced the following year when again the Allies failed to open the second front before the Germans embarked on their summer offensive. At the ensuing massive and decisive tank battle at Kursk over two hundred thousand Russian soldiers perished before they won the day. The Soviet Generals believed that this battle would never have taken place if the Nazis had faced an invasion in France. Stalin believed the western allies were happy to sit idly by and watch while the two mighty armies slaughtered each other, hoping they would fight on until the terrible attrition rate rendered them both impotent. He never trusted the allies again, despite the fact that after Kursk it was the Russians that had the real momentum.

Now, even more suspicious of their post-war intentions, he wanted the Home Army destroyed so that he would be unopposed when turning Poland into a satellite communist state and a buffer with the west in the oncoming 'Cold War'. Ironically he didn't want the Home Army to take Warsaw but he required them to inflict maximum casualties on the Germans whilst themselves suffering massive and crippling losses in the attempt. With the Germans weakened and the Poles' spirit to fight broken, his forces could then simply march in and take the city without the bitter and costly house-to-house battles that would severely drain his resources. Warsaw and its inhabitants was just another dispensable obstacle in the way of his rush for the real prize, Berlin, which he was determined to take before the allies were in a position to do so.

FIFTEEN

Meeting the Past
8th November 2008

The letter from the MoD was surprisingly short and after the usual references and salutation the author, Jane Mitchell, merely apologised for the delay in responding, informed me that the matter had become more complicated and intimated that a formal reply letter would probably only generate many more questions on my part. She added that she wished to save me time and avoid any protracted correspondence that would inevitably cause me annoyance and frustration. She repeated that she wished to help as much as possible and suggested that I should telephone her in order that she could release the authorised information, explain the various limitations and answer any questions I wished to ask.

I was not too disappointed because it was my experience that you are far more likely to obtain detailed and more useful information over the telephone than in writing. People are always far more reluctant to commit themselves on paper, especially when there are issues of policy or data protection involved and in any case, there is no spontaneity in a letter. On the telephone, however, I could explore the inevitable grey areas and do my best to provoke off the record comments and opinions. I quickly recapped my file, made a note of a few key questions, and then made the call. I thanked her for her letter, waited whilst she gathered up her papers and commenced with an interviewer's typical open question, "What can you tell me Jane?"

"I'll start with Tomek. I can confirm that he served with the Polish 2nd Corps and was demobilised in Amersham in 1946. We heard nothing from him until his application for naturalisation in 1967. His application was successful but we have nothing on him since."

"Can you tell me when he joined up and where he served?"

"He served in Italy but as I don't know whether he is still alive or the identity of his next of kin, I have been told that I cannot give you any more information from his file."

I couldn't stop myself, "What about his address in 1967?"

Jane chuckled and said, "Nice try, but you definitely can't have that."

"What about his date of birth or age?"

"When he left the army he was twenty two, now that's really all I can tell you."

As I made notes of what she had told me I decided to try to exert some control over the direction of the conversation and steer her away from the standard, well-practiced, policy answers by asking, "What did you mean when you said in your letter that things had become more complicated?"

"When I spoke to you before we had no trace of Jan on our computerised nominal index but when the files arrived I found him. His file contents had been placed inside the jacket of Jacek's personal file, but despite a further search, there still isn't any trace of Jan's own original file jacket. That explains why there was no record of him on the computer because the names were computerised in the early nineties when the entries were created from the information contained solely on the file covers. It follows that if there was no file jacket then there couldn't be a nominal index record. The actual contents of the files were never computerised because such a project was beyond our resources and not cost effective. Therefore there was no need to open any of the tens of thousands of files or examine their contents when the nominal index was created."

"So you now have a full file on Jan that had presumably been misfiled in Jacek's cover, well, you did warn me that these things happen."

"It's a bit more complicated than that because it wasn't just simply misfiled. I found a hand written unofficial note with Jan's papers. It's very unusual and somewhat intriguing so I've spoken to my boss and I've been told that under these unique circumstances I can explain it to you. It's probably best if I read it to you first. It was written by a member of the old Polish Records Office in January, 1946 and says and I quote, 'when looking for Jacek Nowaski's file, following up on information received from Flight Lieutenant Godwin, Bomber Command, RAF, I also found a file for a Jan Nowaski. The files indicate they are brothers (same place of birth, same parents, same home address and same siblings). Full details of both given to the RAF for the information of Lt. Godwin', unquote. Now the fact that the brothers were suddenly identified as such is, in itself, not unusual because they joined when the whole of Europe was in turmoil and close relatives were often in the same Division but in separate units and they were frequently completely unaware of each other's existence. From the other papers in their files it's clear to me that while they were in the army neither of them had any idea where any of their brothers were. The fact that such a note was written into the file tends to suggest that the record's office clerk came to the same conclusion, but he took some form of action to inform them of each other's service. He may have done it through their units or the RAF officer might have had something to do with it. It appears that once the matter had finally been dealt with all the papers were mistakenly put back into the jacket of Jacek's file and have stayed like that ever since."

I followed most of what she was saying except how the third party fitted in, "What's the role of the RAF officer in all this?"

"We don't know exactly, there's nothing to indicate what the information mentioned in the note could be, but whatever it was it was nothing detrimental or official because no disciplinary or any other action was taken or any further information added later. My best guess is that it was something personal but very important to all three parties."

I had a sudden idea, "Can you or anyone else give me more information on the RAF chap? There could be more to it than we think."

"We can't and to be honest, even if we could we wouldn't because you have no legitimate right of access to his personal details. The RAF wouldn't give you the time of day over it."

I asked her to hang on while I made some more notes and gathered my thoughts then asked, "If the staff put two of the brothers together, why didn't they also find Tomek's file and include him in the information given to the RAF officer?"

She was silent for a moment before replying, "The records for the two Corps were kept separately and to be honest, during the war itself, they weren't that accurate and a great deal of information was added retrospectively, using the information provided on demobilisation in 1946 and 1947. It could be that they only checked against 1ˢᵗ Corps records and that's why they found only Jan's and Jacek's, or it could be that when they checked the 2ⁿᵈ Corps records Tomek's was missing or incomplete."

I thought we had taken that issue as far as we could and so, whilst Jane was being so helpful and talkative I changed tack and asked, "What have you got on Jan?"

She answered straight away, "Well, he joined the 1ˢᵗ Polish Armoured Division in Scotland in 1942 when he was 17 and then went into France in August 1944 and fought until the end of the war. We have his complete history and war service up to 1946. After that it's a complete blank. That's probably because his papers were inside Jacek's file cover from then on and so if anything else came in subsequently it must have been put in a temporary file and then destroyed after a few years or was simply lost."

"What about his demobilisation papers, where are they?"

She was obviously embarrassed by the apparent inefficiency and replied, "To be honest, anything could have happened to them but there's no way of finding out now. We don't know whether he is still alive or whether he settled here or got married or anything. I'm really sorry about that."

I thought any further comment about the loss would be pointless and so I moved on, "What about Jacek?"

Expecting another completely negative reply her answer this time surprised me, "I can confirm that he joined up in France in the summer of 1944, after he had escaped from the Germans and then surrendered to the Canadians. He was demobbed at Winchester in February 1947, when he was twenty-two and in 1950 we received a letter from him in which he stated that he intended to return to Poland. We have nothing on file since, but there is one other thing I can tell you: Jacek and Tomek are twins."

I let that sink in and then wondered why the problem with the combined files had not been spotted in 1947 or 1950 when Jacek's demobilisation forms or his subsequent letter were filed away. I had to ask, "When those documents were placed in his file in 1947 and 1950, why wasn't Jan's file also discovered inside and matters put right then?"

Jane had already seen this coming, "Almost certainly because the papers were just filed away inside the jacket. Neither of the documents would require a thorough examination of the file contents, it was only when I searched them properly that it all became apparent."

We seemed to be getting bogged down on this issue and so, in order to try and get her talking freely again rather than feeling defensive I asked, "As you say, you've studied all the files and my written request and thought about what you were able to reveal to me. Is there anything else you can tell me that we haven't yet covered?"

"Well I put all the names contained in your written summary through our system and there were no other matches. The Italian connection you speak of is almost certainly with Tomek as he was fighting there throughout most of the campaign."

I tried to get just a bit more personal information, "I know you can't tell me anymore about Jan but can you make up for it by letting me know whether Jacek was married before he told your predecessors that he was going home?"

"Just this once but please don't push your luck: he got married in September, 1946 in Hampshire and his wife Marta Dudek, a concentration camp survivor, had worked for the Polish Red Cross in Germany before she travelled to England with him."

I then moved on, "What do you know about Sergeant Vranek?"

"It's unfortunate but I often find in this type of enquiry that I can supply the most comprehensive information about the people on the periphery of the case and not the central characters. It's the same this time and the reason I can release so much to you is because Sergeant Vranek is now dead and we have no next of kin listed."

She was more accurate than she thought because things had moved on since I had written my letter to her and I was not now as interested in him as I used to be. Nevertheless, I had learnt time and time again to always accept information when it's on offer, no matter how insignificant it may seem, because it could prove priceless sometime in the future. "Fire away, I'm ready with pen poised."

314

"He returned to the UK in late 1945 and worked for the Resettlement Organisation as an interviewer and interpreter. He then travelled around the various transit and resettlement camps all across England. This next bit is of particular interest to you: in December 1946 he was definitely working at the Pipers Wood camp at Amersham but his visit was only temporary, as part of his administrative duties, and he moved on to Yorkshire in February, 1947. He left the army a month later but continued to work for the military as an interpreter, on a self-employed basis until 1950 when he started full time civilian employment at Leeds City Corporation as a housing officer. He stayed there until he died from a heart attack in 1966, aged 52."

I scribbled down the information as fast as I could and asked, "What can you tell me about his service in Holland, I am particularly interested in the 28th October, 1944?"

I waited whilst she again shuffled through papers. After a moment or two she said, "Well, his Division liberated Breda on 29th October and it attracted a great deal of comment at the time and since, because the city was hardly damaged and in gratitude all the soldiers were given the freedom of the city. Unfortunately there's no indication of exactly what he or his battalion was doing the day before but he was almost certainly fighting on the outskirts of the city."

I wondered if the Sergeant had provided the Crutzen family with details of any of the Nowaski soldiers and asked, "Was the Sergeant in exactly the same unit as either Jan or Jacek whilst they were in Holland?"

"Yes, you're right, Jan and the Sergeant were both in the same company of the 9th Rifle Battalion when they took Breda but Jacek was in the Highland Rifle Battalion."

"Just one more thing, when Sergeant Vranek was working for the Resettlement people would I be right in assuming that he would have had complete access to the records showing where Jan, Jacek and all the others were stationed or resettled?"

Jane replied, "Yes, most certainly and it would have been easy for him to have visited them in his official capacity, if he had wanted to."

I needed some idea of how resettlement worked, "I take it that these soldiers didn't just sit around in the camps waiting to be demobilised, there must have been some sort of a structured process to prepare them for civilian life in England?"

"It was structured in the sense that there were English language lessons, education programmes and trades courses but they also had a lot of free time and many found immediate part-time work in the local area. The resettlement officers forged strong and productive links with industry and commerce and they would use their contacts in order to match the soldiers' skills to the local job market. The Poles are hard workers and so a huge number quickly found full-time work, a significant proportion utilising their pre-war skills. In fact there were more vacancies than could be filled as offers of employment came from around the world and soldiers left for America, Canada, Australia, South Africa, virtually any country you would care to name. Some also married local girls and this was a great help in quickly settling down to life in what was still a strange and very different country. A few found it very difficult to adjust to the British way of life and so their release dates were very fluid and it was not uncommon for them to be working full-time locally but still officially be in the army. They had been through a great deal and they were cut a lot of slack, at least for a while."

I thanked her profusely and was just about to hang up when I noticed an unticked item on my checklist, "I'm sorry Jane but you must be aware that the Rubens Hotel was used as the Polish Military Headquarters during the war. Could you throw any light on why Jozef in Poland, who had certainly visited the hotel in 1943, should be using it as an accommodation address to communicate with Jacek in France?"

This time she did not hesitate, "If Jozef was getting in and out of Poland and visiting the Rubens then he was almost certainly an intelligence agent or a courier. Poland had a very sophisticated intelligence service that covered almost all of occupied Europe and they were particularly successful operating inside France and Germany itself. British Intelligence Services were delighted when they assumed control of the hundreds of Polish assets, including a network of penetration agents, when the Government in Exile was set up over here. It's only recently come to light that the Poles were running a spy codenamed 'Knopf', a German who operated alongside a number of informants within the top military echelons and provided the highest grade intelligence including details

316

of German intentions on the Eastern Front, the battle order for Operation Barbarossa and the location of the Wolf's Lair."

"I didn't realise that they were so successful and I've never heard of Knopf. How come you're so well informed?"

"This job brings me into regular contact with researchers, historians and intelligence documents of the time and a great deal of this once secret information is now available in such places as the Churchill Archives and National Records. Anyway, getting back to your original question, the Poles also supplied the Allies with huge quantities of other critical data particularly on the V1s, V2s and the Enigma machines and codes. They were so numerous, active and successful that the SIS (MI6) spied on the Government in Exile and intercepted all their radio traffic in case they were running any additional operations outside British parameters. So, if Jozef was involved within this widespread intelligence organisation, then he would have had no trouble communicating with someone anywhere inside occupied Europe. I have no doubt that he would have made contact if he had found out where Jacek was being held in France."

I thanked her once again before hanging up and she invited me to get back in touch if there was anything else she could do and requested that I inform her of the outcome of my search. I then sat and thought about the situation and concluded that I probably wouldn't be able to find out much more about what happened to the Nowaski family during the war and so it was time to actively search for them and their descendants in the present. As three of them had been demobilised in the UK and the fourth had also visited I decided to search using all their names.

I went on-line and searched the obvious sites such as UK telephone numbers and newspaper archives for the Amersham, Winchester and Codford areas but after two hours I had drawn a blank. This didn't surprise me because so many people are now ex-directory and others have discarded their landlines and only use mobiles, which are not normally listed in directories. I then tried the County Archive Offices for Buckinghamshire, Hampshire and Wiltshire and, although I learnt a great deal about the Polish communities in those areas, I found nothing on the name Nowaski. I then searched the internet for UK sites that dealt solely with tracing individuals and was surprised to see that there were so many. All required registration and they were not cheap but many offered their services by the hour or on a daily rate, rather than requiring a hefty full year's subscription. I then looked amongst those for sites that provided searches across the widest spectrum of categories and finally made my choice. This particular site offered combined searches in the areas of births, deaths, marriages, electoral roll and neighbour details, covering the dates from the 1980's to the present, right across the UK. The other advantage was that dates of birth were not required, only an estimate of age. This was just what I was looking for because I could now search countrywide for both the subjects themselves and possible children. They also offered to provide, at a price, the telephone services of an experienced search assistant if I ran into any real difficulties.

I had only recently become aware of the existence of these sites and discovered that they were regularly used by private detectives, who were now able to conduct quite protracted and complicated investigations from the comfort of their own offices. These sites, together with those covering such things as credit rating, property and land registers, deeds, debtors, genealogy and school reunions etc have now made the image of the archetypal care-worn, bedraggled sleuth, banging on doors in all weathers, a thing of the past.

I signed up, paid the fee and entered in the details of my four subjects. It was money well spent and I punched the air in delight as I saw the results, twelve hits on the first site and as I looked closely I just could not believe what I was seeing. Surely it had to be two of mine: Jan Nowaski and there, four lines below in the list, Tomek Nowaski, with addresses for both. Jan lived in Kidderminster and Tomek in London, but as I sat there the euphoria started to fade and doubts began to creep in. Both of them must be well into their eighties, could they both still be alive and, if so, did one of them leave the case in the hotel in Salisbury in the 1970's and if this was true, why didn't he collect it if he's been over here all this time? I ran over all the old issues again but it didn't get me any further and so I scanned down the rest of the list. None of the forenames meant anything to me but I was aware that any of them could have been a child or other relative.

I contacted directory enquiries to check again now that I had addresses, but as I expected, that came up negative. I thought about taking the bull by the horns and driving straight to one or both

318

of the addresses but I was unsure of the reception I would get, particularly as I could be interfering in very personal and painful experiences. It was quite possible that by just going in cold I could exacerbate a difficult situation or even cause a heart attack in someone so old and perhaps very frail. I decided there and then that I would try to make contact with a son or daughter and then visit them to explain everything and hand over all the property. This would give them the opportunity to discuss matters privately with their father and thus accommodate any concerns or expectations that he may have without causing any anxiety. All I had to do was find a son or daughter.

I did a separate electoral roll check on both addresses but no other occupants were listed. I then conducted a neighbour search on both addresses and printed out details of the occupants living in the three properties numbered on either side of the target addresses. In each case several of these occupants had telephone numbers listed. Twenty minutes later I had confidentially and, without telling too many untruths, confirmed with neighbours that both addresses were solely occupied by old gents of Polish origin and that a son and his wife were regular visitors to Jan's address. I went back to the original list and found a David Nowaski living in Stourbridge only six miles from Kidderminster. I then searched the births' index and found that a David Nowaski was born on 10th January 1950 in Kidderminster and the entry gave me the Registrar references. Within half an hour and one telephone call to the local county library I had learnt that David was born to Jan Nowaski and Magda Nowaski nee Macuta. Jan's occupation was shown as a bricklayer and Magda's as a nurse. I then repeated the procedure searching the death records and was saddened to see that Magda died in Kidderminster on the 23rd August 2000 aged 76. I also found that Tomek had married Halina Chepenko in London in 1946 and they had at least two children, Jack (who also appeared on the same search site list as his father) and Dorcus (on a census list) and that his wife had died of cancer in 1996. Further checks revealed that Jack had two children of his own and in 1986 they were living in Slough.

I then tried directory enquiries with all the new names but without success, so I checked the Web-directories as well but with the same result. I found it hard to believe that I had collected so much information in such a short time and marvelled at the search powers of the Internet, yet was dismayed that not one of the names had a telephone number listed. I was still reluctant to directly approach any of the relatives and decided to try one other long-shot first.

I registered with two family history sites and then searched under Nowaski and although I did not find a direct male line/family tree for that name there was a Jan, who was shown as born in 1926 in Poland, mentioned in the family tree of a Mary Redland. As with all these sites I was not able to communicate directly with Mary Redland but I sent an E-mail via the site's own system. I briefly outlined why I was trying to trace Jan without giving too much detail but making it as intriguing as possible. I decided to wait a week and if nothing developed I would drive up to Stourbridge.

Five days later I had an e-mail reply from Mary Redland who was Jan's married daughter! She was very interested in my enquiry and confirmed that Jan had a sister Maria and brothers called Jozef, Jacek and Tomek and that he was born in Pelplin. She provided me with a telephone number and invited me to ring as soon as possible.

I spoke to Jan's daughter later that evening and explained the whole story to her. She revealed that her husband had been researching his family tree and her father's name had only been added, almost as an afterthought, to bring it up to date. It had been entered on the family history site over five years ago and they had forgotten all about it and she was now amazed by the coincidence. She told me that she saw her father on a regular basis but her brother and his wife visited nearly every day because they lived much closer. Her father hardly spoke about the war and she was sure he had not seen Maria, Tomek or Jozef since he was a boy in Poland. She then explained that as far as she knew, he had last seen Jacek in about 1950 when they had a serious disagreement and went their separate ways.

She asked if we could meet so that she could arrange for her brother to be present and they could both see the documents. In the meantime they would pick their moment and discuss the whole matter with their father and see where he wanted to go with it. I again stressed to her that I was as certain as I could be that I had traced Tomek to an address in London. After further discussion we both agreed that it would be best if we held off any further action on that front until after we met because it would need careful management. As I was semi-retired and she worked full-time, including Saturday mornings, I offered to drive up and meet them at her home in Evesham the following Saturday afternoon. I prepared a written report for Jan and his children covering details of my involvement, the sequence of events and also listing all the enquiries I had made, together with contact numbers in case they wished to follow up on any particular area or make contact with those who had originally supplied the information. As I did so I experienced the occasional and frustrating 'senior moment' of forgetfulness, finding the various names, relationships, dates and locations a little confusing, even though I had developed a detailed working knowledge of the letters, documents and my notes, so I also prepared a basic family tree to serve as an aide-mémoire.

THE NOWASKI FAMILY

Henryk (brother of Roman) married **Ewa**
He died in 1939 shot by the SS in Pelplin
She was murdered in 1942 at Auschwitz

Their Children:

Maria	Jozef	Jacek	Tomek	Jan
b 1920	b 1922	b 1925 *Twin*	b 1925 *Twin*	b 1926
Alive in Warsaw 1940.	Alive in Warsaw 1943.	Married Marta Dudek in Hampshire 1946.	Married Halina Chepenko in London 1946. Had a son Jack and a daughter Dorcus. Jack married with 2 children.	Married Magda Macuta in Kidderminster 1947. Had a son David b1950 and a daughter Mary. Married name Redland.

Notes:

- **Halina** also a Gulag survivor died in London in 1996 and **Magda** the nurse died in Kidderminster in 2000.
- **Jacek** and his wife **Marta** the Red Cross worker and concentration camp survivor were last known to be living in Poland.

- **Tomek** is now living in London and **Jan** in Kidderminster. **Tomek's** son Jack is living in Slough.

When I arrived at the Evesham address I was given a warm welcome and we soon got down to the business in hand. We briefly talked through the report I had prepared for them and I could see that they were both eager to examine the contents of the small brown case. I opened it carefully and handed it across without any further comment. Mary immediately picked up the rosary, held it reverently and said, "Dad has just told us that he believed this saved his life and it gave him immense comfort all through the war. He wore it with his dog tags and never let it out of his sight."

As soon as they saw the photographs they both homed in on the ones that showed the young man in Polish army uniform alongside the hut. David immediately exclaimed, "That's Dad, there's no mistake about that."

He then passed it to his sister and she was in no doubt either, "Up until now there was a part of me that thought it couldn't possibly be our father, the coincidence with the find in the attic and the Polish connection with you and the police, it just seemed too unlikely. Although he's told us he did leave the case there, the whole story with the huge time scales involved and the fact that the people who found it didn't just throw the case away. It all seemed so improbable and I had my doubts as to whether this really was his stuff. Now I can believe it, that's him and there's no mistaking that, thank you, I can't wait to see his face when he sees it all."

I sat quietly for another ten minutes while they sorted through the postcards and photographs and I then handed over the English translations of all the letters together with their originals. "I made these translations to help track your father down but I felt uncomfortable doing so because I was intruding on private and personal matters that were really none of my business. Like me, you'll find the contents very moving and the revelations powerfully graphic and in places shocking, but the spirit, resolve and honour of the Nowaski family always shines through. I thought it best if you both have them all and you can decide how you would like to deal with them."

I then asked, "Do you know what your father was doing in the Salisbury area when he left the case at the hotel all those years ago, because I haven't found anything to suggest he lived or worked there?"

Mary was the first to answer, "We've asked Dad but he's not keen to talk about it yet. He said he would look through what you've found and then talk to us some more."

David looked up from the letters and added, "I expect everyone who's been involved with these documents are as intrigued as we are as to why Dad never went back to collect them."

"That's certainly what my friends would like to know because it seemed that the contents were so very important to him and yet he just seemed to disappear off the face of the earth. Even from their limited contact the licensee and his wife took a shine to him and thought it was so out of character, and from what I've learnt since, I must agree with them."

I was invited to stay for tea but I declined as I could see that they had so much to discuss and were anxious to read the letters together and meet with their father. As I left Mary said, "We really appreciate what you've done but it's still hard to believe and there's so much to take in and so much of Dad's life that we know so little about. I promise we'll let you know where we go from here. I know David wants to contact Tomek as soon as possible but Dad hasn't even agreed to that so we'll have to be patient."

I drove back home feeling reasonably content that I had achieved my aim in returning the case and its contents to its rightful owner but I was also hoping that the two brothers would get back in touch. A reunion after seventy years would really be an achievement! Perhaps I was asking too much.

Four weeks later just as I was beginning to think that I would hear no more and was immersing myself in the business and my own domestic affairs, Mary rang me. "A great deal has happened to us since we saw you, and Dad would like to meet you if that's alright. We can come to you or meet half way, whatever's more convenient."

"I would love to meet Jan, I have this fixed picture of him in my head as a young man and the story needs bringing up to date but only if you feel he's up to it."

She laughed and said, "It's as if he's had a new lease of life since he saw the letters and photographs and we've spent hours talking about all that happened to him. He has never spoken about these things before, but now we're learning all about his incredible life before we were born. The discovery of the case has acted as a catalyst and once he started he couldn't stop. He really wants to see you and explain why he left the letters in Salisbury. He's told me to get on and arrange it and won't rest until I report back. He's treating it all like a military operation. There really is a lot to tell you but he wants to speak to you himself. He's so grateful for the trouble you've taken and he says he owes you and your friend an explanation."

We met at a hotel in Cirencester and in the plush surroundings of the conference suite foyer I had my first sighting of Jan Nowaski. He looked younger than the person I had now mentally prepared for, and although very well built, he walked upright with a light, steady and purposeful gait. As I stood up to greet him a wide smile lit up his entire weather-beaten face and his handshake was warm and strong. He stood back, looked me over with alert intelligent eyes and then pulled me into a hug and kissed me on both cheeks. This took me by surprise and before I could recover he said in his delightful Polish accent, "Well, I managed somehow to escape the Russians and survive the Nazis, even when it seemed to me as a boy that thousands of them were hunting me down and yet you found me so easily. I'm so glad that you're my friend and not my enemy."

We ordered our drinks and settled down and almost at once any anxieties I had were dismissed in the exclusive and relaxed atmosphere. Jan was a delightful old man: warm, friendly and humorous with a witty, mischievous side and an obvious love of life in general and his family in particular. He opened the two top buttons on his shirt and smiled broadly as he showed me that he was again wearing his mother's rosary. "Thank you so much for bringing this back to me. It's played a major part in the turning points of my long and rewarding life. Despite the hardships, I've been blessed and most fortunate to have experienced more than my fair share of true love and friendship."

He told me that he had read my report many times and was astonished that such detailed records and search facilities existed on the Internet and he was worried about the potential for abuse and the infringement of peoples' right to privacy. I got the distinct impression that, although he was glad to have the letters back, he was delivering a mild rebuke concerning my willingness to intervene and make use of questionable sources. I found myself agreeing with him and was glad that Mary was eager to change direction when she said, "Come on Dad, he did what he had to do to find us and we're very glad he did, now why don't you tell him what we came here for."

He looked at me and asked, "Do you know what happened to your own father during the war and at home in Poland before that?"

"Until recently I knew very little but he's now told me most of his life story. He strongly believes that one day the grandchildren should know and really understand their heritage but he waited until he was well into his seventies before he went into any great detail. He once explained to me that whenever he speaks about it he is instantly transported back in time and he physically shudders at the memories. I've learnt that it's both difficult and painful and that's why he tried to bury it for so many years."

Jan nodded and said, "Unless you've been through similar experiences it's hard to understand and although we all deal with things in our own way, nearly everyone involved would rather forget all about it and just live in the present. However, when you reach my time of life there is another and sadly, final factor that comes into play and it makes you review the important decisions you have made in your life. I want to tidy up the loose ends before I leave this world and now I can clearly see how to do it, but we'll come to that later. First of all I'll try to fill in the gaps for you."

David suggested, "Why don't you start with the Tomek update."

"Well, as you know from the letters I last saw him at Luck in 1939 when the Russians beat us up and separated us. I always thought he must be dead but last week we went to see him. It's been a long time since I cried and yet I wept like a baby when I saw him again and met his whole family for the very first time. I can't believe that God, through your efforts, has given me another chance. All these years we've been so close but unaware of each other and Tomek thought we were all dead. He'd been through hell himself and although he survived he'd lost hope of any miraculous family reunions, so when it happened it was so much the sweeter."

The brothers' reunion was the very news I had hoped to hear

and I bought a round of drinks on the strength of it and we all toasted, "Jan and Tomek, brothers again."

After Jan had regained his composure he continued, "There were some incredible parallels in our stories, he too had his Jerzy but his name was Wladyslaw, although everyone called him Doc and they too fought side by side and became the greatest of friends. After the war Doc went back to medicine and completed his training back here in Scotland. He studied at the Polish School of Medicine that had been established in 1941 at the University of Edinburgh and he completed his Clinical training at the city's Polish hospital and the Edinburgh Royal Infirmary. He went on to specialise in the treatment of burns and became an eminent plastic surgeon at the Radcliffe Hospital in Oxford. He retired in the early 1980's and died peacefully in his sleep at the ripe old age of eighty-five in 1999. Tomek had kept in touch with him all those years and he was Godfather to both of Tomek's children, who he visited regularly."

He paused again and Mary prompted him, "Tell Mick what you've decided."

Jan replied, "Yes OK, we both know that we've wasted too much time apart and we aren't going to waste another moment." He then settled back in his chair and said, "You've already helped us more than we should reasonably expect and yet I'm going to ask one more rather demanding favour of you, but before I do, let me tell you how we all arrived in this position. The English pilot who had known Jozef in Warsaw traced Jacek through the army headquarters at the Rubens Hotel and they told him about me. All three of us got together in London in the spring of 1946 after the RAF officer had been released from hospital. He'd caught pneumonia in the POW camp and had taken a long time to recover but he'd kept Jozef's letters all that time and as promised he handed them over and told us Jozef's story."

Jan then explained to me how Jozef and Zenon had escaped from Auschwitz and joined the Home Army to fight in the Warsaw Uprising and with watery eyes he told of how they had died. We all listened in rapt silence and then he continued, "Neither Jacek nor I knew what had happened to Tomek or Maria and we had no way of finding out. In those days millions of families had been split up and you just made the best of it. For several years Jacek and I were happy enough with life in England and we didn't want to go

326

home and live under the communists. We'd both got married and settled down, but as time passed Jacek's wife became more and more restless here and decided she wanted to go back to Poland despite the obvious risks. It became an obsession with her and Jacek eventually came around to Marta's way of thinking and asked Magda and me to go with them."

David said, "You turned them down though Dad. That must have been very difficult."

"Yes, but Magda wouldn't hear of it because of her terrible memories and the horrendous stories she had heard immediately after the war when nursing the Jewish camp survivors. It was ironic really because Marta, who had experienced the full horror of the camps first hand still wanted to go back and Magda who had not, refused point blank. In the end Jacek and I fell out because he insisted that we should return as it was our duty to our dead parents and that we owed it to Jozef and in any case he was the elder brother and I should do what he said. He went back in 1950 and I've heard nothing from him since. So you see I had lost my parents and then I lost my sister and brothers but, by a turn of fate, one was returned to me but I failed to hold on to him. My own children have again taught me that family is the most important thing in life. An even stranger twist of fortune has now brought Tomek back into my life and together we've decided that we'll not squander this opportunity. We want to go to Poland and find Jacek if he's still alive and if not we'll find his grave and I'll make my peace. Can you do one more thing for me and help us find Jacek?"

I just sat there for a while trying to work out what I could possibly do that would assist Jan with his proposal when Mary asked, "Do you think you'll be able to help, Dad is determined to do this and we all support him, but we don't really know where to start?"

There was only one idea that I could come up with and as I explained it to them they all became very enthusiastic and asked me to put the wheels in motion.

I agreed, but disliking loose ends and inconsistencies, I then started to ask the questions that had been bothering me, "If neither you nor Jacek found Tomek after the war then what was the significance of the postcard of Osimo in Italy and the photographs of what I assumed to be troops in Italy. I came to the conclusion that they were Tomek's?"

Jan smiled broadly and said, "Things are often not what they seem. They belonged to my friend and guardian angel in the army, Jerzy. His older brother was in Italy and was killed at the Santerno River in their last battle of the war when they liberated Bologna. Jerzy received his possessions and he kept the best photographs of his brother but gave me the others and the postcard and I kept them safe with my collection of letters and keepsakes from the war. Some of the other photographs you recovered were also his and the Easter card was from him. Jacek had also given me some of his photographs and postcards and others were sent between Jerzy and I, immediately after the war."

"How did you come to have the postcard to Sergeant Vranek from the Crutzen family?"

He then told me the story of the Crutzens and Barry Reigal and added, "Sergeant Vranek came to see me just after I had been demobbed at Codford and handed it over for me to show Jerzy, because he had recently heard from the Crutzens and in response to their request he had sent them details of Barry's parents and other family members as they wished to see them personally to thank them and explain how their son had saved their lives. We'd been Barry's comrades at the time of the incident and so Sergeant Vranek wanted to update us about the Crutzens progress and their intentions."

I then asked the one question that had intrigued everyone who had been involved in finding the documents, "Why did you leave the case at the hotel in the first place and why did you never go back?"

Jan's smile disappeared and was replaced by a look of intense concentration and I could tell that he was mustering his thoughts on a subject he did not find easy to deal with. He cleared his throat, reached across and held his daughter's hand and then related the answer to the questions that I had asked myself a dozen times.

"Jerzy was like a father to me and it's no exaggeration to say that without him I would have died in 1939 and probably a dozen times since. He was like a rock and set such a wonderful example of strength and compassion and even today I freely acknowledge that I owe him everything."

He explained that after the war Jerzy also settled in England, married an English girl from Southampton and eventually became a gamekeeper on a large estate at Romsey. At first they kept in touch and saw each other regularly but as the years passed by they gradually saw less and less of each other until it was just the exchange of Christmas cards. Then, out of the blue in the winter of 1970, Jan received a brief and barely legible letter from him begging for help. He went straight down there and discovered that his wife had been killed in a road accident two years before and he had been drinking heavily ever since. They had been unable to have children and in his loneliness he'd lost his reason and taken to wandering the streets at night and had been arrested for being drunk and incapable on many occasions. He was in a terrible state, had lost his job and been evicted from the cottage they had shared for twenty years.

"When I got there I found him in a church hostel near Salisbury and the doctor told him that if he didn't stop drinking it would kill him. The change in him was hard to believe and I couldn't understand why he hadn't come to me sooner or even told me of the death of his wife. He was deeply depressed, had aged twenty years and was in very poor general health but I could still see glimpses of the courageous and inspirational man I'd known."

He stood up to stretch his legs and then leaned on the back of his chair and continued, "The staff at the hostel recommended that I should arrange for him to be admitted to a private clinic outside Salisbury that specialised in the treatment of alcoholism. As with most people with his condition he had already spent all his money on drink and didn't have a penny to his name. In fact he owed money everywhere. I had a few hundred pounds saved up and after discussing it with Magda I went home, drew out our savings and settled most of his debts and paid for the first week of assessment at the clinic."

Mary asked, "How was he with you, was he aware of what you were trying to do for him?"

"Not at first, he was sedated and couldn't even talk coherently so I stayed at the hotel in Salisbury and visited him every day. As time passed and he gradually sobered up he started to talk about the old days and although he was still very confused I was hopeful that things might improve."

Mary asked, "What about the case and the letters?"

"Patience please dear. I'm getting there. I took the case with the letters from home as I thought the photographs, postcards and such like would remind him of the resolve and determination that we'd all once shared and help him to regain his confidence and aid his recovery. On the sixth night when I was thinking things over at the hotel I decided to give him my rosary. I'd felt so useless and guilty at the time and I desperately wanted to do something positive to help him, so I took it off and put it in the case with the photographs ready for my next visit the following day. I hoped, foolishly probably and forlornly as it turned out, that it would rescue him from his desperation and isolation as it had saved me from mine all those years before."

David asked, "What happened?"

"I never had the chance to give it to him because in the morning, just as I was leaving to visit him, the clinic telephoned and coldly told me that Jerzy had slashed his wrists and killed himself. As you can imagine I was in a bit of a state and feeling even more ashamed that I hadn't acted sooner, and that's when I suddenly noticed the owner in the bar. He called me over but in the circumstances I couldn't face explaining things to him and I just stood there, rooted to the spot. As he approached me, on the spur of the moment and to avoid having to talk about it or answer any questions I thrust the case out at him and told him that I had an emergency to deal with and needed to rush away. As best I remember I asked him to look after it and said I didn't know how soon I'd be back. I went straight to the clinic and found I had to deal with the doctor, policemen and the coroner because he had no relatives or friends other than me and over the next few days I made all the funeral arrangements."

David said, "I can only imagine how difficult that must have been for you, dealing with it entirely on your own."

"I was feeling rather low but the owner of the clinic felt a degree of responsibility and insisted that I stay in their guestroom whilst I dealt with everything. I had paid for a week in advance at the hotel and so had no pressing reason to go back there and, to be honest, things were so fraught that I didn't want to have to explain all that had happened. Magda was very understanding but soon began to worry about all the money I was spending and the wages I was losing because I wasn't at work. As soon as the funeral was over I rushed back home and it took us the best part of a year and a good deal of overtime and week-end work to get back on our feet."

I asked, "Did you never go back there?"

"I went to visit Jerzy's grave several times since then but I always resisted the temptation to enquire about the case. As strange and over-sentimental as it now sounds, I really regretted that I hadn't given him the rosary when I first booked him into the clinic. Who knows, if I had perhaps things would have turned out differently and so I couldn't bring myself to collect it. I was worried that in doing so I would cut that final, tenuous link between us, especially as I had already failed to help him when he really needed me. At first I felt that it was meant to stay in Salisbury, close to my loyal friend but as the months passed I convinced myself that the case and contents would have been disposed of in any event and it ceased to be an issue."

Again we sat in respectful silence for a moment, all reflecting on the tragedy and no doubt wishing things had turned out differently. When I felt the time was right I suggested, "We've dealt with the past in some detail and now it's time for all of us to look to the future, so while you start planning Jan's trip back to Poland I'll see if I can find your brother." Ten minutes later, after a cup of coffee and fond farewells we were all on our way home.

SIXTEEN

Chains Asunder
14th December 2008

The very next day I started the hunt for Jacek. For the last ten years I have been a member of the International Police Association, an independent body that links police officers and retired officers worldwide to develop friendship and cooperation in a social, educational and travel context. One of the excellent services offered is the provision of a dependable travel contact anywhere in the world. Members in one country offer practical assistance, share their local knowledge, provide emergency help and even offer accommodation to fellow members who are visiting from another country. I contacted the head office for the UK, complied with their proof of membership procedures and asked for details of a contact in Warsaw. I then telephoned and explained to the contact that I needed the services of an experienced and reliable Private Investigator from the Warsaw area.

The next day I was on the telephone speaking to a retired senior detective who had worked with the Fraud Squad in the centre of the Polish capital. I immediately apologised for the unusual nature of my request and spent the next twenty minutes giving him the details of the Nowaski story, as I knew it. He asked a host of questions to confirm his understanding of the key family relationships involved and I then sent him a comprehensive e-mail outlining my complete involvement along with the family tree. He confirmed receipt and promised to ring me back the next day after he had spoken to colleagues and made some preliminary enquiries. Like most police officers around the world he would not commit himself on the chances of success.

He called the following evening but had little to report, as he himself had been very busy and the archivist he wished to talk to was on holiday and a key computer expert was tied up in court for a couple of days. Ten days later he called again and told me that he had found Jacek and he was still alive. I could hardly believe what he was telling me; he had even obtained a telephone number but had not made any approach because he wanted to know how the family in the UK wished to handle it. He did say that a local police officer had told him that Jacek was a semi-retired music teacher living a simple but comfortable life just outside a town called Ketrzyn in the wild and beautiful Great Masurian Lakes area. He explained that less than three miles away was the village of Gierloz where Hitler had built the secret bunkers for his hideout and main wartime headquarters known as 'the wolf's lair', and where the failed assassination attempt had been made by Claus von Stauffenberg. It seemed to me that the Nowaskis were inextricably linked to so many of the monumental events of the war.

The ex-detective gave me Jacek's telephone number and I promised to contact him again when I knew how Jan wished to proceed. Genuinely impressed, but puzzled, I asked him how he could have found out so much in such a short space of time and he replied, "It was relatively simple because the Russians and the Polish communists kept records on everyone. There were 'Russian Advisors' running everything and informers in every street and in every building and when they were kicked out in '89 we inherited millions of their records and although it's different now, if you know your way around and have the right contacts you can still find out anything."

Jan and Tomek telephoned their brother many times over the next two weeks and, after the initial surprise and shock, Jacek quickly agreed to the final arrangements for their reunion in Poland. Jacek had also told them of the fate of their sister Maria and Uncle Roman in Warsaw. Parts of Roman's story had been published by one of the survivors of his underground unit, along with dozens of similar personal accounts of the uprising, in a Warsaw magazine in 1953. Jacek had read it and then, from his own research, pieced together the following account. When the family had left him on the 3ʳᵈ September 1939 he was again unable to sign up for military service, not because he wasn't needed but because the army was already in disarray and recruitment abandoned.

He had stayed in Warsaw and then joined the Home Army and during the uprising he was with the units defending the Old Town area. It was here, in an underground bunker on 12ᵗʰ August 1944 that his niece traced him after she had revealed her true identity to her local commander. She had made impassioned appeals for his help and he used his influence to bring them together. From then on they fought together, side by side protecting each other as much as possible and refusing to be separated. They endured two weeks of continuous bombardment from 'the cows' and from German artillery positioned in the Praga district on the east of the river. Enemy bombers also attacked them every day from bright blue skies and yet not one Russian fighter ever challenged them.

The Russians could have controlled the air space had they wanted, such was their superiority in numbers, but they chose to stand off and watch as the Poles were being picked off like sitting ducks. On the 27ᵗʰ August whilst holding out at the State Mint building, Roman's unit, of which only fifteen of the original sixty men and women were still alive, also came under heavy ground attack from infantry and tanks. Roman, Maria and two others stayed behind to buy enough time for the others to escape and they were all buried under the rubble as the Germans deliberately brought the building down on top of them. Their bodies were never recovered.

Whilst the brothers were catching up on their individual experiences I had been back in touch with the retired Warsaw detective and unbeknown to the Nowaskis I had arranged to fly out a few days before them to meet him as we had some arranging of our own to organise.

On the 5ᵗʰ January, I arrived in Warsaw to be greeted by a sunny but cold winter's day and was still airside when I was met by the ex detective and quickly ushered through the immigration and customs sections. My host, Zygmunt Jaworski was a jovial extrovert in his early sixties who had recently travelled a great deal and was eager to practise his English. We went straight to his home and he explained that he had seen Jacek the previous day and they had discussed the visit in some detail. He then brought me up to date with Jacek's life in Poland and although they had found it hard when they first returned and were harassed by the authorities, they managed to avoid any serious consequences and deliberately shunned all political activity. He became a respected music teacher and they led a quiet but reasonably contented life, despite the hardships and shortages of every day existence in Eastern Europe.

Zygmunt then talked me through the itinerary they had prepared and, after a couple of alterations, we were both content that it allowed plenty of time for the informal and private family reunion but also added something special that only the authorities could provide. He then adopted a far more serious tone of voice, leaned towards me and asked, "Do you subscribe to the view that the sins of the fathers will be visited on the sons for generations to come as it says in the book of Exodus and does it mean that the whole family are culpable?"

I was somewhat taken by surprise and couldn't see the relevance of such a theological question, but Zygmunt ignored my momentary hesitation and waited patiently, obviously expecting a response. I gathered my thoughts and somewhat reluctantly answered, "I'm not persuaded that should be the case. It doesn't seem logical or fair if, as I do, you believe that everyone has free will. Each of us is responsible for our own actions whether viewed in a religious, legal or social sense. In any case if you search through the bible you can always find contradictory passages and I'm pretty certain there's a section that says that neither the son nor the brother or the father should bear the iniquities of the other. Why do you ask?"

"This is a deeply Catholic country and the communist occupation, with its hardships, oppression and anti-religious stance, only served to further reinforce our beliefs. It's against this background that you and I need to make a decision that might well have a profound effect on the Nowaskis' future. You should also remember that we are a very superstitious people and this generation of the Nowaskis do seem to have had more than their fair share of bad luck and tribulation. Some may think that they're being made to pay for their ancestor's crimes. I fear I may not be as objective as I should be and I wanted you to understand that the issues may be more complicated than they first seem."

Although curious and suspicious as to where this was leading I was also anxious not to be drawn further into the private lives of a family that I felt should now be left in peace and voiced my concerns accordingly. He nodded sympathetically, looked down at his comprehensive notes and then said, "Let me explain. While searching our files in response to your original request I also discovered that Roman and Henryk had an older brother. Although, in an attempt to leave the past behind, they had changed their surname when they left Gdansk, it didn't take the all-seeing authorities of the time long to make the connection and a close examination of the extensive German records clearly proves the family relationships."

He explained that, at the time, the whole of northern Poland was German (Prussian) territory and the ethnic Poles, particularly the political activists, nationalists and those considered to be anti-German, were closely monitored until the confusion of the Great War and European political turbulence allowed the Nowaskis to disappear off the radar and then, following Versailles, they found themselves safely back in the newly recreated Poland.

I still couldn't see where this was leading and asked, "But why would the German authorities want to keep tabs on the Nowaskis?"

"Be patient, it's all in the original files which were captured by the Russians. There's a full account of their brother's life and his family history and interestingly he was also known to the Soviet Authorities. His name was Franz and he was the eldest, born in 1891. As he grew up he became very disgruntled with the way the Germans oppressed and abused the Poles in Gdansk and he was officially listed as a threat to authority and a destructive agitator, being regularly arrested for assaulting bureaucrats, fighting the police and general public disorder. When he was thirty and on home leave he shot down a man, in broad daylight on the street in Gdansk but he didn't stand trial for the crime. Instead he was detained in a mental institution but within a year he had escaped and was on the run."

"Did the Authorities catch up with him?"

"No, he travelled all around the world and later, as the Nazi Party started to hold sway his hatred for authority homed in on them, but it didn't end there, because his criminality escalated and he went on to become a political assassin! He publicly shot to death a senior and well-known German Diplomat in Lisbon in 1930 but his motivation has never really been satisfactorily explained. There may even have been a cover up."

I could not contain my incredulity any longer, "Why on earth would he do such a thing? This is all a bit too much to take in, even at face value, without you over-complicating matters with yet another conspiracy theory."

"You've got a point, but let me clarify what I've discovered and then you can judge the merits or otherwise for yourself. From examining translations of the original Portuguese papers and the German and Russian files I've a pretty good idea of what happened. On the very day of the assassination it was immediately announced that he was to be tried by a military court within a week and face execution. The initial investigation following his arrest ruled that there was no political significance to the crime and that he had acted alone."

"Well, perhaps he did. What was his motivation? Once we know that, things may become clearer."

"Let's stick with the facts and the context first then we can consider the why. Although the nature of the crime caused consternation across the city and Portugal's Cabinet instantly met in extraordinary session, the records show that, in stark contrast to what would surely happen today, there was no media furore. This seems strange, even for that time, because the gravity of the event was reinforced when all official functions were suspended and before his body was returned to Germany he was given a full state funeral, attended by the highest-ranking military, civil and governmental leaders from many countries across Europe and beyond."

"Was there a press blackout?"

"No, not entirely, but with hindsight it's clear that media coverage was controlled, probably even censored and an indecent haste was shown by all the countries involved to settle the matter without further complication or repercussions. This seemed to work because there was no public clamour or political will to look beyond the assassin. The imperative was to move on and avoid any suggestion of a conspiracy or governmental involvement. It was then officially announced that the assassination was the work of a Polish lunatic with a persecution mania and that the trial would have to be delayed. He was detained at the Miguel Bombarda psychiatric Hospital in the capital where he was forensically examined by the most highly qualified and eminent Portuguese psychiatrists including the world famous Sobral Cid."

I took the opportunity to buy a little time to try and take it all in, "I'm obviously not as well read as you so I've got to admit I've never heard of him."

"Don't feel too bad because I hadn't either, but I've since done my research and discovered he was definitely at the top of his field. One of the best and most progressive European psychiatrists of the early twentieth century and being at the forefront of modern psychoanalysis he was a renowned world expert. Anyway, he was asked to give an opinion as to whether Franz was fit to stand trial. The case papers show that when he had first been interviewed by the police on the 8th June they found him to be calm, serene and unresponsive. He showed no signs of regret or remorse and offered no detailed explanation. He merely stated that he was acting in self-defence against those who had plotted against him."

"What did the psychiatrist find out?"

"Between the 19th and 23rd June 1930, following further Police interviews of what had become an increasingly reticent suspect, Sobral Cid conducted **fourteen** sessions of mental examinations and tests. He concluded that there was no doubt that Franz was not responsible for his actions and shortly after he completely disappeared from the public eye. Some five months later the medical experts sitting on the closed court-martial panel adjudged Franz to be insane and he was sentenced to confinement in a mental asylum."

"Is that where he saw his days out?"

"No and there's yet more confusion, because evidence in the file alleges that he was detained for months, maybe even years, in a prison outside Lisbon but there's no reference to any mental institution. What's more, local Police sources suggested that he might have been a Russian agent, basing their belief on his travel history and incriminating documents found in his possession addressed to the Russian Foreign Office and the League of Nations. Curiously they took this line of enquiry no further but officially maintained their earlier finding that he had indeed acted alone, driven by purely personal motives. Yet it's clear from the German documents that they suspected him of being groomed or manipulated by the

Soviets and were convinced that they'd helped with the planning, preparation and support leading up to the assassination."

I found it difficult to accept what I was hearing, "Are you really now telling me that this man was a Soviet agent and that he was merely a pawn in some political assassination?"

"I wouldn't go that far because there's no firm evidence, but I can't rule it out altogether. You see, it's so difficult to separate out the real facts contained within the documents from just the opinions and suspicions of the various authors. Nothing is conclusive and some documents are actually contradictory with much of the circumstantial evidence being ambiguous in respect of his motivation and planning. This is compounded by the fact that so much time has now passed that we don't know what the various personal agendas and political imperatives were for all the people connected to the offender, either before or after the crime. We should keep an open mind, but from what I've read there can be no doubt at all that he suffered from a very serious mental illness, as you English say, he was as mad as a hatter, but that in itself doesn't make him a killer. Perhaps something else was also at work."

"Surely you're not going to suggest that this gets even more sinister?"

"I think that's possible, even probable, because over the years he had been given numerous injections of mercury and arsenic to treat his syphilis. He was doubly unfortunate because he lived during the time before antibiotics and was treated during the few critical years when the recognised treatments were changing from salts of mercury to organic arsenic preparations. Unusually he was subjected to both and I can only imagine what the toxic effect of receiving a cocktail of those 'treatments' must have been when they were injected directly into his muscles. If he wasn't insane before, he certainly would've been afterwards."

"Do you think he was deliberately being poisoned then?"

"Not necessarily, because they did have him nailed down as a paranoid schizophrenic with a criminal history of violence and they may have been using an experimental treatment with his best interests at heart. On the other hand, when you look at his work record, his travels all around the world, his documented ability to constantly change identities and quickly learn foreign languages and his incredible resourcefulness, all whilst avoiding capture for years on end, it makes you wonder. Perhaps the Soviets, if not directly controlling him, were grooming him for the future and provided practical help or maybe they just took an initial interest in using him but once they discovered the full extent of his mental problems and realised he was too much of a liability, they cut him loose. Either way it certainly seems as if he had received some support."

I needed to know the outcome, "What happened to him in the end?"

"After hearing what I've told you so far, you probably won't be surprised to discover that his story gets even worse. On 27th March 1934, nearly four years later, when memories had faded and the authorities deemed that a suitable period of time had elapsed, he was quietly handed over to the Germans who transported him back 'home' on a Steamer called the Cape Arona. He was then interrogated and, bearing in mind the nature and era of the crime, probably beaten and abused before again being detained in a secure lunatic asylum, this time at Gottingen in Lower Saxony where he was considered as something 'out of the ordinary' and was presented to the students of Gottingen University Clinic as an exceptionally interesting case study."

"That seems rather pitiless to say the least. If they felt he was fit enough for that sort of scrutiny and examination why didn't they put him on trial in Germany?"

"I'm afraid things became even more sinister for poor Franz and his fellow patients. As soon as the war started Hitler extended his euthanasia programme from children to also include adults who had a physical handicap or mental illness. The first to die were Poles. No sooner had the Germans taken over than tens of thousands of patients were cleared out of hospitals in Pomerania, Gdansk and Gdynia by soldiers of the Einsatzkommando 16 and either shot, beaten to death or poisoned by carbon monoxide fumes in specially modified trucks."

"Is that how he met his end?"

"He was situated further east and his institution escaped the initial massacre but his reprieve was short-lived and yes, he too was later selected as one of some two hundred thousand considered 'unproductive members of society,' and 'not worth living.' On the 22nd May 1940 along with two hundred other patients he was taken

340

from the Mental Institution at Tapiau in East Prussia and transported west. By the way, the visiting German warship central to Franz's assassination plan in Lisbon was named after East Prussia's capital city Konigsberg. It was renamed Kaliningrad in 1945."

Astonished at the breadth and depth of Zygmunt's research I asked, "How reliable is all this information? I can understand that the broad historical aspects are probably a matter of record but where did you get hold of all the personal detail?

"Oh it's pretty reliable, the records are numerous, comprehensive and authentic and, as I said before, the Nazis and the post-war communists were meticulous in their record keeping and second to none when it came to state control. For example, during the fifties and sixties here in Poland one third of the adult population were considered to be anti-Soviet and subjected to some degree of surveillance and monitoring. Anyway that's another story for another day, so let's get back to Tapiau and Franz. A special 'Aktion T4' detachment of SS troops transported the patients to Brandenburg Havel, one of the six purpose built killing sites."

"They had special facilities to murder patients?"

"Yes. They were brutally clinical and shortly after final documentation he would have entered a gas chamber, which had been disguised as a shower room and there he was gassed by means of carbon monoxide emitted from hidden gas cylinders. This was in the early days of their mass killing programmes, at about the same time as Auschwitz was opened, before they had reached their 'maximum efficiency and throughput' and so it took the callous, cold-hearted bastards five days to kill all the patients in that one transport from Tapiau. He died along with all the thousands of other innocents from all over occupied Europe, not because he was a ruthless assassin, but because he had been certified as an incurable manic schizophrenic." Zygmunt then paused to give me the opportunity to speak but my mind was once again racing to catch up with the significance of the revelations and I found myself temporarily speechless.

He filled the silence, "To sum up, I would say that although he was a deeply troubled and dangerous man he felt a justifiable sense of persecution and outrage and so he was looking for revenge, justice, and notoriety, but in the end he failed even himself. He didn't create a diplomatic incident. There was no public enquiry, no international crisis, not even the publicity of a trial. Despite all his plans, hopes, fears and crimes, he passed almost unnoticed into oblivion and, as history has shown us, he changed nothing."

As he spoke the whole sequence of events finally started to fall into place and I was suddenly struck by the tragic irony of what the extensive files didn't spell out but what Zygmunt had just alluded to. Despite the diagnosis of 'rampant paranoia', the years of anxious self-reliance, suspicion of all authority, and most latterly, hostile incarceration and conditioning, at the end he was completely oblivious to the massive conspiracy of genocide that was then truly unfolding around him. He was also totally blind to the deception of his own individual betrayal and persecution, engineered by the same megalomaniacs of the Nazi party who paradoxically he had identified and accused long before they were to become the common enemy of humanity. Finally, unknowing, compliant and trusting, the erstwhile dissenter and master of suspicion had fallen easy victim to their obsession and its fatal subterfuge.

I sat quietly for a moment trying to absorb everything I had learnt and consider the implications, and then I asked, "How much of this do the brothers know?"

"From my guarded conversations with Jacek I'm pretty sure that the family today know nothing at all. They're not aware of Franz's existence or the fact that their father changed the family name. As children they had been puzzled as to why Henryk and Roman were so secretive about their past but they put it down to a domestic family breakdown or simply the effects of the depression and the social upheaval of the Great War. In fact Henryk and Roman last saw Franz in 1913 and they heard nothing further from him. I also learnt that after he went to sea they both had a very hard time of it."

"Well that's something that's definitely been passed down through their generations."

"Yes, and it was particularly difficult then. Food was scarce and their father found it impossible to get work because of the mass unemployment and, as poverty burgeoned, the Poles were increasingly treated as second class citizens and their needs ignored. Because of Franz's early behaviour his whole family were treated particularly harshly by the authorities and, as there was no safety net or social support in those days, they probably only survived with the help of neighbours, friends and the Church. Their father was killed in the Great War at about the same time that they ran away from home in the city and started a new life in what was soon to become rural Poland and, as best as I can gather, they've never had any further contact with their mother or anyone else in Gdansk."

"Hearing these terrible things certainly makes me appreciate how lucky my generation has been."

"Yes, they had a terrible childhood, even by the standards of the day and we don't know whether there are any other skeletons in their ancestral closet so it's easy to understand why they would prefer not to speak of it but completely put it behind them, start afresh and keep it from their new families. Which brings me to the crux of our present and pressing problem and the million-dollar question? Bearing in mind the considerable failings and reputation of their uncle and the stigma of his terrible, some would say unforgivable crimes, the nature of his incarceration and death, the fact that they are now the only descendants and their own succession of harrowing experiences since, should we tell Henryk's sons what I have discovered or keep quiet?"

My first reaction was that the family already had enough to deal with and we should leave well alone. They obviously bore no responsibility whatsoever for Franz's behaviour, the suffering and hardships of his family or the murder eighty years ago; but as I thought through the consequences certain doubts began to creep in. They had all shown great resilience and character over the years and one could easily argue that they had a right to know what had happened. The more I thought about the decision and considered the issues, the more ambivalent I became and when I eventually answered, no nearer to a conclusion, I felt as if I was really just avoiding the issue. "Right now we shouldn't do anything to detract from the reunion. I suggest we wait until their last day here and in the meantime we both give it some more thought and finally deal with it, one way or the other, before we all go home."

The private detective tapped his fingers on the table as he made up his mind, "I don't know what to do for the best, so I'm more than happy to go along with your suggestion. Strictly speaking, you're my client and I take your instructions and so on this basis I'm content for you to deal with it, as you think fit. As far as I'm concerned I will say no more unless I'm approached by the family in the event that you tell them." With that the buck was firmly and finally passed and I realised that I had been out-manoeuvred by the wily Warsaw detective.

Two days later the Nowaskis arrived with their families and at a champagne reception in the VIP lounge they were greeted by their brother, his wife Marta, their three children, four grandchildren and great granddaughter. They were later taken by limousine to the Marriott Hotel, one of the best in the city and as Jan noticed straight away, it was also situated just opposite the railway station where they had been bombed all those years ago. They were deliberately left to their own devices for the rest of that day and the next, but they had been given Zygmunt's contact details in the unlikely event that they should require any help that the hotel couldn't provide.

They then travelled 1st class by train to Pelplin and on arrival were all met by the station master and, following drinks in his office, they were shown the plaque which had been unveiled in 1959, marking the anniversary of the murder of their father, the station master and the other townsfolk. The Mayor, local dignitaries and all the current staff gathered in support around the family and they stood in mutual understanding and respectful silence. They were deeply moved as they looked up to see their father's name in the long list of station staff and other locals who had perished at the hands of the Germans. Jacek who had never been back here himself was later pleased to see that, although many of the sheds and sidings had disappeared under the post-war development, the station had retained its old charm and character.

They then walked the short distance to their old home where they met the current occupants and were proudly shown around the house. The memories came flooding back and they were all surprised at how easy it was to see Maria's, Jozef's and their parents' faces and imagine their presence throughout the building. In his mind's eye Jan could also see his brother Jacek as a boy, sat at the piano and hear him practising. How sweet the music sounded as the years fell away and a smile of contentment stretched across his face. Tomek wandered into the garden and immediately noticed that the old vegetable plot now had a garage built on it and for no logical reason that he could fathom, he felt a real sense of disappointment that the well had been filled in. He looked around the once familiar setting

344

and wondered if the large and gnarled apple trees still standing like sentinels were the very ones that he had climbed and played in when he was an adventurous and optimistic, yet unknowing boy. In the distance he could see the front of their old school building. It was still being used and looked totally unchanged and as he stared he laughed out loud, as he remembered how they used to ski there and back every day for what seemed like weeks on end in the wintertime: throwing snowballs, shouting, clowning around and teasing one another.

Later they all sat around a large dining table in their old living room and spoke at length with energy and delight about the really happy days of their childhood before the war changed everything. They recalled the rivalry and childish exhilaration every Christmas eve when they ran outside to scan the evening sky, each hoping to be the one to spot the first star so that festivities could start. Jacek was visibly moved as he spoke, "Being here is almost spiritual for me, exactly like Christmas used to be. We always gathered in this room on Christmas Eve as a happy and excited family full of expectation as we solemnly broke the blessed wafer and shared it out. It was only when I saw the nativity scene on that thin and delicate symbol of love and friendship that I really believed that the spirit of Christmas had arrived. With mouth watering I used to stare at the ornately laid table in anticipation of the twelve special courses and I thought to myself that heaven must be just like that; being surrounded by your whole family, eager to open your presents and feeling totally safe and specially privileged. But now we have been changed by the war and ever since, even when I go to shepherd's mass or set up the Christmas tree it's not quite the same because sadness always seems to choose those moments to seek me out."

"I have similar feelings," replied Jan, "We still stick to the custom of keeping an empty chair and place setting at the Christmas table and placing some hay under the table cloth, but now they have an added significance, the chair isn't just there for the unexpected visitor as tradition demands and the hay isn't just a representation of the stable. No, together they're a Yuletide commemoration to those we have lost and remind us that we must never, even in the happiest of times, forget their sacrifice." Despite the shadow of their sad memories they all felt a sense of renewal and happiness,

345

reliving the wonderful times they had shared as such a strong and vibrant young family.

That evening they dined at the Town Hall in Gniew as guests of the civic authorities of both Pelplin and Gniew. Their staff had combined their efforts and traced two survivors from 1939 who knew the Nowaski family and twenty descendents of their old friends and neighbours and also a handful of relatives of Ewa's, and brought them all together in an amazing reunion. The occasion and its organisation had attracted considerable local media interest and Jan was 'volunteered' by the rest of the family to be interviewed on local radio and television. Afterwards, during a small thank you speech he told the guests, somewhat tongue in cheek, that appearing on the television was more of an ordeal than the worst of his wartime experiences.

They were particularly pleased to meet the son of the railway porter who had helped Jozef and his mother and probably saved Jacek's life in Pelplin. His father had survived the war and had been employed on the railway for the rest of his working life. He enjoyed a very long and successful career and for the last four years of his service (following the fall of communism) he had held the very prestigious post as the Station Master at Torun, the old capital of Pomerania. He had died peacefully only six months previously, surrounded by his family and following fifteen years of very happy and contented retirement. They all talked for hours about the sad and happy times of their event filled lives and the party was a huge success, carrying on into the early hours before the family finally retired to a local hotel for a few hours sleep before travelling back to Warsaw.

They had another day at the Marriott hotel before Zygmunt escorted them to the monument to the Warsaw uprising. As Jacek examined the massive sculptured figures representing the fighters of the Capital defending the barricades and descending into the sewers, he remembered Maria, Jozef and Roman and he asked himself why the Poles had to wait to the 45th anniversary on 1st August 1989 before the monument was erected and they could officially commemorate such sacrifice. They all stood in silent prayer for Henryk and Ewa and agreed that this would be a fitting place to commemorate them, as there were no graves to visit and Warsaw was halfway between the locations of their murders. Jan solemnly walked forward and in a final and impromptu act of respect and remembrance he took off Ewa's rosary, kissed it for the last time and placed it at the base of the memorial. As the old soldier he was, he came to attention in respect and tribute to his lost family and friends and his memories flooded back, bridging those seven decades with the clarity and vividness of a cinema screen. As he saluted, the tears ran down his cheeks and the guilt of survival that he still carried daily was tempered by recognition that all they had struggled and fought for with such patriotism, passion and pride had now been achieved. He looked up into the grey sky and thanked God that no one had died in vain but fervently prayed that their children, grandchildren and future generations would be spared such unspeakable suffering.

From there they went to the Katyn Tomb memorial, also in the capital, where Tomek explained to the whole family his personal connection with those dreadful events and the reality of the Gulag. They said a prayer for Red, Lech, Boris Zansky, Anna and his dead and cherished wife Halina. He remembered them all with happiness, pride and an intense affection. None of the family, despite all they had been through, or perhaps because of it, could steel themselves to visit Auschwitz.

On the last day of the visit they were taken to the church of the Holy Cross and the children learnt that, in accordance with Chopin's will, his heart had been preserved in cognac and brought back from Paris after his death and placed in an urn behind an epitaph to him. It had been removed for safekeeping during the war and was now in a jar sealed inside the imposing commemorative pillar that stood before them. Zygmunt went on to explain that during the uprising a fierce battle lasting for many days had taken place in and around the church and it was also here that Father Antoni Chepek (who had somehow managed to avoid arrest and transportation to the camps for so long) was murdered when he bravely and persistently tried to protect wounded soldiers and the nuns who were being abused by German troops. He said, "Many thousands of members of the Home Army including your Maria, Jozef and Uncle Roman have no known burial place and so it is fitting that we, all four generations, remember them and Father Chepek in this holy church. It has witnessed so much and even in the worst imaginable days it offered solace and hope for the future.

347

It is because of their sacrifice that we all live in peace and freedom today and these words, inscribed on the altar, are a most fitting epitaph." He then translated the lines for the benefit of the English speakers:

Eternal rest grant them Oh Lord,
Beneath the ruins of the buildings,
In the cemeteries and in the streets,
In the squares or buried alive in the cellars,
Wherever they fell and died.

Although I had deliberately kept in the background throughout their visit and was sure that they hadn't spotted me as I entered the church, nothing could have kept me away. I was so determined to be there and witness these three decent, honourable men, who had won my admiration and respect, reach the end of their epic journey that had taken seventy years. They had been tested time and time again but their resourcefulness, faith and courage had brought them back together and seen them home at last. What an example to the rest of us!

I had originally struggled to appreciate the enormity of the horrors unleashed against them, but now I had come to understand the terror of their memories: the sights, sounds, smells and nightmares that must have haunted this family for far too long. At that very moment, in the shadows at the back of the church, the huge weight of uncertainty and indecision that I had carried over the last few days was lifted away. I was now absolutely convinced that for everyone's sake it was finally time to let the past go and I would not add to their burden.

I would say nothing of Franz.

Epilogue

Call of Duty
Salisbury 3rd November 2009

I opened the brown paper parcel and read the note inside:

Dear Mick,

I thought you should know that Dad passed away last month. I am so sorry that I have not told you before now but it was purely an oversight on my part and I know that he would have been most annoyed at my negligence. He died peacefully in his sleep and only a few days before he had told me that the last year had been the most joyous and rewarding passage in his long and challenging life. He was true to his word and spent no end of time with his brothers and their families and his obvious happiness and contentment was in itself a source of great comfort to Mary and me. The positive change in him was incredible and his enthusiasm and energy was an inspiration to us all, we will miss him so very much.

Yesterday, I started to put his affairs in order and I came across the enclosed sealed package in his desk. It had a 'post it' attached on which Dad had written, 'I've kept this for seventy years and when I'm gone I want Mick at Salisbury to have it. I'm sure he'll know what best to do.' I have not opened it and have no idea what it is. I must admit I am intrigued. It's so typical of Dad to have his fun

*and keep us guessing, even at a time like this, so please let
me know as soon as you can.*

With kind regards and grateful thanks for everything,

David.

I cut the string, opened the package and found a small diary wrapped inside an oilskin cloth. It measured five inches wide by six inches long by three inches thick. The fold over leather cover was dirty, water stained and fraying at the edges, but the clasp still worked and inside the tiny but immaculate copperplate handwriting was clearly legible. Inscribed on the first page were the following words:

Duty bade me fight.

The Life of Dominik Dabrowski:

A Polish Soldier.

Author's Notes

The book concludes with a number of historical annotations just in case you are left wondering which characters and events are real and which imagined: but I must emphasise that the terror, suffering and steadfast spirit of the Poles is not overstated and all the major events outlined actually took place. I have tried to portray these historical facts as accurately as possible, but limited changes and compromise have been necessary to fully accommodate the characters, to facilitate the development of their journey and in some small way to do proper justice to the heroism of all those who resisted the Nazi persecution and to honour the innocent victims. Time has also affected some personal perceptions and recollections but I fully accept that the mistakes are all mine. My apologies to those who were present at the time and their descendants, some of whom will no doubt readily identify the few liberties I have deliberately but regretfully taken.

This book is dedicated to the memory of those heroic fighters and the non-combatants who gave so much in the battle to defeat a truly evil dictator yet, by a combination of cruel fate and the procrastination of their allies, were destined never to see their homes again. Their families and surviving fellow citizens were abandoned to an equally evil but far more insidious dictator and his successors. For these Poles and their children, the Second World War and its horrors did not end until the Russians finally withdrew in 1989.

The United Kingdom's own ability to do more to recognise and mitigate the Polish plight was controlled and then hampered by the Superpowers who were flexing their muscles at the onset of the cold war. There is no better or more injurious example of this rancour than that of the battle hardened and proud Polish forces being excluded from the Victory Parade in London in 1947. At Stalin's insistence and despite their unquestioned allegiance and massive sacrifice to the cause of freedom they were to be snubbed and marginalised.

The 70th anniversary of the outbreak of that war served as a timely reminder that in our own lifetime millions of fellow Europeans endured decades of almost unbearable sacrifice, before they could finally experience freedom from fear, persecution, torture and the ultimate malevolence of state sponsored murder. Such suffering, however, still continues in many countries across the world and whilst our attention, political influence and resources are focussed elsewhere, dictators and tyrants still abuse, starve, rape and murder thousands with relish and impunity. For these poor and defenceless victims, so exploited at home and seemingly abandoned by the rich and powerful nations, there exists no war on terror - real or rhetorical. So this could also be their story – a personal, family account of a war for liberty and self-determination and one that exemplifies the triumph of the human spirit over the fanaticism and depravity of unbridled power.

Historical Annotations

German Minister Herr von Baligand

He was indeed shot to death, exactly as described, in Lisbon on 7th June, 1930, just after visiting the warship Konigsberg. He was promoted to the Lisbon position by the famous Foreign Minister Gustav Stresemann who, despite having won the Nobel Peace Prize in 1926, was no friend to Poland, wishing to reclaim lands ceded to them after the Great War. He was determined to bring Poland to its knees economically and to that end he established a trade war with his neighbour. In his words 'there should be no settlement until Poland's economic and financial distress has reached an extreme stage and reduced the entire Polish body politic to a state of powerlessness. Then they will settle according to our wishes.'

The assassin was Franz Piechowski, a disgruntled German sailor of Polish origin from Danzig who refers to Stresemann in negative terms many times in his letters. The minister's escort, the Counsellor, miraculously survived the attack. Franz Piechowski's tragic and turbulent life has been traced through the official archives, his medical history, press reports and his own correspondence. He was killed exactly as described, a victim of the Nazi T4 euthanasia programme designed to eliminate all those that were 'a drain on the rations'. At the Nuremburg trials it was estimated that about 275,000 such patients were murdered and almost 10,000 were children or babies.

The SS Konigsberg

This K Class Light Cruiser was only a year old when she visited Lisbon to show off the might and technological advancement of the new German Navy, which was being trained and inspired to challenge British and American maritime domination. She had been built to the most modern and exacting standards by exploiting every possible loophole within the international treaties restricting

German rearmament. With her considerable firepower, speed, manoeuvrability and a highly trained crew of over five hundred she was a formidable and potent addition to the Kriegsmarine.

She was sunk on 10th April 1940, by Fleet Air Arm Skua dive-bombers from 800 and 803 squadrons based in the Orkney Islands. Over the preceding two days she had provided naval support to German troops when they landed in Bergan (flying British flags to confuse the defenders) during the Nazi invasion of Norway. She was damaged by fire from the harbour battery before she helped to destroy all the coastal defences. Being then unfit to take to deep waters she stood guard at the harbour mouth, her formidable guns preventing any British naval intervention. This was the first sinking of a major warship by aerial bombing and was also noteworthy because dive-bombing was being ridiculed and discouraged by the RAF establishment.

The Polish or Pomeranian Corridor

This was a strip of land between twenty and seventy miles wide (consisting mainly of West Prussia and Poznan province land), which ran north along the lower Vistula from Torun to the Baltic coast. The Treaty of Versailles transferred this ribbon of territory from Germany in order to give Poland access to the sea and its trade routes. Historically, it had been Polish territory and the majority of the population were still Poles. Although Germany was given free transit across, it caused a great deal of animosity towards the Poles because it separated East Prussia from the German Reich and the Nazi party bitterly resented the imposition.

Danzig (Gdansk) and its hinterland

After the 1st World War it was not ceded to Poland, but established as a free city state and became virtually autonomous under the protection of the League of Nations. Nevertheless Germany exercised her dominance and control over the port to such a degree that the Poles became second-class citizens and her government could exert little or no political or practical influence. She was powerless to prevent Germany building up her forces within the city and using the shipyard to build her warships: indeed her first submarines were also constructed there. It was here that the war started in 1939 after Hitler had demanded that Danzig should be ceded to Germany and German highways be created across the corridor to East Prussia. Poland refused and also secured French and British guarantees against German aggression. On the 31st August the Germans mounted the Gleiwitz attack on its own territory to falsely establish Polish aggression against Germany and thereby justify the invasion of Poland. Gestapo agents dressed and equipped as Polish soldiers attacked and seized the Gleiwitz radio station just inside the German border and broadcast anti-German messages to give the impression that the station had been taken by Polish Nationalist saboteurs. They even left behind the bullet ridden body of a German: a prisoner who had known Polish sympathies who they had murdered and then prepared to look like an insurgent who had been shot whilst attacking the installation. They later showed the body to journalists as proof of a Polish plot.

This was just one of over twenty such incidents staged along the border in the days leading up to war: all part of a Nazi conspiracy codenamed Operation Himmler. On the 1st September the German battleship Schleswig-Holstein fired the first shots of the war over Westerplatte at the entrance to the port of Gdansk.

Pelplin

This was an early mediaeval settlement (34 miles due south of Gdansk) that became the home of Cistercian monks in 1274 and for five hundred years the abbey was the centre of the community. Its church is one of the largest and some say the best in the country and it acts as a cathedral served by its own bishopric. The town has a religious and historical significance far beyond its size, a population of only eight thousand.

Luck

The old Polish city of Luck, sited on a bend in the Styr River, is now better known as Lutsk, being the centre of the Volyn province in Ukraine. In 1941 the Germans forced the town's 10,000 Jews into a ghetto and following a year of immense suffering and deportations, thousands were machine-gunned just outside the town and buried in mass graves. There were only a handful of survivors. All the buildings and infrastructure remained intact but the very life and soul of the city was totally destroyed by the slaughter.

Partition

The Germans invaded Poland on the 1ˢᵗ September 1939 from the west, south and north and then on 17ᵗʰ September the Soviet army, on the fraudulent pretext of defending Ukrainians and Belarusians (now living in a disintegrating Poland) from the Nazis, invaded from the east. On the 27ᵗʰ, in accordance with the Molotov-Ribbentrop Treaty approved by Stalin himself, the two aggressors partitioned Poland into three predetermined areas. Western territories were annexed into Germany, eastern lands into The Soviet Union and the central section became a German 'protectorate', known as the General Government and was controlled by Germans. After the war, in accordance with the Yalta Conference, the Polish Eastern border was redrawn to its present position. In effect it lost nearly half of its land and although Poland received territorial compensation in the west from Germany, the whole of the country became a Soviet Satellite and there was to be no democracy. In order to ensure the Soviet Union's participation in the United Nations, Stalin was given practically everything he wanted, particularly in Poland. The Polish Government in Exile and the Polish Free Forces were excluded from having any role whatsoever in the future of their own country.

The Atrocities of Terror

Both the Germans and Russians murdered, mistreated and abused the Polish population on an unprecedented and monumental scale. In the first few months of the war tens of thousands of intellectuals including teachers, authors, poets and musicians were slaughtered by the Germans. As the war went on their atrocities grew worse and, if anything, the events portrayed in this book understate their capacity for inhuman treatment. Millions were forcibly driven from their homes and imprisoned, tortured or sent to concentration camps or labour battalions. The German Authorities and the military leaders regarded the Poles as 'sub-human' and the Polish Jews were considered even more inferior and both groups were subjected to the most horrific brutality. The Russians' treatment of the two hundred and fifty thousand captured Polish soldiers was no better and thousands were worked to death, starved or succumbed to disease or torture in the Gulag. There was great historical bitterness and mistrust between the Russians/Ukrainians and the Poles who regularly rose up and fought against the Russian occupation. These rebellions were savagely and ruthlessly put down but it would not be fair to say the terrible losses in recent history were all one-sided. Following the 1920 war, tens of thousands of Russian prisoners were placed in a camp at Tuchola. Famine and the cold, but mainly epidemic disease, contributed to a death rate of 25%. Some reports suggest that as many as 25,000 Red Army POWs perished while in Polish captivity and there was undoubtedly a degree of physical abuse by the Polish guards which contributed to their suffering. The Poles maintain that their soldiers and general population succumbed proportionately to these privations and that they were not responsible for the vast loss of life, but the Russians insist that the Poles were culpable.

Katyn

There was almost certainly no prison camp such as I described situated at this site 12 miles west of Smolensk in Russia, but for years historians had no clear idea of what had happened to the captured Polish military personnel between the time that they had 'disappeared' from their prisons until the discovery of the mass graves. They first assumed that the NKVD Rest and Recreation facility, which did already exist there, was a holding area and also the execution and burial site for nearly a fifth of the unfortunate Poles who found themselves in Soviet captivity in April and May 1940. It was believed that the victims had been brought to the forest (in groups of two to three hundred) by train and then truck, but post-Cold War revelations suggest that, although some may have indeed been executed at the burial site in the forest itself, the vast majority of the victims were transported from the monastery prison at Kozelsk, some 150 miles to the south east and were shot in the basement of the local NKVD headquarters and at an abattoir in Smolensk.

In any event, the Katyn Forest is (and will probably long remain) the main symbol of the atrocity, even if it was not the actual killing field. Here alone two generals, an admiral, 24 colonels, 79 lieutenant colonels, 258 majors, 654 captains, 17 navy captains, 3,420 NCOs, 7 army chaplains, a prince, 43 civil servants, 85 privates, 200 pilots, 20 university professors, 300 doctors, 300 lawyers, teachers and engineers, 100 authors and journalists and 131 refugees, who had been shot in the back of the neck whilst their hands were tied behind their backs, were dumped like discarded rubbish into mass graves. Similar executions took place at other prison sites, including Starobelsk near Kharkov and Ostashkov near Kalinin - a total of *twenty one thousand souls*. Hundreds of boy scouts, police officers and firemen were also murdered alongside the military personnel and, in total, half the Polish officer corps was eliminated to prevent any resurgence of Polish nationalism. Only in 1992 did post-communist Russia publicly admit its guilt and provide the Polish authorities with documents proving Stalin's culpability and describing the subsequent cover-up. In addition, about one and a half million Polish citizens living in the Russian annexed area were also forced into labour camps and the Gulag. The intelligentsia, other professionals, the clergy and political activists were also rounded up and imprisoned or murdered.

Sighet

Between 1940 and 1944, whilst being administered by Hungary, twenty thousand Jews from Sighet town were sent to Auschwitz and other concentration camps and today the Jewish population numbers only about one hundred of its forty-five thousand general population. One of the Hasidic Sighet survivors of Auschwitz and Buchenwald was Eliezer (Elie) Wiesel, the famous Jewish writer, who went on to provide dramatic and thought provoking literary testament to the destruction of European Jewry. He was awarded the Nobel Peace Prize in 1986. The Treaty of Paris at the end of the war returned Sighet to Romania.

Auschwitz

Himmler ordered the building of the first camp, Auschwitz 1, in April, 1940 and initially it was reserved for political prisoners, mainly Poles and Germans. It was supplemented in October 1941 by Auschwitz 2 (Birkenau). The total number of people who were murdered at this camp alone is estimated to be one million six hundred thousand. It is not commonly known that there were more than one thousand Nazi death and labour camps scattered across Europe from the Ukraine to the Channel Islands. Some like Treblinka had no barrack blocks at all because the prisoners were herded straight into gas chambers on their arrival. Nobody sent there survived longer than six hours. This slavery and slaughter was on an industrial scale and encompassed every brutality imaginable, culminating in 'The Final Solution', which was discussed and promulgated at a conference of the Nazi hierarchy in a Berlin suburb on 20th January, 1942. The carefully sanitised but chilling minutes of this meeting later became an exhibit at the Nuremberg trials and are commonly referred to as the Wannsee Protocol.

On 20th June 1942 Kazimierz Piechowski and three fellow prisoners at Auschwitz concentration camp made an audacious escape by wearing stolen Nazi SS uniforms and driving the Commandant's own car out of the main gate. Their bid for freedom was spectacularly successful and recently, from his home in Gdansk, at the age of eighty-five, Kazik has told his story to the world. In total eight hundred prisoners escaped from the Auschwitz camps and about one hundred and forty successfully evaded recapture.

Polish Free Forces

The 1st Corps consisted of the 1st Polish Armoured Division and The Independent Parachute Brigade. It was commanded by General Maczek and fought in north-west Europe through France, Belgium and Holland and into Germany. The Parachute Brigade were specifically trained and equipped to be dropped into Warsaw in support of the general uprising but because of fierce Soviet objection this was shelved and they were later deployed in operation Market Garden.

The 2nd Corps was commanded by General Anders and was mainly made up from his refugee army brought out of Russia following the Sikorski–Maisky agreement of July 1941. It consisted of the three major units of the 3rd Carpathian Rifle Division, the 5th Kressowa Infantry Division and the 2nd Independent Armoured Brigade. Although some sections had taken part in previous battles it first fought as a full Corps in the Italian campaign.

General Stanislaw Maczek

Was the last surviving senior army commander of the war and when he was demobilised he made his home in Edinburgh, working with the Polish Resettlement Corps. Like most of his soldiers he felt unable to return to Poland and in any event the communist puppet government stripped him of his Polish citizenship. Despite the gallant assistance he had provided in the struggle against the Axis forces he, like his men, were not considered as allied soldiers and did not receive any form of pension either from their home country or the United Kingdom. As times were not easy he worked as a part time barman in a hotel run by a former Sergeant from his Division. Old comrades would regularly visit the hotel and, as a sign of their respect and the high regard in which he was always held, they would proudly salute him before ordering their drinks or meals. When he died at the age of 102 in 1994, in compliance with his wishes, he was buried alongside his fallen comrades in the Polish military cemetery at Breda in the Netherlands.

General Wladyslaw Anders

Who had led a regiment of Lancers during the Polish Soviet war of 1920 was captured by the Russians twenty years later whilst he was fighting the Nazi invasion. He was incarcerated at the infamous Lubianka prison where he was interrogated and tortured by the NKVD, but his life was probably saved when the Germans invaded Russia and he was then released to command the Polish army to be formed from his fellow prisoners. He was considered to be an outstanding General by the British military hierarchy and unusually many British troops were placed under his direct command. For example, at the battle of Ancona on the 17th and 18th July 1944, the 7th Queen's Own Hussars fought with distinction alongside the 6th Lwow Rifle Brigade and the 5th Vilno Infantry Brigade. Whilst troops from these units were giving their lives for the allied cause, British and American politicians were already negotiating to give the cities of Lwow and Vilno to the Soviet Union. At wars-end the General lived in England but did not survive to see a free Poland, the very thing that he had fought all his life for. He died aged seventy-seven in May 1970 and at his own request was buried with his men in the Polish Military cemetery at Monte Cassino.

Wojtek

The Syrian brown bear orphan cub adopted by the Polish 2nd Corp in Iran lived a long life and when he finally passed away in Edinburgh Zoo in 1964 he was famous, well loved and had often been visited by his wartime colleagues and their families. Among the very few possessions recovered from the Sikorski crash site was a photograph of this cherished animal.

Pilots serving with the RAF

Two thousand of the seventeen thousand Polish airmen serving with the RAF died in combat and per capita they had the highest success rate of any of the many nationalities fighting in the air war. In addition, during the Battle of Britain, the all Polish 303

Fighter Squadron had the most 'kills' within the whole of Fighter Command (originally credited with over 120 - although historians now believe the confirmed figure to be about 80).

Mont Ormel

Today Mont Ormel is a Polish Memorial with a visitors centre and the fallen are buried in the Polish war cemetery at Granville-Langannerie, between Falaise and Caen.

Sturmbrigade Dirlewanger

Often referred to as the Dirlewanger Brigade, it was a Waffen SS unit that fought alongside the Kaminski Brigade in Warsaw. Its troops behaved atrociously: raping, looting and killing civilians without compunction. In the Wola district it was responsible for murdering tens of thousands of men, women and children. Oskar Dirlewanger, the commander and an alcoholic sex offender had himself previously been sent to a concentration camp for his crimes and was only released so that he could specifically form a unit of ex-convicts for use on the eastern front. After his capture by the allies he was sentenced for war crimes but whilst in the custody of the French he was handed over to Polish soldiers serving with them on occupation duties and in June 1945 he was taken to a prison camp at Altshausen. A few days later he was killed there, reportedly while being beaten and tortured by the Polish guards and liberated concentration camp victims. The massacres at the hospital, the school, the church and the park all occurred as described, but they represent only a fraction of the mass murder carried out by this unit and the Kaminski Brigade.

The Kaminski Brigade

Or RONA (Russian National Liberation Army). When deployed in Warsaw it comprised of some seventeen hundred men and their behaviour was horrendous, spending more time looting, murdering, raping and consuming liquor than fighting. They were mostly Russians with a minority of Ukrainian and Belorussian prisoners of war and deserters from the Red Army. Even the German High Command demanded their withdrawal following numerous atrocities, as they believed its actions were actually slowing down the process of suppressing the insurgency. Bronislaw Kaminski, who was born in the USSR of a Polish father and a German mother, was held personally responsible for his troops' misconduct in Warsaw and in August 1944 he was arrested, tried and executed by the Germans because he was an embarrassment to the SS! His death was blamed on Polish Partisans.

The Polish People's Army

In 1943 Stalin organised a Polish Army to fight alongside the Red Army and the first units were formed under the command of General Zygmunt Berling and many recruits came from those left in the prison and labour camps when Stalin had stopped them leaving to join General Anders. As the Soviets marched west into Poland they also recruited from the inhabitants of the Polish eastern borderlands (Kresy Wschodnie). Because of the Katyn murders there was a drastic shortage of officers, which meant that Russians commanded many of the units. This army, which numbered some four hundred thousand by the end of the war, played a major role in the drive on Berlin and made up some fifteen per cent of Zhukov's and Koniev's armies. The Poles fought with great distinction and they even raised the Polish flag over the damaged Brandenburg Gate, which had been used by the Nazis to symbolise their power. It was then standing defiantly in its isolation surrounded by total ruin and devastation, and the irony of the symbol of Polish nationhood flying over the Red Army and the Nazi ruins was not lost on their Russian commanders who were incensed at the perceived effrontery. The Poles paid dearly for their share of victory in the east with over seventeen thousand dead, forty thousand wounded and nearly ten thousand missing in action, some three times the casualty rate suffered by the Polish Forces fighting in the west.

The Home Army or the AK (Armia Krajowa)

Resistance to both the German and Soviet occupation of Poland was immediate and widespread, with many different underground groups emerging across the whole country. By 1943 virtually all these groups were organised or controlled by the Home Army, under the command of General Stefan Rowecki and then, after his arrest by the Gestapo, the role was taken on by General Tadeusz Komorowski. Some three hundred thousand strong, this well organised and popularly supported insurgent group operated under the control of the Sikorski government in exile, based in England. It carried out many spectacular actions and was a constant threat to the German forces by fighting a guerrilla war attacking communications, factories, fuel stores and enemy personnel and equipment. Its biggest test and greatest battle was the Warsaw uprising, where the death toll on both sides was exceedingly high and, although the AK failed to achieve its political and military objectives, its heroic performance came to symbolise the struggle for freedom and independence that has inspired generations of Poles since.

It was renowned amongst the allies for the vast amount of high quality military intelligence and captured German technology that it provided: including an Enigma code machine and parts of a V2 rocket. In total it provided almost fifty percent of all the information received from within occupied Europe throughout the war years and it also distinctively operated to great effect within France and Germany. It also encouraged, organised and financed a massive and continuous programme of industrial sabotage carried out, at great personal risk, by many of the thousands of slave labourers forced to work in German munitions factories and on related armament and defence projects. This undoubtedly saved innumerable allied lives and seriously frustrated the Nazi war effort. One small example of particular relevance to this story is that the normal operational failure rate of the stick grenade, through the separate time delay fuse failing to ignite or the factory sealed warhead failing to explode, was significantly increased by deliberate disruption on the assembly lines.

The cost

At the end of the war a total of nearly seven million Poles had been killed, of which over three million were Jews (It has been estimated that 95% of Poland's Jews perished).One hundred and fifty thousand of her troops had died on the battlefield and many thousands more in the camps. Many of Poland's brightest young men and women lay buried in the Warsaw rubble or in unmarked graves across the whole of Europe. Over another million of her citizens who had been deported to Germany and occupied Western Europe found themselves scattered across the various allied sectors with little more than the rags on their backs. As a result, there were over three hundred and fifty ghost villages in Poland that were completely uninhabited: all the occupants had either been killed in reprisal for the activities of the underground movement or had been deported as slave labour.

Of the one and a half million Polish citizens who were forced into slavery in Siberia only about three hundred thousand survived. A large proportion of those who made it out owed their lives to General Anders who insisted on taking as many of the children and elderly men and women as possible, along with his half starved but undaunted army.

If you should now slowly flick through this book from cover to cover and consider that every single letter of every single word on every single line of every single page (including what you are reading at this moment) represents ten Polish citizens who perished between 1939 and 1945 as a direct result of the war, then the enormity of the crime becomes almost tangible. As revealing as this simple demonstration is, we can still only begin to imagine the extent and depth of the suffering involved.

What might have been

As so often in times of major conflict the accuracy, interpretation and use made of military intelligence was to have a profound and almost unimaginable effect, not only on those directly involved but

365

also upon generations to come. Whilst the world, its political leaders and its military commanders were being staggered by the speed and destructive power of the German 'Blitzkrieg', the allies did not seem to realise that the practical consequences of the lightening drive to Warsaw and the brief but brave Polish defence could have ended the war there and then. As the capital was being besieged and Poland was beseeching France and Britain to honour their promise of military action, the German invasion forces had almost run out of ammunition, supplies and most critically, fuel. They were certainly in no position to quickly reinforce or re-supply their sparse deployment along their western borders. At best, the critical military significance of this weakness was not fully appreciated by the allies' intelligence network or at worst, yet more self-serving political argument and procrastination allowed such a unique and golden opportunity to pass. If France and her allies had attacked in force in the west whilst the German forces were so committed and over-stretched in the east, then perhaps Hitler might have been forced to settle with the allies. What a prize for humanity that would have been: no Holocaust, no invasion of the Low Countries and France, no Battle of Britain, no Blitz, no further destruction of Poland or her people and perhaps even the prevention of four more long years of total world war. The list of suffering over that time is almost endless and with the benefit of hindsight we can now see that during a very small window of opportunity the allies had it within their grasp to save not a handful of fictional characters as depicted in this book, but millions of real, equally desperate, families and tens of millions of lives.

It was not to be.

Acknowledgements

I must mention Mike and Carol Andrews who so kindly and thoughtfully provided the letters, photographs and other documents that led me to Edmund, his son Nic and his uncle Czeslaw. They were the inspiration that fired my curiosity and when my own father Henry and my Godfather Wladek gradually told me of their incredible experiences during the war years I knew that I wouldn't rest until I had the story down on paper. Even recalling those events proved painful to them and, along with the other veterans who have spoken to me over the years, they fully deserve my heartfelt respect, admiration and thanks.

I am grateful to Ernst Volker and the staff at The Bundesarchiv, who kindly provided background information and access to the records of Franz Piechowski and to Hagai Aviel of The International Association against Psychiatric Assault. He was the first to inform me of Franz's dreadful fate and describe the true extent and utter ruthlessness of the horror. Thanks also to Doctor Astrid Ley of the Sachsenhausen Memorial and Museum, who supplied additional and vital information regarding Franz's personal treatment at the hands of the Nazis during their despicable 'euthanasia' programme.

A special reference and praise is due to Luis Quintais, Professor of Social Anthropology at Coimbra University Portugal, a very successful poet and author, for his unstinting encouragement and also for allowing me to draw both information and motivation from his book, *Franz Piechowski*. This was made so much easier thanks to the excellent translations from the original Portuguese, carried out with such attention to detail and good humour by Regina Arnold - a talented student at Bath University. Thanks also to my neighbour Bill Fritsche who so graciously and enthusiastically provided a first class German translation service and who, together with his charming wife Frances, was ever supportive and reassuring.

The professional and friendly assistance provided by the staff at The Polish Enquiries Section of the M.O.D. at RAF Northolt was critical during my original investigation and I cannot pay sufficient tribute to their vital, longstanding and painstaking contribution to the welfare and support of Polish veterans and their families. I also point out that the contacts, communications and interactions with them and other organisations and agencies as described in this book are purely fictional. Thank you also to the Polish Ex-Servicemen's Association at Hammersmith who work tirelessly in the most worthy of causes.

I am proud to be a member of The International Police Association and I extend a huge 'thank you' to the representatives here in the UK and also in Poland who have so freely offered up their spare time and their considerable investigative and research skills in support of my project.

I must also compliment those who have read the manuscript and provided an invaluable critique. My thanks go to Steve and Marcia Higgs for bringing me the letters in the first place, then listening to my endless progress reports and still being there towards the end to act as my first proof readers and make valuable suggestions. Furthermore, I am so grateful for the encouragement, sound advice and constructive recommendations put forward by my brother-in-law Philip Tolerton and my sister Mary who read the final draft.

My greatest thanks go to my wife Becky who has been a rock throughout what has been a long and rewarding but occasionally difficult process. Her understanding, support and infectious enthusiasm have never wavered and her wise counsel and sound judgment have always carried the day. I am lucky indeed!

Finally, this project would not have been possible without the extensive support, encouragement and advice that I have received from countless other individuals and organisations throughout the last four years. Their generosity and enthusiasm for my subject has been uplifting and, although the numbers involved preclude me from citing them all individually, they know who they are and I am only too glad to pay them a collective debt of gratitude.

In Memoriam

Today we are alive and humbled because
You cared so much
You gave so much
You lost so much
You were alone, without home, language or family
Bearing sorrow, grief and unimagined hardship
Yet your valour, tenacity and selfless example
Will forever live on in these islands
Be honoured in your treasured homeland
And inspire all those who would be free
We owe you so much
We must never forget!